ELVIS:
IN THE TWILIGHT
OF MEMORY

ELVIS:
IN THE TWILIGHT
OF MEMORY

June Juanico

Introduction by
Peter Guralnick

LITTLE, BROWN AND COMPANY

A *Little, Brown* Book

First published in Great Britain in 1997
by Little, Brown and Company

Copyright © 1997 by June Juanico Taranto
Introduction copyright © 1997 by Peter Guralnick

The author and publisher would like to thank the following
for kind permission to quote from copyright material:
CARLIN MUSIC CORP.
'Blue Suede Shoes' (Carl Lee Perkins) © 1956 Hi-Lo Music, Inc.
'Love Me Tender' (Presley/Matson) © 1956 Elvis Presley Music, Inc.
'Good Rockin' Tonight' (Roy Brown) © 1948 Fort Knox Music, Inc.,
and Trio Music Co., Inc.
MPL COMMUNICATIONS LTD
'Unchained Melody' (North/Zaret) © 1955 Frank Music Corp.
REDWOOD MUSIC LTD
'Are You Lonesome Tonight' (Turk/Handman)
FARON YOUNG MUSIC
'Is It So Strange? (Faron Young)

A CIP catalogue record for this book
is available from the British Library.

ISBN: 0 316 63967 2

Typeset by M Rules in Sabon
Printed and bound in Great Britain
by Clays Ltd, St Ives plc

Little, Brown and Company (UK)
Brettenham House
Lancaster Place
London WC2E 7EN

To the memory of Gladys Love Presley: this is the Elvis we both knew and loved.

CONTENTS

$\mathscr{I}$NTRODUCTION

There have been lots of books written about Elvis Presley, of course, with probably as many personal memoirs among them as have attached to any other cultural figure or entertainer in history. Some have been spurious, a number seem to have been written out of little more than personal rancor, motivation has ranged from love to money to self-adumbration (never has one man had so many chief advisers). Virtually none have actually been put together by their narrators.

That is one of the things that makes June Juanico's book different. It is not simply that she has written a book that is filled with feeling and insight, that conveys an experience with truth and without rancor, about a real, not-mythic Elvis Presley. She has also written (and re-written) every word herself and in the process produced an account that is as touching in its unadorned honesty as it is refreshing in its feisty and unself-censored voice.

I should have known that June was a writer when we first met. It wasn't the fact that she had saved up her experience over the years, avoiding interviews for the most part and keeping her memories to herself. Nor was it the confidence with which she told her story. Lots of people can recite anecdotes with assurance and humor. No, it was the extent to which she had reflected upon her experience, fleshed out her story with three-dimensional portraits, created a narrative persona removed from the nineteen-year-old girl at its center, provided a structure which, far from distorting the experience, defined it. When she produced the manuscript that she had been working on, I really should not have been surprised.

Everyone has his or her own way of telling a story, and most of us, when recounting our own experience, paint a 'truthful' picture. It is not necessarily a complex one, though. For reasons of convenience most of our stories boil down to anecdotes, in which our own roles may be enhanced, the punch-line delivered more crisply, the world more a 'like' world (a world in which these things *could* have happened, these verbal ripostes could have been made) than the real one, in which motivation is often confused, people are necessarily a combination of contradictory elements, the picture is not postcard-perfect.

It's hard to scrutinize these accounts realistically – particularly if one is a participant in the story. It can be painful to look too closely at one's own past. But that is what June has done. Without for a moment sacrificing the immediacy of what can only be called a 'love story', the narrator has told a tale filled with autumnal regret, a bitter-sweet account filled with vivid detail that portrays a particular time and place (Biloxi, Mississippi, the summer of 1956) and carries with it its own charm and its own truth. It also captures a 21-year-old Elvis Presley with 'Hound Dog' just about to start climbing the charts, on the brink of movie stardom (he receives his copy of a script titled *The Reno Brothers*, soon to become *Love Me Tender*, while he and June are in Miami), enjoying a brief moment out of the spotlight just before the curtain of privacy is forever lifted. June Juanico's book carries conviction in its very simplicity – but don't be misled by that simplicity. There's a writer there, too. And we are getting the benefit not just of her experiences but of her insights as well.

Peter Guralnick
January 1997

Elvis:
IN THE TWILIGHT
OF MEMORY

PROLOGUE

*I*T WAS A two-hour drive from Biloxi to the station in New Orleans where Elvis would be changing trains. Because of his phobia about flying, he chose instead the long train ride from California to Memphis. Being on the train for days at a time didn't bother Elvis. It gave him time to relax and collect his thoughts. He had selected a route slightly out of his way, because it would be convenient for me to rendezvous with him in New Orleans. He had no idea, however, that I would be making the trip to say goodbye.

In October 1956 he'd held me in his arms and said he couldn't live without me, and wanted me to stay with him forever. Now it's March 1957, and he sends me a telegram asking me to meet him at Union Station, as if nothing has changed. Maybe things hadn't changed for him; his life was moving at a rapid pace, but my days and nights seemed to last forever. In the past five months he had phoned me only three times.

After reading about his latest house-guest, a Las Vegas showgirl, I decided it was time I too started dating again. I wasn't trying to forget about Elvis, I was just tired of staying home and being faithful. It wasn't long before I was reading about another new friend, a different Las Vegas showgirl, and that she was spending the Christmas holidays with Elvis and his family in Memphis. This was the last straw, as they say, so I decided to make Elvis Presley a memory.

I began dating Fabian Taranto, a local businessman ten years my senior. Fabian was recently divorced from a bad marriage that lasted less than two years. Bearing a striking resemblance to a young Clark Gable – without the big ears – he was very handsome with his black hair and blue eyes. He was also the perfect date, literally sweeping me off my feet. My thoughts of Elvis soon began to fade away. I'd made it through the hurt, and my broken heart was slowly mending. I no longer cared how many showgirls Elvis brought home for Christmas, or at any other time. I stopped reading articles about him, and listened to records instead of the radio (Elvis was on every station). I refused to talk about him to anyone, especially persistent reporters. My mother was answering the phone by saying, 'Sorry, June's not here, and I have nothing to say.' I stopped reading all the fan mail; it piled up for months. If you're in love – really in love – you pick up the phone and call. Elvis had left me on hold for too long. Even in a Continental Mark 2, I could never take a back seat to anyone. If I couldn't be right up there by the hood ornament, then I didn't need the ride.

When Fabian asked me to marry him, I didn't think twice. I said yes immediately.

On the way to New Orleans, I got into a heated discussion with Pat, my best friend, about my new relationship with Fabian.

'Are you really gonna tell Elvis?' Pat asked.

'Certainly I'm going to tell him. That's why I'm going to see him.'

'Are you serious about all this marriage stuff?'

'Yes, I'm serious! Why is it so hard for you to understand? We've already set a date.'

'Jesus, June, I hate to ask!'

'It's going to be the first of June. I'm going to be a June bride.' My words were pronounced and deliberate.

'Do you think this is a joke, June? You can't be serious!'

'I *am* serious. I'm in love with Fabian and we're going to be married. That's all there is to it.'

'June, you were in love with Elvis just a few months ago! You're not thinking straight. And I'm not concerned with Elvis, June, I'm worried about you! You're going too fast! Don't you realize you're on the rebound? You're so hurt and mad with Elvis for not calling you, you're gonna show him or else!'

'That's not true. I love Fabian and we're getting married, and I don't want to discuss it any more. Okay?'

'Okay, I won't say another word. You're so mixed up now I wouldn't want to confuse you with the facts. I only have one more thing to say, and then I'll shut up. Okay?'

'I'm listening.'

'You're about to make a decision that will affect the rest of your life, and I feel you should take a little more time to think it over.'

'I'm tired of thinking, Pat, and I'm tired of hearing about Elvis and who he spends Christmas with. It's over!'

I felt a big knot in my stomach as we passed a sign reading WELCOME TO LOUISIANA. I reached over and turned on the car radio – *loud* – but, typically, it was blasting out 'Don't Be Cruel' so I switched it off as quickly as I'd turned it on. Pat looked over at me and just shook her head. I was nineteen years old, and damn well capable of making my own decisions – or so I thought.

PART ONE

1
EARLY HEARTBREAK

As a young girl, I remember my handsome father leaving for work, always wearing a starched and meticulously ironed shirt, and smelling of Old Spice. His jet-black hair and bronze skin came from his Spanish and American Indian heritage. A natural athlete, he not only excelled at basketball, baseball and track, but was named All-American High School Quarterback, leading his undefeated Biloxi High Indian team to victory three years in a row.

He had his choice of cheerleaders, but gave them all up when he first saw my mother at a Junior High track meet, catching his eye as she crossed the finish line winning the fifty-yard dash.

My beautiful mother dropped out of high school to marry my father after completing her freshman year. She was sweet sixteen. Although she'd feared she was going to be childless, my mother finally conceived my brother after five years of marriage. I was born two years later. We were thought to be the ideal American family. However, we rarely spent time with us all together; it was usually just my brother Jerry, Mama and me at suppertime. Daddy always came home late, and most of the time was either drunk or had been drinking. Having a few beers made him jolly, but whiskey brought out his angry side and he was often verbally abusive. He made all the family decisions and Mama was afraid to disagree.

While most families considered Christmas a time for togetherness, my parents left Jerry and me with grandparents while they went out to party. Every year of our young lives, we woke up on Christmas morning to open gifts with our grandparents, and never saw our parents until sometime Christmas evening. I didn't realize how odd this was until I had children of my own. The thought of never feeling the excitement of seeing the expressions on your children's faces as they tore open their gifts from Santa, nor hearing their screams of delight, made my heart ache for all my mother had missed.

Mama started acting strange. She was spending most of her days alone in her room. I could tell she was crying a lot, but she said it was only a head cold. One evening she borrowed a car to follow my father when he got off from work. Thinking I was too young to be left alone, she insisted I ride with her. My father's first stop was at a drug store. He came out carrying a huge red heart-shaped box of candy, too large to be put in a paper sack. It was Valentine's Day. His next stop was a liquor store, where he purchased what my mother thought to be a bottle of champagne. We followed at a safe distance; I thought we were playing some kind of game. His dark green truck then pulled off the main road and turned into a trailer park. We waited at the entrance for a few moments before driving in through the narrow rows of trailers. We saw Daddy's truck parked on the last row. As we drove slowly past, my mother and I were both shocked to see him embracing a strange woman. I can still picture her bright red hair. They were standing in front of an open window, locked in each other's arms. My mother was devastated. Her hands were shaking on the steering wheel, and her face so streaked with tears she couldn't see where she was driving.

She pulled the car over to the side of the road, opened the door, and started to vomit. I got out of the car and went round to her side. I wanted to help her, but didn't know what to do. I patted her on the back of her head and kept telling her over and over, 'It'll be all right Mama, it'll be all right.' I was ten years old.

Daddy didn't come home that night. The next morning, very early, I helped Mama throw all his belongings out on our front porch. We were both crying and throwing clothes in a pile. We went back inside, she locked both doors, and we waited and watched through a crack in the venetian blinds for my daddy to come home. After several hours he finally drove up and parked in his usual spot. He was clean shaven; his hair was still damp from a recent shower. He came straight to the door, trying to ignore the big pile of clothes. Finding the screen door locked, he knocked gently. 'Honey, let me in; the screen is locked. Honey, please let me in. What's the matter?'

After a few moments of his pleading, my mother opened the door. She looked at him through the screen.

'Go live with your valentine whore!' she said softly, slamming the heavy wooden door in his face. It took him several trips back and forth to load his belongings into his truck. She held me close as we watched him drive away.

'Don't ever let this happen to you, my baby. Promise me you'll never let this happen to you.'

'I won't, Mama, I promise.'

After a few weeks of crying, I believe Mama would have taken him back, but he never made any attempt to save their marriage.

Night after night I would wake to hear Mama sobbing as if every breath would be her last. Often I'd get out of my twin bed and crawl in next to her. It seemed to give her comfort, so I soon stopped sleeping in my bed altogether. I considered Mama's room to be my room too. At least it was better than sharing a room with a brother who was always bossing me around. Jerry, busy with his after-school paper route, had disassociated himself from our family crisis. He was just pleased to have a bedroom all to himself.

Mama got a job to support Jerry and me after my father disappeared from our lives. Soon after their divorce was final, he married the valentine whore. Mama got the house. Thank

God it was paid for – child support wasn't even mentioned and my father never volunteered one cent.

My happy-go-lucky childhood was suddenly turned upside down. I was in charge of the cooking and the cleaning, while Mama was making a living. I didn't mind; to me it was like playing house. I taught myself how to cook and how to sew. I attempted to do the laundry, but was soon told to leave it alone after all the white clothes, including Jerry's underwear, turned a bright shade of pink. Having that much responsibility quickly turned me into an adult way before my time.

My mother, a devoted wife, mother and home-maker, finally got over the pain and started dating again. She was thirty-six years old, and for the first time for as long as I could remember she was laughing and having fun.

2

*T*HAT FACE

*E*VERY ONCE IN a while we all reminisce and think about our special memories. The memory that stands out most in my mind was that face. The face that was soon to be the most recognized face in the world. The deep-set eyes that would make girls scream and cry; the full, pouting lips that would make them swoon. I'll never forget the first time I saw that face: the flawless face of Elvis Presley.

It was June 1955. I had just gotten home from work when the phone rang. Glenda Manduffy, a close friend, was calling to ask me to go with her to see a singer named Elvis Presley.

'I saw him last night at the Slavonian Lodge, and June, he's the most gorgeous man I've ever seen in my life. You've got to go with me, June. Okay?'

'Slow down, Glenda! Now, where, when, and how are we going?'

'It's tonight at the Airman's Club. My brother will take us there and pick us up when it's over.'

'I'm so tired, Glenda, I just want to take a hot bath and relax before Norbie gets here.' Six feet four inches tall, Norbie Ronsonet was the most gorgeous man I had ever seen in my life. We'd been dating regularly for the past six months.

'The show doesn't start until 7:30, June, you've got time to bathe and relax. Call Norbie and tell him you have to go to Keesler Field with me. You can call him when we get home, at around 9:30. Better yet, I'll call Norbie, you go get ready. We'll pick you up at seven sharp!'

Reluctantly I agreed and went to take a bath. Afterwards I had to decide what to wear. Ladies wearing slacks were not allowed on the Air Force Base. I had a new figure-flattering white dress, the one I'd worn under my cap and gown for graduation. It would be perfect. I even had a new pair of white high-heel sandals to match. I was dressed and ready to go by 6:45.

With a few minutes to relax, I sat on the couch and turned on my favorite radio station. The DJ announced a hot new song by a hot new singer – Elvis Presley. I sat up straight, as if that would make me hear better, and paid close attention. The song, 'Blue Moon Of Kentucky', was recorded with so much reverberation that it sounded to me like an old man – a nervous old man.

'Elvis Presley,' I said to myself. I wonder how old you are. And where *did* you get that name?

About that time, my mother came home from work. She looked me up and down.

'Well, don't you look pretty. Where are you going?' I told her where I was going and promised to be home by 9:30. Glenda's brother, Chester, came to the door and walked me to the car. Glenda's mouth was still going at 90mph when I got in.

'Do you think I can pass for eighteen? I'm glad you're wearing a dress! You have to be eighteen to get into the club, and you have to wear a dress!' Chester assured us we would both pass, whistling his approval of my dress.

We got to the Airman's Club early. All visitors had to sign in at the door. We were worried that someone would ask for ID, but they didn't. Luck was with us; we made it in and found a table right up front. The club seated about three hundred people, and was filling up fast, mostly with young airmen who gave us loud wolf-whistles as we made our way through the tables. Glenda was pleased to see so few women – no more than thirty-five or so.

'Good,' she said. 'Now maybe we can get a chance to talk to him. Last night at the Slavonian Lodge it was wall-to-wall screaming girls; you couldn't get near him.'

'Maybe tonight you'll have your chance, Glenda.' She was squirming in her seat; I couldn't imagine why she was so excited.

The house lights dimmed, the music started, and Elvis made his entrance. I don't remember what he was wearing; I couldn't get past that face. 'That's All Right' was his first song. He was dancing all over the stage. Now I knew why my friend was on the edge of her seat. This young man was absolutely beautiful!

Several couples got up to dance, and it wasn't long before Glenda and I joined them. His live rendition of 'Blue Moon Of Kentucky' sounded much better than the recorded version. After eight or nine songs – his repertoire was very limited back then – the band took a break. Elvis was standing by the side entrance to the stage, talking to a small group of people. Glenda was dying to go talk to him, but I was being a little cool. He had looked my way a few times when he was singing, so I didn't want to appear anxious. Glenda noticed an arrow on the wall, just above Elvis's head, pointing to the ladies' room.

'Come on, June, let's go.'

As we slowly passed by, Elvis looked in our direction and smiled. I took Glenda by the arm and we kept on walking.

'June, let's stop and talk to him on the way back. Please?'

'You can if you want to, Glenda, but I'm not.'

Elvis, standing a head taller than anyone in the crowd, was looking our way when we came out of the ladies' room. As we were passing him again, he reached through the crowd and took me by the arm. I was trembling when I heard this low sexy voice speaking to me.

'Where're you going? You're not leaving, are you?' He was still holding my arm. I turned and looked up; his face was inches away. Somehow I managed a nervous little smile. For the first time in my life, I was at a loss for words.

'No, I'm just going back to the table.' My heart was racing,

I could feel the blood rush to my face. I'd figured that before the night was over, I'd get up enough nerve to go and say hello, but I was totally unprepared for this. He caught me completely off-guard.

'I'd like to see you after I finish here. Are you staying for the rest of the show? I'd like you to show me the town.'

'There's not much to see. Biloxi is a very small town.' I was babbling like an idiot, playing hard to get, and I didn't even know why.

'Just show me what you can, I'm not hard to please. I'll be through in about an hour. Wait for me; I won't be long. I have to load up a few instruments, okay?'

I nodded yes, and Glenda and I went back to our table. She was slapping me on my hand, and kept saying over and over, 'I don't believe it! You lucky dog! You lucky dog!'

Elvis came back on stage and sang for another forty minutes. Our table was surrounded by young airmen, wanting to dance. They were blocking our view of Elvis, so if we wanted to see him, we had to get up and dance whether we liked it or not.

After the show Glenda waited with me at the front of the club. Elvis drove up in a light pink and black 1955 Ford Crown Victoria. An upright bass was strapped to the top of the car. It was the funniest-looking thing; like some kind of war machine. He jumped out, came around and opened the door for me. We said goodbye to Glenda and Chester and drove away.

'Would you mind if we went back to the motel?' he asked. I swallowed hard, wondering what he had in mind. Before I could answer, though, he put my mind at ease.

'Just long enough for me to take a quick shower.' He had worked hard on stage; his shirt was soaking wet.

'Sure,' I laughed.

'I don't even know your name, pretty girl.'

'It's June. What's yours?'

'My name is Elvis.'

'No, I mean your *real* name.'

'My *real* name is Elvis.'

'Oh, I thought Elvis was just a stage name.'

'Nope, I've had it all my life. Would you mind waiting in the car, June? The boys are real messy, and there's no place to sit. I won't be long, I promise.'

'Sure, go ahead, I don't mind.'

Two men came out of Elvis's motel room. One went to the left side of the car, the other to the right. They opened both doors, then stood on the edge of the doorways to take the big bass down. At first I didn't know what they were doing, and I slid to the middle of the seat.

'Hi, I'm Scotty, and the one over there is Bill. Hope we didn't scare you, little lady!' Scotty played guitar and Bill was the bass man. I was happy to see the big bass come down. I could just imagine everyone in town staring at this thing – the car looked like a tank with a cannon on top. Elvis came out just as the boys were going in with the big bass. He told them not to worry; he'd be back before it was time for them to leave. They were leaving in the morning, heading for Alabama, to do some more shows.

'Okay, pretty girl, show me the town.'

'Have you already forgotten my name?'

'No, June, I haven't forgotten, it's just that you're so pretty.'

'Thanks. I'll bet you say that to all the girls.'

'Nope, only the pretty ones. Where to, pretty girl?'

'What are you in the mood for?' I asked, innocently. He raised his brows, looked at me and laughed.

'I can't answer that, June, you'd slap my face.' We both laughed. Not only did he have that great face, he had a sense of humor to match.

'Okay,' I said. 'What *else* are you in the mood for?'

'How about a nice place where we can get something to drink and get better acquainted.'

We drove a few blocks down the beach to Gus Stevens's restaurant and went into the lounge. We found a little table for two in the corner, away from the crowd. The band was to start at ten, and a comedian named Dave Gardner was coming on at eleven. When the waitress came to take our drink order, I was afraid she was going to ask me for an ID. I had a driver's license clearly stating that I was only seventeen.

'What would you like, baby?' Elvis asked, giving me a wink.

'I'll have a VO and 7-Up,' I answered, smiling at the waitress. My father had always kept a bottle of Seagram's VO whiskey on the kitchen table.

'Make mine a Coke, please.' He winked at me again.

'Never mind, I'll have a Coke too.' The waitress walked away smiling. She was so busy looking at Elvis that for all she knew I could have been a hundred.

'It's okay if you want a cocktail, June.'

'No, I really don't. I was just trying to make the waitress think I was older.'

'How old *are* you, June?'

'Not old enough to be in here,' I whispered.

'You mean you're not eighteen yet?'

'Not yet. I'll be eighteen in November.'

'I just turned twenty in January. Let's finish our drinks and get out of here.' But the band was good, so we ordered more Cokes, enjoyed the music, and each other. We decided not to stay for the comedian, so we went for a ride on the front beach. The night was perfect, with a slight breeze coming off the water. The edge was dotted with gas lights: it was that time of the year when people in Biloxi, usually two to a light, go looking for soft-shell crabs and flounder. I explained to Elvis what they were doing, and he got all excited.

'Can we go find some the next time I come to Biloxi?'

'Sure, my brother has a light and some gigs.'

'What in the world is a gig?'

'It's like a spear. You stick it in the flounder. It's lots of fun; I think you'll like it.'

'What about crabs? How do you catch them?' He realized what he'd said right after he said it, and we both started laughing. After I'd finally pulled myself together, I told him.

'You just reach down and pick them up. If they're soft they can't run very fast. If they're hard they'll bite you.'

'In other words, June, you're telling me you can't catch them from a toilet seat, right?'

We were laughing so hard Elvis had to pull the car over. We

found ourselves parked right in front of the White House Hotel, which had one of the longest piers in the city, jutting out over the water. We talked for a while and then decided to go for a walk on the pier. The full moon lit our way. It was a long walk, especially in high-heel shoes. He held my hand until we got to the end, then he turned me to face the rising moon and stood behind me with his arms around my waist.

'Have you ever seen the moon on the water before?' I asked.

'Not this much water! If you think this is pretty, you should see the moon on the snow. It's the most beautiful sight you'll ever see. Everything sparkles, and you can see for miles.' I leaned my head back on his shoulder, and he kissed my neck. I'd been kissed on the neck before, but never like that. It gave me chills! He said my name, and kissed my neck, again and again. I was trembling; I felt like I was going to melt.

'Right now, I can't think of any other place I'd rather be.'

'I can't either.' My voice was weak, and cracked slightly when I spoke. 'I'm glad I live here.'

'I'm not talking about living here, June, I'm talking about being here with you.'

'Well, thank you, Elvis Presley, I'm glad you're happy to be here with me.'

He turned me around, held me at arms length, and looked in my eyes.

'June, you don't have to be afraid of me; I'm not going to hurt you, I promise.'

'I'm not afraid of you, Elvis.'

'Why are you trembling, then?'

'I guess I'm a little nervous, that's all.'

He pulled me close, and took my face in his hands. He kissed my forehead, each eye, my nose, and finally my mouth. It was the most gentle, and yet the most passionate kiss I had ever experienced in all my seventeen years. We spent the next few hours kissing and talking, talking and kissing, and watching the moon move slowly across the sky. Elvis thought it funny when I told him I never kissed on a first date.

'It's the truth, I promise. This is the first time.'

'I believe you, baby. I'm glad it was me.'

'My mother always told me, if I ever got carried away, and found myself in a compromising position, to *stop* and ask myself, "What would my mother think, if she could see me right now?" It works! Speaking of Mother, what time is it?' He tried to see his watch by the light of the moon.

'It's either 1:15 or 3:05, I can't tell.'

'I've got to go home! I've never been out this late!' We ran back to the car. Dear God, I hoped it was 1:15, but the clock in the car said 3:15 – and I knew I was in big trouble.

Thank goodness my house was only five minutes away. When we pulled up in front, the house was in darkness, and everything was quiet.

'Maybe she's sleeping,' Elvis whispered.

'I hope so. Why are we whispering?' We giggled as if we were little kids getting away with something.

'Don't go yet, June, stay with me for a little while longer. Better yet, let's go wake her and tell her you're going with me.'

'Are you crazy? She'll kill us both! I'll stay, but if I see a light come one, I'll have to run.'

We were parked under a street light, and I could see his perfect features clearly. It was hard not to stare.

'What's your last name, June?'

'Juanico.' I had to spell it and say it over and over.

'It's pronounced like the name Juanita, but it has "co" on the end. Think you can remember that?'

'I'll never forget it – June Juanico.' He repeated it again and again.

'Do you have any brothers or sisters, Elvis?'

'I had a twin brother, but he died at birth.' When he said twin brother, my first thought was, Gee, there's another one just like you. My second thought was to wonder about the twin's name, because in the South it's a very common practice to give twins rhyming names. I could only think of one word to rhyme with Elvis.

'What would your mother have named your twin, if he had lived?'

'His name was Jesse Garon; mine is Elvis Aron.' His mother

chose to rhyme their middle names. I had a smile on my face, thinking that at least he had a name. I remember visiting my grandfather's grave and seeing several grave markers inscribed with just 'Baby Boy Smith' or 'Baby Boy Jones'. These babies had died at birth, and no one had bothered to give them a name. It always made me sad. Elvis misinterpreted my smile.

'I know what you're thinking, June: the only name you can think of that rhymes with Elvis is Pelvis. Can't you just see me introducing myself and my brother to strangers? "Uh, hello, my name is Elvis, and this here feller is my brother Pelvis".' He said it with such a red-neck Southern drawl, we both laughed.

'It's really no laughing matter, June. Believe it or not there's people out there who call me Elvis the Pelvis.'

'Why would anyone call you such a tacky name?'

'I guess when you start making a little noise in this business, you're gonna run into a few assholes along the way. Pardon my language. I try not to let it bother me. How about you? Any brothers or sisters?'

'One brother, his name is Jerry. He's two years older, but everyone thought we were twins when we were younger.'

'June, can I call you sometime?'

'Sure, my number's in the book. It's listed in my mother's name – her name is May. I was named after her: June comes after May. Do you think you'll get down this way again?'

'I'll make sure I do. I'll call you.'

'You promise?'

'I promise. I hate to leave you, baby, but I've got a long road ahead. I've been looking for you for a long time, June. But I've got to go; the boys will be worried about me. I've never been this late before.'

'Neither have I!'

'Take good care of yourself, baby.'

We got out of the car, he hugged me real close, and kissed me all over my face again. He didn't want to leave, and I didn't want him to leave either.

'I'll walk you to the door, June.'

'*No!* Mama's sleeping right there.' I pointed to the window.

'I hope you don't get in trouble, baby.'

'Me too.' I kissed him real quick and ran up to the house. He blew me a kiss before he got in the car. I watched him pull away, his arm out the window waving goodbye.

I tiptoed into the house to find Mama sitting on the side of the bed. I was sure she could hear my heart still pounding in my chest. Her voice was stern.

'Where have you been?'

'I've been sitting out in front of the house, talking. I'm okay, I haven't done anything wrong, I promise.'

'Well, come to bed, we'll talk about it in the morning.' She glanced over at the clock. 'June, do you know what time it is?'

'Yes, ma'am, it's 6:00 A.M. It won't ever happen again, Mama, I promise. It won't ever happen again.'

I crawled in next to her and shut my eyes. I had a hard time going to sleep; I couldn't stop thinking about this Elvis Presley. I wondered when I would see him again. Would he call me? He'd promised he would.

3

$\mathcal{O}$PERATOR #4

*T*HE AROMA OF freshly baked cinnamon rolls and crisp fried bacon was the one sure way Mama had of getting me out of bed in a flash. It was 10:00 A.M.; I'd been in bed only four hours, and two of those were spent recapturing the splendor of the night before. My stomach pangs told me I needed food more than I needed sleep. I hadn't had a bite to eat in twenty-four hours, and now I was starving. I brushed my teeth, washed my face and staggered blindly to the kitchen. I poured myself a cup of coffee, grabbed a hot cinnamon roll and sat down at the kitchen table. Mama was at the stove, with her back to me.

'Would you like some eggs? And would you mind telling me why you were out so late?'

While she was frying eggs, I started telling her all about Elvis Presley and the wonderful time we'd had. I was talking so fast she didn't have time to fuss at me.

'The next time this Elvis person comes to town, you'd better let me meet him, okay?'

'Okay, Mama, I will. Did Norbie call?'

'He called twice; I told him you got in late and were still sleeping. Is this Elvis as handsome as Norbie?'

'Well, they're both handsome; it's just that Elvis is real different; kind of sexy-looking.'

'*Sexy*! June, what do you know about sexy?'

'Oh, ma, you know what I mean.'

Someone was knocking at the front door. I was still in my PJs, so I ran to the bathroom. It was Norbie; I heard Mama tell him I was getting dressed. She came in the room shaking her head.

'I don't know, June, I've never seen anyone as handsome as Norbie Ronsonet!'

My mother was crazy about Norbie. He was not only handsome, he was a perfect gentleman as well. Good manners were important to Mama. It meant you came from a good family.

Norbie was in the living room, reading the sports section of the newspaper. He smiled at me over the top of the paper.

'Let's go spend the day at the river. Get your bathing suit on, the gang's waiting in the car.'

On the way to the river, one of Elvis's records came on the radio. A few of our friends had seen him the night before. One of the girls told me I should've been there, that Elvis Presley was so good-looking he had all the girls going wild. Feeling a little bit guilty, I looked at Norbie and smiled. We were free to date others, but until last night, I'd never done so. When I wasn't with Norbie I spent time with a group of girlfriends, and, like me, they all loved to dance. It was more fun going stag with a group of girls – then you could dance with all the guys. We could all be found every Sunday afternoon at the Beachwater Club jam sessions. Featuring some of the best dance bands in the South, the Beachwater was the gathering place for all the best dancers on the Gulf Coast.

Our group consisted of five girls. Marie; her sister, Rosalie; Rita Mae; Pat; and me. Pat Napier was a newcomer to the group. Her father, a sergeant in the Air Force, was stationed at Keesler. Pat and I spent a lot of time together, in her father's car, checking out all the local teen hangouts. Sergeant Napier, angry because his gas gauge was always on empty, started checking the mileage. The streets were never crowded, so whenever possible we drove around in reverse. Pat would look through the rear window to see where she was going, and I would look through the windshield to let her know if any cars were behind us. We still laugh about all the crazy stunts we used to pull.

One night, after going to an early movie, Pat came in to visit for a while. My brother Jerry was home having a snack. I didn't see much of him since he'd started working a night shift. As children we'd had our little fights, but basically we got along well. One day he removed a metal ice-tray from the freezer and told me to touch it with my tongue. I was dumb enough to do it, but smart enough to run to the kitchen sink and stick my tongue, along with the dangling ice tray, under the tap. In spite of his boyish pranks, he was still my hero. He could run faster, jump higher and throw a ball farther than anyone in the neighborhood.

'You should have been here ten minutes ago. You had a person-to-person phone call,' Jerry said as we walked in the door.

'Who was it?' I said curiously.

'I don't know,' Jerry answered.

'You don't know? Why didn't you ask?' My first thought was that Elvis had called, and when I get excited my voice gets louder and louder.

'Hey girl, don't yell at me! Why don't you stay home some-time and answer the phone yourself!' he yelled.

'I'm sorry, I didn't mean to shout. You don't know who it was?' I said meekly.

'No, I don't know who it was.' He was imitating me. 'But it's not the first time he called.'

'Why didn't you tell me?' I could hear myself getting loud again.

'"Cause I forgot, that's why!'

'How many calls have I had?'

'One other one, about two weeks ago.'

'How do you know it was a he?'

'Because when the operator asked him if he would like to try his call again, he said, no thank you, operator. All I know is he had a country twang.'

'Will you please do me a big favor? The next time, will you

please get the number or ask who's calling?' I knew it had to be Elvis; I didn't know anyone else who spoke with a twang.

Week after week went by, and no phone calls. Maybe it wasn't him after all. I was busy having a good time, and didn't give it too much thought.

Norbie was a High School senior and a football star, so I wasn't seeing much of him. Occasionally I would have a date with a guy named Edval Hughes. I felt very grown-up with Edval. He was a few years older, and would take me out for dinner and dancing – a lot different from hamburgers and Cokes at a drive-in. I loved getting all dressed up, and was spending all my money on clothes.

One day Pat and I went to Bernie's Drive Inn for a Coke. It was a local hangout, only two blocks away, so we didn't have to worry about the mileage. We were gone less than an hour, but when we got back Jerry told me I had just missed another person-to-person call.

'Did you ask who it was?'

'Dial O and ask for operator number four.'

When I called the operator and told her who I was, she said the caller hadn't left a name and couldn't be reached at that number any longer. The only thing she could tell me was that the call had come from Prichard, Alabama. I didn't know anyone in Prichard.

'Pat, do you know anyone from Prichard?'

'No, I don't even know where Prichard is!'

Curious about my phone call, Pat called the next morning.

'Did you ever figure out who you knew in Prichard?'

'Oh, yeah, it was Richard,' I answered, jokingly.

'Richard who?'

'Richard from Prichard! You remember him, don't you?'

'I don't remember any Richard from Prichard.'

'It's just a joke, Pat, just a joke.'

We laughed, and nothing about the calls was mentioned again.

4
$\mathcal{H}$E CALLED IT FATE

I WAS ALWAYS LISTENING to a pop radio station, so I didn't
hear much about Elvis. It wasn't until January 1956 that I
heard 'Heartbreak Hotel' for the first time. Boy, was I
impressed. He had come a long way from 'That's All Right'
and 'Blue Moon Of Kentucky'.

The first part of May, 1956, Marie had a vacation coming,
and asked the four of us if we wanted to go to Memphis. I
said I'd rather go to Florida, but she had the car, so we'd go
where she wanted to go. It really didn't matter, we always had
a good time regardless of where we were. We all started saving our money and making plans. Marie was more excited
than anyone. She had just bought a brand-new 'hot pink'
1956 Ford Fairlane. We were going in style.

We left Biloxi early one morning and arrived in Memphis
well after dark. We checked into the Holiday Inn, just outside
Memphis, across the Wolf River. After breakfast, we drove
downtown to check out all the stores and pick up a few souvenirs. We were browsing in a store on Beale Street, and
Marie was talking to an employee at Lansky Bros., asking him
for Elvis's address. She kept insisting that we were all close
friends, and had been invited. The man finally gave her the
address, saying it didn't matter, because Elvis wasn't in town;
he was on tour.

We had no trouble finding 1034 Audubon Drive. We parked the car on the street in front of the house. We could see a hoe and other equipment in the back yard, behind the privacy fence, and figured he must be building a swimming pool. We sat in the car, wondering if the pool was going to be in the shape of a guitar. There was no fence across the front, and curiosity got the better of us, so we decided to go take a peek. We piled out of the pink Ford and started walking up the driveway. We were almost to the house when we heard a car turn. Everyone stopped in their tracks. Everyone but me, that is; I kept walking toward the fence.

Elvis was behind the wheel of a big pink Cadillac; his mother and father were next to him in the front seat. Elvis and his father were both dressed in dark suits. Mrs Presley was wearing a black hat with a veil and a black dress. They looked as though they were returning from a funeral. Mr and Mrs Presley went in the house and Elvis walked over to where the girls were standing. By this time, I was standing by the fence, looking over at the pool, with my back turned to everyone. I don't know if I was playing hard to get or just embarrassed to be caught trespassing. Probably both!

'What are you doing home? You're supposed to be on tour,' Marie asked.

'I got called home yesterday. My cousin drowned and we had to go to the funeral. What are ya'll doing in Memphis?' He looked my way and I just smiled. Marie answered.

'We thought it would be a nice place to take a vacation.'

'Nice car, Marie. It is yours, right? I love the color.'

'I knew you'd like the color, Elvis. I thought of you when I bought it.' The Ford and the Cadillac were the same color. I was wondering why Marie had never said anything to me about knowing Elvis. He knew her name; would he remember mine? He motioned to the back yard.

'I'm having a pool put in.'

Everyone walked to the fence to have a look. Elvis came up behind me, put his hands on my waist, and lifted me off the fence.

'What are you doing here, June? You vacationing too?' I

just smiled, not saying anything. At least he remembered my name.

'The last time I was in Biloxi, someone told me you were engaged to be married.' He looked at Marie and then back to me.

'Well, someone told you wrong. I'm not, nor have I ever been, engaged to be married. How are you, Elvis?'

'I'm doing great, June. I can't believe you're here. How long are you going to be in Memphis?'

'We're supposed to stay a week.'

He wanted to know where we were staying, and what we were going to do that night. All the while, he was holding my hand.

'We were talking about going to a movie tonight. I guess we're still going.' I looked at Marie and she nodded yes.

Mrs Presley came to the door and told Elvis to come eat. She was giving him a polite way of saying goodbye, saving him from his fans. He told us goodbye and said he hoped he'd see us later. I thought he was just being polite; I didn't think we'd see him again. We went back to the motel. His name wasn't mentioned.

That night we went to see *The Man Who Knew Too Much*, with Doris Day and Jimmy Stewart. We'd been in the show about fifteen minutes when Elvis came in and sat down next to me.

'What are you doing here? I didn't expect to see you,' I whispered.

'Well, are you glad to see me or not?' he whispered back.

'Yes, I'm glad to see you, just surprised, that's all. How did you know we were here?'

'I spotted the pink Ford.'

He was holding my hand, and every now and then he would give it a little squeeze.

After the movie – I haven't the foggiest idea what it was about – Elvis invited the five of us back to his house. He could have easily fit us all in the huge black Cadillac he was driving, the one used by his band, but he wanted to be alone with me. Elvis led the way, with the pink Ford following close behind. He had opened the passenger side for me to get in, and that's where I was sitting. The car was so wide I felt like I was a block away.

'I tried to call you, June. I even asked about you the last time I was in Biloxi. I called several times and no one was home, and when I did get an answer, it was always a man's voice. I figured it was the man you were engaged to.'

'Did you call person-to-person?'

'Yes, I always do.'

'Do you remember me telling you I had an older brother?'

'Was that who answered the phone?' he said with relief.

'Why didn't you leave a number? I would have called you back.'

'I was on the road, June. I wasn't in any one place long enough. Well, anyway, I'm glad I found you again. What are you sitting way over there for? Come sit next to me.' He put his arm around me, and pulled me so close I was almost in his lap.

'I still think about that night on the pier, June. Somehow I knew we'd be together again, I just knew it.' Country twang and all, I loved listening to his voice.

Elvis's parents were sitting in the den when we walked in. They excused themselves and went to the kitchen, leaving the room for Elvis and his guests.

Marie started the conversation by telling Elvis she'd seen him every time he was on television, on the *Stage Show* and the *Milton Berle Show* too. I sat quietly, unable to join in the conversation because at that time I was totally unaware that Elvis had ever made any television appearances. We didn't have a television set at my house. We were lucky to have food in our stomachs and clothes on our backs. I was glad when Mrs Presley entered the room carrying a tray of cookies and Cokes for everyone. Now maybe the TV talk would stop. Elvis said 'excuse us' to the girls, pulled me up from the couch, and took me down the hallway to his bedroom door.

'I want to be with you while you're here. Is that okay with you?'

'Sure, I'd like to be with you, too.'

'I'll call you in the morning; we can spend the day together, maybe go motorcycle riding. You're at the Holiday Inn out by the river, right?'

'Right! Boy oh boy, you're the fastest worker I've ever seen. You don't waste any time, do you?'

'I only have so much time for myself, June, and if I don't take advantage of it, then it's lost forever. I'll call you in the morning, baby.'

I gave him the room number, kissed him gently on the lips and we went back to join the girls. I could tell Elvis was tired, so I looked at my watch, announced that it was getting late and suggested we call it a night. He gave me a wink.

5
$\mathcal{T}$HE RIDE OF MY LIFE

IT WAS AROUND 10:00 A.M. when Elvis drove up to the door of
our hotel on his 450 Honda motorcycle. The room was pool-
side, a short walk from the parking lot and through the
courtyard. Elvis didn't park the bike and walk; instead he
drove through the courtyard, around the pool, and up to the
door. He didn't have to announce his arrival – the roar of the
motorcycle did it for him. He had phoned the room at nine,
telling me he was on his way. He was all dressed in black, and
so was I. I climbed on the bike behind him, and he reached
one arm around me and pulled me in close.

'Is that as close as you can get, June?' he said, joking.

'If I get any closer, I'll be sitting in front!' I said.

'That's not a bad idea.'

Off we went for the grand tour, riding all over the city. The
first stop was to buy me a motorcycle hat like the one he was
wearing, cocked slightly to one side. He parked the bike in
front of the store, and we went in to look around. We were
the only customers. Elvis knew the owner and chatted with
him about how things were going in the record business. By
this time, Elvis had cut over twenty records, not including 'My
Happiness' and 'That's When Your Heartaches begin',
recorded for his mother back in 1953. He had just last month

received his first gold disc, for selling a million copies of 'Heartbreak Hotel'. He introduced me to the owner of the store.

'This is my sweetheart from Biloxi, Mississippi. Ain't she the prettiest little thing you ever did see?' The man looked me up and down, smiling. While giving me the once over, an alarmed look came on his face.

'What happened, little lady?'

I looked down where he was staring, and discovered my right foot was covered in blood. I was wearing black ballerina pumps, not exactly the perfect shoe for a motorcycle date, but it was either that or barefoot sandals. Blood was even down in my shoe. The man ran to the back of the store and returned with a wet towel. Elvis took the towel, sat me on some boxes, removed my shoe and started cleaning my ankle and foot. The blood had already dried in most places. Elvis was being very gentle, trying to find out where the blood was coming from. He paused for a moment, looking at my foot from all different angles.

'Damn, June, has anyone ever told you you have pretty feet?' He was smiling as he said it. I'd heard the same thing from a few shoe salesmen, but I thought it was just a line. To me, feet were just feet.

'No, Elvis,' I lied. 'You're the first.'

When all the blood was removed, he found the cut and nodded.

'How did that happen?' the store-owner inquired.

'I know exactly how it happened, and this isn't the first time either.' I looked at him; I was puzzled.

'I don't remember this ever happening before.'

'Oh no, not to you, baby,' he laughed. 'It happened to another friend I took riding one day. Same cut, same leg, same place. It's that damn tag on the back of my bike.'

The cut was actually a deep thin scratch, about an inch long, on the top inside of my right ankle. I still have the scar today. I wonder if Elvis's other friend still has hers?

We left the store wearing our matching hats, mine cocked to one side, too. When we got to the bike, the first thing he did was feel the edge of the license plate; it was razor sharp. He covered the tag with his hand, and told me to raise my leg real high whenever I was getting on.

Our next stop was a man's clothing store on Beale Street. The store catered mainly to black men, and a few customers were browsing around. The owner of this store was also Elvis's friend.

'This is where I buy most of my clothes,' he said proudly. The owner and the customers greeted Elvis.

'Where you at, man? What's happenin'?'

'I'm just doing my thing, man, trying to make a buck.' You could tell they all liked Elvis; he was 'cool' and he was singing their kind of music. After shaking hands with everyone, he introduced me again as his sweetheart from Biloxi, Mississippi.

'She even has pretty feet!' he said. We picked out a few shirts and Elvis gave them to the owner, saying he would pick them up later.

Our next venture was to Mudd Island. When Elvis said 'island', I was expecting to see white sand and palm trees, like the islands off the Mississippi Coast, but this was nothing more than a long stretch of blacktop.

'How fast do you want to go, baby?'

'As fast as you can!' I answered.

'Okay, pull your hat down and hold on tight.' My heart was pounding; I was holding on for dear life. After about five minutes of flying fast, we slowed and came to a stop.

'How fast were we going?' I had my head buried in his back, too afraid to peek over his shoulder at the speedometer.

'Oh, about 120mph. Why? Were you afraid?'

'Who, me? No! I know you wouldn't let anything happen to me.' If he'd suggested we did it again, I'd have wet my pants.

'Well, I was! Feel my heart!' I put my hand on his chest – his heart was pounding faster than mine, and mine was about to jump out! I didn't know if it was from fear or the excitement of the ride. We laughed and hugged; we were both out of breath.

We sat at the edge of the island and watched the churning waters of the muddy Mississippi river. Elvis started singing.

'Ole man river, that ole man river, he don't say nothin', he must know somethin', he just keeps rollin', he keeps on rollin' along.' His voice was so smooth and deep I couldn't believe it. I had goose-bumps; it made me shiver. He put his arm around my shoulder, thinking I was cold.

'I had no idea your voice was so powerful. Why aren't you using it? You should let everyone hear you sing like that.' I was being complimentary, but he mistook it for criticism.

'You really can sing, Elvis Presley. I'm impressed.'

'What do you mean, *really*? I thought I *was* singing. You don't like the way I sing?' He was getting a little upset.

'I love the way you sing! It's just that you have this rich powerful voice, and no one knows about it. Have you ever heard of Mario Lanza?'

'Yeah, but he's an opera singer, June. I sing rock'n'roll and ballads.'

'I'm not talking about the type of songs, I'm talking about the way he sings them. You have the same quality – the power, the strength. It's music you can feel. You have that same kind of voice. You can make people feel your music as well as hear it. It's a great gift you have, and I think you should share it with everyone. Has anyone ever heard you sing like that before?'

'Only my mama,' he said tenderly.

Evidently, I'd said the right words this time. He didn't seem to be upset with me any more.

'Why only your mama?' I asked.

'Because she loves to hear me sing, and never criticizes. She's the reason I became a singer in the first place. She convinced me I had a beautiful voice, and gave me the confidence to get up and sing in public.'

'Well, thank heaven for your mother. She was right. I got goose-bumps listening to you sing just now. Mario Lanza was the only singer who ever gave me goose-bumps before. Have you ever heard a song called "O Sole Mio"?'

'I don't know. How does it go?'

I tried to sing what little I knew, and ended up la-la-la-ing the rest of it. He smiled, he liked it.

Four years later, in 1960, Elvis recorded 'It's Now Or Never' the English version of 'O Sole Mio'. I wonder if he was thinking of our time on Mudd Island when he was in the recording studio. I'd like to think he was; I know I do, whenever I hear it playing.

Sitting there on the edge of the island, so immersed in conversation and each other, we didn't realize how hot we were getting, sitting in the sun in our black clothes, until Elvis gently wiped the beading perspiration from my upper lip. We got back on the bike and rode until the wind had dried our shirts and cooled us down.

We stopped at a children's amusement park, and Elvis went straight to a concession stand advertising foot-long hot dogs. We found a shady spot and enjoyed our dogs, a bag of chips, and a Coke. Elvis walked over to the concession stand to dispose of our trash and came back with two tickets to ride the train.

The train had a smoke-stack, about ten cars, and a caboose. It looked just like the real thing only it was about a quarter of the size. Except for the engine, all the cars were topless, so you could sit inside. It was in the middle of the week, so the park wasn't crowded – there were only about six other passengers, mostly parents with children, also boarding the train. We ran and jumped in the caboose. We noticed a little boy, having a temper tantrum, wanting to ride in the caboose, but it was already occupied by two other children – Elvis and me. His dad was telling him they'd ride in the middle this time and next time they could ride in the caboose. He refused to get on the train; it was the caboose or nothing. The father was embarrassed by his son's behaviour, and gave us a little smile.

It was a short ride around and through the park, lasting maybe ten minutes. When we got off the train, the daddy gave us another smile while the little boy gave us his meanest glare. A woman, standing behind the little boy, probably his mother, said to us sarcastically, 'Some people never grow up!'

Elvis smiled politely. She was still saying something when Elvis started up the bike and revved the engine. He shook his head as we drove away.

'No wonder the kid is so bad; he takes after his mama,' he yelled at me over the roar of the engine. I was proud of him for not swapping remarks with her.

I learned a lot about Elvis Presley that day. It was always yes ma'am, no ma'am, yes sir, no sir, please and thank you very much. Mrs Presley was doing a fine job of raising a real Southern gentleman.

Cramming a two-day tour into one, we rode all over the city of Memphis that day. He took me by Humes High School, proudly showing me where he had graduated, and even the electrical company where he had worked as a truck driver. When he pointed out the kind of truck he drove, I teased him about it.

'When you said you were a truck driver, I thought you meant a *truck* driver, like an eighteen-wheeler.'

'A truck is a truck, June.'

'I know, Elvis, but there are *big trucks* and little trucks.'

'Okay, so I was a little truck driver. I know one thing for sure June, big or little, when a truck pulls up next to you, you'd better have your skirt down and your legs together, cause they all have a good view. I know! It was my favorite part of the job. I'm only kidding – you know I wouldn't do that.'

We laughed. We both knew he would.

We then went to the radio station and the recording studio, where he introduced me to Dewey Phillips, a close friend, who had helped him get his start. Everywhere we went, people were glad to see him. It was easy to see how much Elvis was respected and loved in his home town.

Later that afternoon, we were riding down a four-lane street, in the middle of town, and had to stop for a red light. A dozen or more sailors were crossing the street in front of us. One of the sailors said, 'I know who you are, but I'd rather know who that is on the back of your bike.'

Elvis took off, ran the red light, and had the sailors

scrambling for safety. A few miles down the street he stopped the bike and we got off.

'You asked for that, June!' he said angrily, his arms folded across his chest.

'Asked for what?' I answered innocently.

'You were flirting with those guys – don't tell me you weren't!' I had to laugh. He was so far off base, I couldn't believe it.

'Well, Elvis Presley, I think you're jealous!'

'I'm not jealous, June, I think that was uncalled-for.'

'Well, so do I! You should have ignored them. And don't accuse me of flirting! That was a crazy thing to do driving off like that; you could have hurt someone.' I was pretending to be angry.

'Yeah, I guess it *was* a dumb thing to do. It just made me mad, that's all. I won't stand for anyone making any kind of smart remarks to you.' Now, he was pretending to be nice.

'But it wasn't a smart remark to me, Elvis, the guy knew who you were and wanted to get a rise out of you, that's all. Do you realize we've only been together a few days and we're already having a lovers' quarrel?'

'That's 'cause I'm crazy mad about you, June. I've never been this crazy over anyone before, and I don't know how to handle it.' He sounded sincere, but I'd heard lines from guys before, and usually when they got that sweet they wanted something in return. I could feel the blood rushing through my body, so I tried to take his sweet confessions of love lightly, or, as my mother would say, with a grain of salt. Or else be swept off my feet and into his bed.

'You're so full of bull, Elvis Presley, your eyes should be brown.'

'And just what is that supposed to mean, June?'

'You know, Elvis. Brown – as in bullshit.'

'You're crazy, June, that's why I love you.' He said, laughing. He didn't know it, but my silly remarks were sometimes my shield. He lifted my feet off the ground and whirled me around, kissing me ever so tender before putting me down. I was crazy mad about him too, and I think he knew it. There were times when we wouldn't say a word; we just got lost in each other's eyes. Trying not to fall in love with Elvis was next to impossible.

I hated to think of the day coming to an end, but it was getting late. When we got back to the hotel I kissed the back of his neck, got off the bike, and started to walk away. He hadn't mentioned anything about seeing me again. He grabbed me and pulled me to him and kissed me on the forehead.

'Go rest for a while, baby, I'll be back to pick you up in a few hours. Okay?'

'Okay! I'll be ready!' I said anxiously.

Elvis had been gone long enough to shave, shower, and get dressed. He knocked on the motel door to the rhythm of Shave-and-a-Haircut-Two-Bits. I invited him in to visit with me and the girls for a while, but he had to decline.

'We can't stay, June, Mama and Daddy are expecting us back at the house to have dinner with them. I hope you haven't eaten.'

'No, I haven't had time. It took me an hour just to get the tangles out of my hair.'

The girls were leaving too, going to see another movie. Even though Memphis was a large city, it offered very little in the way of entertainment for the average tourist. We all walked to the parking lot, where the two pink cars were parked side by side. Elvis had to give them all a goodbye hug.

'Sorry about the rush, June, it was a last-minute thing. When I got out of the shower, Mama called me to come eat. When I told her I didn't have time, she was disappointed. I felt bad about it June, I really haven't been spending much time with her, so I told her I'd pick you up and be right back, then we could all have dinner together. I hope that's okay with you.'

'That's fine with me, Elvis, I'd like to meet your parents.'

Mrs Presley was waiting for us at the door.

'Mama, this is June. June, this is my mother.'

'It's good seeing you again, June. Elvis forgot his manners

the other night, and didn't introduce anyone,' she said, teasing him.

'It's nice seeing you again too, Mrs Presley.'

We followed her to the dining room, where Mr Presley was already seated at the table.

'C'mon and sit right here across from me, June. Both my men always sit on each end.' I started to sit when Elvis introduced me to his father. Mr Presley was about to stand when I grabbed his hand and gave it a hearty shake.

'Please, don't get up, Mr Presley. It's nice to meet you.'

'It's not easy getting out of these chairs with arms. It's nice to meet you too, June.'

He was speaking of the big Captain's chairs at both ends of the table. This was one of the few times Mr Presley said more than three words to me. Mrs Presley brought some food to the table.

'Can I help you with something, Mrs Presley?' I asked.

'No thank you, hon, I just have to get the biscuits out of the oven. The rest is done.'

Mrs Presley didn't have much to say that night, either. Elvis told me later they'd had a little disagreement about eating so late. I was relieved; I thought it was because of me.

The Presleys went to bed shortly after dinner, and Elvis and I watched a little TV. We decided to go for a ride, this time in the car, and went back to Mudd Island. Elvis wanted me to see how pretty it was at night. It was pretty; lights, off in the distance, were twinkling all around us. We parked down by the river and watched the lighted tug boats passing by. It was very romantic. I couldn't help but wonder how many girls he'd brought here before me.

'I have a confession to make, June—' I didn't give him a chance to finish his sentence.

'I know, Elvis, I'm not the first girl you've brought here.' He laughed as if that was the funniest thing he'd ever heard.

'That's not what I was going to say. You're right, though!' Now we were both laughing.

'Now let me finish, before I forget what the hell I was talking about in the first place. Too late, I already forgot.'

'You were talking about a confession, remember?'

'Oh yeah! Remember how fast we went today, on the motorcycle? Well I've never been that fast before. I was scared!'

'*You* were scared! I almost wet my pants.'

'Uh oh, June, don't tell me you're a little PP britches.' Apparently Elvis's mother called him that when he wet his pants as a little boy.

'It was close, Elvis, real close!'

We laughed and hugged and kissed until we got close to being carried away. We were both breathing heavy, and decided we'd better stop before it was too late. It was getting late, and we were both tired. He didn't want to, but finally agreed to take me back to the Holiday Inn. I was in his face so much, I don't know how he could see where he was driving.

'I don't wanna leave you, June, come home with me, stay with me tonight,' he pleaded.

'I can't do that, Elvis! I've never done anything like that before.' I was confused by his invitation, but I knew I wanted to go with him. I didn't know what was holding me back.

'I wouldn't do anything but hold you close to me, June, I promise.'

'I can't. I just can't, please don't ask me to.' Now I was pleading. I was afraid he'd think less of me if I said yes.

'Okay, baby, I guess it's better this way. I'll pick you up tomorrow morning,' he said reluctantly.

'What time?'

'I don't know. I'll call first.'

'Give me enough time to get ready, okay?'

'Okay, baby. Are you sure you don't want to come home with me?'

'That's just it, Elvis, I *do* want to go home with you, but I just can't. What would your parents think? What would my friends think? And what would you think about me?'

'I don't know about them, June, but I think it would be great. I've dreamed about you, June, several times.'

'Go home and dream about me tonight, then I can be with you and not have any guilty feelings. Okay?'

'Okay, baby, whatever you say. You're the boss for tonight.'
We shared a long kiss goodnight, and I watched him walk
back to the car. I felt like running after him, but I didn't. Not
only did I want to spend the night with him, I wanted to stay
with him forever.

6
$\mathcal{H}$ARD FRIED EGGS
AND BACON

W HEN ELVIS CALLED the room early the next morning, I grabbed the phone on the first ring.

'June, is that you, baby?'

'Yes, it's me.'

'I've got to stay close to the phone; will it be okay if we just hang out around here today? Mama would like to get to know you better, anyway. How soon can you be ready?'

'I need at least thirty minutes to shower and get dressed. I'm not even awake yet,' I whispered, trying not to disturb the girls.

'Okay,' he whispered back.

'Don't knock on the door; I'll come out as soon as I'm ready.'

'I'll see you in thirty minutes.'

The room was so dark I had to feel my way to the bathroom. I switched on the light, leaving the bathroom door open so I could find my suitcase in the crowded room. I brought my suitcase into the bathroom, only to find it full of dirty clothes. I opened the door, just a crack, to let some light in. Pat had been thoughtful enough to hang all my clothes. Now where was my underwear? I opened the door a little wider so I could find the dresser. My toes were cracking with every step. My things must be in a drawer, but which one?

I took a quick shower and got dressed. I was putting mascara on my lashes when I heard a little tap on the bathroom door. It was Pat. I opened the door and let her in. The bright light was making her squint her eyes. She looked Oriental.

'What do you want, Patsy Wong?' I asked, teasing.

'Are you just getting home?' she asked in a squeaky voice.

'No, silly, I was in bed next to you all night,' I croaked. My voice was always deep in the mornings; even deeper if I hadn't had much sleep.

'Gee, I was so dead to the world, I didn't know who I was in bed with. Are you leaving again?'

'Yes, Elvis will be here any minute.'

'Where ya'll going?'

'Over to his house; I'll call you later,' I said, in a hurry to finish my eyes.

Elvis was waiting for me in the courtyard, with a big smile on his face. He was neatly dressed in a white shirt and black pants. We both laughed; I was wearing black and white too.

'Have you been waiting long? I tried to hurry.'

'No, baby, I just got here. Why are you out of breath?'

'I've been running around in the dark, trying to be quiet, tripping over shoes, trying to find my clothes, take a shower, and all that without waking anyone.'

'Did you get a good night's sleep?' he asked.

'I'm not sure; I wasn't in bed long enough to know.'

'You can take a little nap when we get to my house.'

'No, I'm fine, really I am.' He turned me sideways, looking at my rear end.

'You can say that again, June. You're fine all right.'

'Elvis Presley, you're crazy!'

'You're right, June Juanico. Crazy about your ass!' I playfully slapped him on the back of the head and ran to the car. He caught me, scooped me up in his arms, and carried me the rest of the way, biting me on the neck all the while.

'Umm, you smell good! What kind of perfume do you have on?'

'Chanel No. 5; you like it?'

'I love it, June, don't use any other kind.'

He put me down to unlock the car and then picked me up again, saying he wanted to carry me over the threshold. We were both laughing as he twice tried to slide me in, bumping my head both times. Every time he banged my head, he laughed even harder. He got so tickled he finally had to put me down and let me get in by myself.

'Sit next to me, baby,' he said, patting the seat next to him. This became a ritual; he'd do it every time we got in the car.

'Smelling your perfume reminds me of the first night we met. Do you remember that first night, June?'

'Like it happened yesterday,' I said, smiling.

'I remember everything about that night, June, I even remember what you were wearing. At first glance, I thought you were a colored girl. You were on the dance floor, and all I could see was this gorgeous figure in a tight white dress. When you got a little closer to the stage, I could see that you were white. You had the darkest suntan I've ever seen. When you smiled at me, all I could see was your blue eyes and your white teeth, shining. What happened to your suntan?'

'I haven't started on it yet. It's still early; the water's still cold.'

'What's the water got to do with it?'

'I don't go to the beach just to get a suntan. I go to swim – the suntan just happens. That's about all there is to do in Biloxi. You'll have to come spend some time down there, and get a little color in your cheeks.'

'Yeah, I am kinda white. I'm gonna have some time off pretty soon; maybe I *will* go to Biloxi.'

'Good, we can swim and fish, and live in the sun.'

'You'll have to teach me to swim, June, I've never learned.'

'You've never learned to swim? Why not?'

'I wasn't raised around the water, and Mama wouldn't let me go to the creek. She's always been a little over-protective because of my twin dying, I guess. Anyway, we didn't have a pool in our back yard, except of course, the *cess*-pool.' He laughed. 'And it was a long time before we even had one of those. Have you ever had to use an outhouse, June?'

'No, thank God, but my mother had to use one when she was little. One time she slammed the outhouse door and a snake fell on her shoulders. After hearing that story I could never go in one. I'd have to wet my pants, or go in the woods.'

'I went in the woods a lot, when I was a kid. We were poor, when I was coming up, June, real poor. My mama and daddy have made a lot of sacrifices for me, June. You can't imagine how good it makes me feel to be able to do something for them now. They really had it rough, but thank God, not any more!' I was so touched by his concern for his parents, I didn't know what to say. I snuggled up close, and kissed him on the cheek.

'I love you, Elvis Presley.' He looked at me and smiled, knowing I meant it in a nice sort of way.

'Let's talk about you for a change, June. I've heard you talk about your mother, but you've never mentioned your father. Why is that? You do have a father, don't you?'

I laughed, thinking of making a joke about being a bastard, but this was a serious conversation and I thought it would be in bad taste.

'My mother and father were divorced when I was eleven years old. When my father divorced my mother, he divorced me too. He's remarried, and I never see him. You want to talk about sacrifices? My mother knows all about sacrifices. She raised me and my brother all by herself.' I couldn't say anything else; I always got a lump in my throat when I thought of my mother and father getting a divorce.

'I'm sorry, baby, I didn't mean to get you upset. I was just wondering, that's all. Let's just talk about you and me.'

'Okay, there's you, Elvis Presley, and there's me, June Juanico. And I'm so glad I ran into you again!'

'It was fate, June. It was meant to be!'

'I guess you could say it *was* fate: all of our meetings have been somewhat arranged, so to speak. If it weren't for Glenda's insistence that night, I'd never have gone to the

Airman's Club. And this time it was Marie's decision to come here. I didn't even know you lived in Memphis.'

'I wasn't even supposed to be here, June. If my cousin hadn't drowned, I'd be in Hollywood right now. We were meant to be.'

Mrs Presley heard the car drive up, and was standing in the doorway.

'Hi, June, it's good to see you again. C'mon in, I just made some coffee. You do drink coffee, don't you, June?'

'Yes ma'am, first thing every morning. I'd love a cup.' Alberta, Mrs Presley's new housekeeper, was shelling field peas with Mrs Presley at the kitchen table. Mrs Presley cleared a spot and Alberta poured Elvis and me a cup of coffee.

'If you get me a bowl, I'll help with the peas,' I said. Alberta got a bowl from the cabinet, and sat it in front of me. It looked like a social gathering out on the farm, with everyone sitting around the table, shelling peas. Elvis picked up one of the long brownish pods, broke it in half, played with it a while and threw it back on the pile.

'Alberta, what do you think of my girl? This is June, my sweetheart, from Biloxi, Mississippi. Ain't she the cutest thing you ever did see?' I thought he was going to say something about my feet again, but he didn't.

'She sure is!' Alberta said, grinning.

'Nice to meet you, Alberta,' I answered nervously. I raked my thumb down the center of the pod, letting the peas fall in the bowl.

'I see you've done this before, June,' commented Mrs Presley.

'Oh, yes, ma'am, I didn't know vegetables came in a can until a few years ago,' I said. Everyone laughed. Elvis got up, came behind me, leaned down and kissed me on the cheek.

'I've got to make a few phone calls, June, you show 'em how to pick peas while I'm gone.' He then kissed his mom's cheek and whispered something in her ear.

I had started getting nervous when we pulled in the drive, thinking about how quiet it was at the table the night before. I was finally beginning to relax when, unintentionally, Mrs

Presley started giving me the third degree.

'Do you live on a farm, June?' she asked, remembering my comment about the fresh vegetables.

'No ma'am, I'm a city girl. My mother always brought home fresh vegetables, and I did most of the cooking.'

'You did?' She looked surprised.

'Yes ma'am! I didn't have much choice. My parents were divorced when I was eleven and my mother had to go to work. I had to stand on a little step-stool in order to reach the stove. I could reach it standing on my tiptoes, but I couldn't see down in the pots without the stool.'

'Do you like to cook, June?'

'Yes ma'am, I love it; I'm always trying new recipes of my own, sometimes they're good, sometimes they're awful,' I laughed. I dumped my little bowl of peas, already filled to the top, into the big bowl. My mouth wasn't the only thing going at high speed; so were my fingers.

'You sure know how to pick peas; you've picked more than me and Mrs Presley put together,' Alberta said, smiling.

'That's because ya'll have been talking and I've been pickin' peas.' Mrs Presley laughed, showing me a handful of peas in the bottom of her bowl.

'June, you've been doing all the talking and the pea pickin' too,' Mrs Presley said.

'I'm sorry! I guess I have been talking up a storm.'

'No, don't be sorry, hon, keep on talking; I like hearing all about you. What else can you do besides cook?'

'Let me see, I know how to sew, I embroider and crochet, and I'm good at cleaning house. I don't do laundry well, but I'm pretty good with the ironing-board and iron.' I wasn't meaning to sound boastful, I was just so nervous I was going down the list, trying to tell her everything in one sentence, so I could get it all out and not feel like I was on the witness stand being interrogated.

'You know how to sew, too?' she persisted.

'Yes ma'am, I make most of my own clothes.' I knew a simple 'Yes' would have been sufficient, but my nerves wouldn't let me slow down.

'You're kidding! You don't look like you could do all that. Most girls your age don't know how to do all that,' she continued.

'I guess it's because I started out so young.'

'It's just that you're so pretty, and you already know how to do all those things. That's very unusual, June.'

'Thanks, Mrs Presley.' I said. Alberta, sitting quietly up to this point, looked at me and smiled.

'Child, you gonna make somebody a good wife.' I smiled with embarrassment and emptied another bowl of peas. Mrs Presley laughed, showing me she still hadn't finished her first bowl.

'Did you make the clothes you have on, June?'

'I bought the blouse, but I made the skirt.'

'Stand up, let me see,' she said with enthusiasm. She inspected the hem, the waistband, the zipper, and even the kick-pleat in the back.

'You did a beautiful job, June, very professional. How long have you been sewing?'

'Gee, Mrs Presley, I don't know. I used to watch my mother sew all the time; she made all my clothes when I was little. I guess I started sewing right after she went to work. I was about twelve years old.'

'You could sew for other people, June. Have you ever thought about that? A good seamstress makes good money.'

'Not really, Mrs Presley, sewing is very hard, plus it's time-consuming. I designed and made Easter dresses for two of my friends who are here in Memphis with me, but I wouldn't want to do it professionally. I like doing it for fun.' Here I was, sounding boastful again, and trying not to. Shut up June, I thought to myself.

'My goodness, June, you have all that talent, and you're pretty to boot.'

'Thank you, Mrs Presley. You're making me blush.'

'I wish you'd call me Gladys, June, I want you to feel at home.'

'I do feel at home, Mrs Presley, but I was taught at a young age to call my elders Mr or Mrs. It was drilled into my head.

My mother said it was a sign of good manners and respect. I'd have a hard time calling you by your first name.'

'Well anyway, June, my name is Gladys Love Presley, and you can call me whatever makes you happy.'

'Your middle name is Love? I've never heard that before, Mrs Presley. Love is a beautiful name.'

'Thanks, June. You're very sweet.'

All the peas had finally been shelled. I helped Alberta clear the table, and Mrs Presley poured us another cup of coffee.

'That's it for now. Let's finish our coffee and go find Elvis. Alberta can start breakfast when we get out of her kitchen.' I gulped the hot coffee and breathed a sigh of relief. My mind was ready for a break.

We found Elvis lying across his made-to-order, larger-than-king-size bed. He was sound asleep, an opened copy of *Billboard* magazine resting on his chest. With his hair hanging in his face he looked like an innocent little boy. Mrs Presley admired her beautiful son for a moment before tenderly brushing his hair from his eyes.

'Wake up, baby boy, you've got company.' Elvis sat straight up, and apologized for falling asleep.

'Elvis, did you know that June can cook?'

'Can you, June?' he said, surprised. 'You'll have to cook something for me one of these days.'

'I'll be happy to. What's your favorite dish?'

Mrs Presley went back to the kitchen. Elvis closed the door behind her and pulled me over to the massive bed.

'You're my favorite dish, June,' he said, laughing. He picked me up and threw me in the middle of the bed. We were rolling over and over, laughing like children. He was kissing me all over my face. He had my arms pinned over my head and was half sitting on my stomach. I stopped laughing and was trying to get my arms free. He stopped laughing too. He could tell by the expression on my face that something was wrong.

'What's the matter, June? Was I hurting you, baby?' Having my arms pinned down reminded me of an unpleasant incident that had happened on a date when I was sixteen years old. This guy had me pinned down in the back seat of his car at a drive-in movie. The fact that there was another couple in the front seat didn't slow him down at all. The more I struggled, the tighter he held me. He was trying to hold both wrists with one hand, leaving the other hand free to fondle my body. He was very strong, and I was almost paralyzed with fear. I got one hand free, and was feeling around the floor for something to hit him with. I had just finished a cold drink, and I knew the bottle was down there somewhere. I came up with the heavy Barq's root-beer bottle and crashed it across his head. The other couple stopped smooching when they heard him yell. We dropped him off at the emergency room to be stitched up, and they took me home.

'What's the matter, baby?' Elvis said. 'You're not afraid of me, are you?'

'We shouldn't be in here. Your parents will think I'm wild – or something worse.'

'My parents won't think anything of the kind, June.'

'Well at least get up and open the door, okay?'

'Okay, June, if that'll make you feel better.' He opened the door as wide as it would go, ran back to the bed and started tickling me.

'Now, does that make my girl happy? Mama wouldn't think anything bad about you, June. She likes you.'

'I want her to keep liking me. And how do you know she does?'

''Cause she told me so just a few minutes ago. When I left you in the kitchen I didn't have to make any calls. I wanted you to spend some time with Mama, so she could get to know you. She really likes you, June, she told me so.'

We got into a playful wrestling match, with a few kisses thrown in here and there, and ended up on the floor several times. When his mouth bumped into mine we didn't think much about it, until we both tasted blood. One of us had a busted lip, but it didn't matter. We climbed back on the bed and continued to wrestle until Mrs Presley came in and told us to come eat.

'I hate to disturb you two; I haven't heard this much laughter in a long time. Go wash your little faces and come get some breakfast.'

When we walked into the brightly-lit bathroom we started laughing again. No wonder Mrs Presley told us to wash our faces; we looked like clowns. My lipstick and Elvis's blood was all over both of our faces. With his face only inches from the mirror, he pulled his lower lip down, and whimpered, showing me the tiny cut.

'Oh, poor baby, do you want me to call the doctor?' I said.

'No, just kiss it and make it all better,' he answered in his baby voice. He and his mother were great at baby-talk. It wasn't long before they had me talking it too.

I thought someone in the kitchen had goofed when the aroma of burning bacon came all the way into the bathroom. When we sat down at the table I noticed six slices of bacon, burned to a crisp, neatly arranged on a plate in front of Elvis. I thought Mrs Presley was playing a joke on Elvis, and I laughed my head off. When I looked around, I realized I was laughing alone. I soon learned that Elvis had been eating bacon prepared this way all his life. He also had to have his eggs fried hard as a brick. Other than these two peculiarities, his eating habits were pretty much normal back then.

Alberta had prepared everything but the biscuits; they were Mrs Presley's speciality. They were fluffy and delicious; the best biscuits I'd ever tasted, and I told her so.

'You see, Mama, I told you, you make the best biscuits in the whole world,' Elvis said proudly.

'I've had lots of practice,' she said, graciously accepting the compliments.

When we finished eating Elvis took his plate and mine and brought them to the sink. I started gathering the rest of the dirty dishes but Mrs Presley stopped me.

'Leave it, June, you two kids go play, we'll take care of the dishes.' Elvis and I went out in the back yard and walked around the unfinished, rectangular swimming pool. About ten inches of rainwater had collected in the deep end. We sat on the edge of the pool, and he started talking about his family and all the changes taking place in their lives – and his life, too.

'June, you can't imagine how good it makes me feel to be

able to give them all of this. Mama, bless her sweet heart, still thinks this is all too good to be true. It's like a dream to her. She's afraid she'll wake up one morning and we'll be poor again. I'm not gonna let that happen, June, I've got to make it, for my mama. She's worked hard all her life, to take care of me, both of 'em have. And now, thank the good Lord, I'm gonna make life easy for them.'

'You're a good person, Elvis. Your mother is very proud of you, and rightfully so.'

'She really likes you, June. When we were having breakfast, she looked at me, then at you, and when she looked back at me, she winked. I know her, June, she don't have to say a word; she talks to me with her eyes.'

'I like your mother too; she's very down-to-earth, easy to talk to. She had me talking my head off this morning.'

'She'll have you telling her your life story if you don't watch out.'

'I know! I think I told her most of it already.'

'My daddy is just the opposite. He don't have much to say until he gets to know you, and then he still don't have much to say,' he said, laughing. Elvis talked jokingly about his father, but when he spoke of his mother you could see his eyes light up.

Sitting on the edge of the pool, his elbows resting on his knees, his smooth hands with long slender fingers dangling from hanging wrists, Elvis would occasionally shake them from side to side like a swimmer standing on his dive platform, trying to relax before taking his position for a race. His eyes were fixed on a bug, swimming frantically in circles in the rainwater at the bottom of the pool. Anxiously awaiting his important phone call, he was glancing at his watch every fifteen minutes. His energy level was so high it was impossible for him to stay in one place for any length of time.

I suggested we go back inside and listen to some music. I requested something by Elvis Presley, and he was more than happy to oblige. His first album, *Elvis Presley*, was the biggest-selling album in RCA Victor's history. He put the album on the hi-fi and we made ourselves comfortable on the floor in front of the speakers. We both enjoyed the feel of the sumptuous carpet; something neither of us had known as children.

Mr Presley came in the den, looking like Santa Claus with a huge duffel bag filled with fan mail slung across his back.

'Where do you want this, son? Do you want to read any of this or do you want me to stack it in the back?'

'Leave it here, Daddy. I'll get June to help me go through it in a while.' I was glad he said in a while: I was so content lying side by side on the floor with Elvis, listening to his album and looking in his eyes, that I didn't want to budge.

When the song 'I Got A Woman' came on, he pulled me to my feet, put his left hand on my forehead, his right hand on my stomach, and played me like an upright bass. It was one of the cutest things he ever did, and he did it often. I knew to be standing on my feet, and ready, every time a song with a good bass came on.

'Bill Black should have a bass like you, June, you never need tuning.'

'Just don't think you can strap me on top of the car, Elvis. There's some things I won't let you get away with.'

After hearing both sides of the album, he put on the album he played the most. It was an album by the Platters, with two of his all-time favorite songs, 'Only You' and 'My Prayer'. He had my undivided attention as he sang along with the record.

When the music stopped, Elvis picked up the duffel bag and dumped the contents on the floor. He had recently hired a secretary to read the mail, and reply to requests for autographed pictures, but when he had time he enjoyed reading it himself.

'My fans are very important to me, June. Without them, I'd still be driving a truck.'

'Geez my knees, I've never seen so many letters! Do you get this much mail all the time?' I asked in amazement.

'This is nothing, June. Most of the time it's two or three bags. Wanna help me read some?'

'I picked one at random; it was from an eighteen-year-old somewhere in Alabama. She wanted an autographed picture, and had enclosed one of herself in a bathing suit. I showed the picture to Elvis.

'Wow! Put that one on the side, June. I'll have to get the name and phone number for my little black book.'

I knew he was teasing. His little black book would've been so big he'd have had to hire a truck to carry it around.

'Where is your book? I'll make a list of all the good ones for you,' I replied, nonchalantly.

'You would too, wouldn't you, June?'

'Sure, I wouldn't want you to miss out on anything.' I continued reading the letters. I started reading the next one aloud, making it up as I went along.

'Wow! Listen to this one. "My Darling Elvis, I think I'm in love with you. I know you could love me too. I never miss a show. The next time you're in any of the Southern states, look for me. I always wear a pink scarf around my neck. Please send me one of your sexy pictures. Love, Ralph."'

'Let me see that, June, you've got to be kidding.' He snatched the letter from my hand and laughed when he realized I'd made it up.

A lot of the letters had been soaked in perfume. They were not only trying to catch Elvis's eye, with fancy little drawings on the envelope, they were trying to attract his nose as well. The combined odors of so many different perfumes was making me so nauseous I had to stop reading the letters. We put all the mail back in the duffel bag and Elvis carried it to a room at the back of the house, where bags and bags were neatly stacked to the ceiling.

For lunch, Mrs Presley had prepared a traditional country-style meal. We had the field peas, shelled earlier that morning, with mashed potatoes, cornbread, made from scratch, and the most delicious fried chicken I had ever put in my mouth. She was flattered when I told her it was better than my mother's fried chicken, and my mother's fried chicken was to die for. She gave all the credit to the new electric deep-fryer Elvis had bought for her recently.

'It uses a lot of grease, June, but if you strain it real good afterwards, and keep it in the icebox, you can use it over and over again.' Elvis was a millionaire, or close to being one, and bless her soul, she was still trying to be conservative.

By four o'clock that afternoon, Elvis realized his important phone call wasn't coming. He stormed in the den, where Mr Presley was stretched out on the couch watching television.

'Go call 'em on the phone, Daddy, and tell 'em if it's not ready by tomorrow they can just forget the whole deal.'

'Be patient, son, be patient. It'll be ready tomorrow.' It took a while, but he finally calmed down, and quit fidgeting.

Skipping supper that night, we went to the amusement park, rode every ride available, and played every game. The baseball throw was our last game. Elvis was saving the best for last. He positioned me on his left side, next to the counter.

'Stand here, baby, and bring me luck. Pick out which one of those stuffed animals you want, and I'll win it for you.' I'd seen this game before, even tried it myself a few times, and it wasn't easy. Not only did you have to knock the heavy milk bottles down; they had to be knocked completely off the stand. After a few warm-up throws, he started to cut loose and let fly. Two other guys were throwing at the same time, but when Elvis started clearing out the bottles, they stopped throwing and started watching in amazement. This was definitely his game. Everyone was cheering, me being the loudest. He was so sure of himself, he would wind up, give me a wink, and let it fly. Within a few minutes he had scored enough points to win the animal of my choice.

I didn't have any problem making up my mind. The shelves were full of teddy-bears of all shapes, sizes, and colors, but the one that caught my eye was a big black and white panda bear, the only one of its kind. We toyed with several names for the panda, all beginning with the letter P. Jesting, I suggested we call the panda Pelvis.

'Why not!' he said, in his favorite drawl. 'This little feller, from this day forward, shall be known as Pelvis.' Elvis took the panda by one paw and I took the other. We walked back to the car with Pelvis swinging between us, and Elvis singing a song.

'*Just my baby and me, and Pelvis makes three, we're happy in my blue heaven . . .*'

We pulled into a drive-in restaurant, ordered two Cokes

and a large order of french fries. He would put one fry half-way in his mouth, and I would bite off the other half. Every fry was a salty kiss.

Ours was the only car left in the parking lot when the car hop came to remove our tray. The lot was in total darkness before Elvis had even had a chance to start the car.

'You think they're trying to tell us something, June?'

He drove slowly back to the Holiday Inn, kissed me and the panda on the forehead, and told us to get a good night's sleep.

'I'll call you tomorrow morning, baby. I had a great time; I just wish the days were longer.'

'I'd like to have a whole year of days like this,' I said, wishing they would never end.

'Me too, baby, me too.'

7

$\mathscr{A}$RE YOU LONESOME TONIGHT?

ELVIS PHONED THE room early the next morning, and again I caught it on the first ring.

'I have some business to take care of this morning, so I'll pick you up at two o'clock. I don't know what we'll do today, but I'll think of something. Will you be there at two?'

'I'll be right here!' I said excitedly.

The girls and I drove downtown to get a bite to eat and pick up a few more souvenirs. I was checking my watch every fifteen minutes; I didn't want to miss him. I felt like a traitor, going off and leaving the girls every day, but I kept telling myself they'd do the same thing, given the opportunity.

It was almost two o'clock when we got back to the motel. Elvis was waiting for me in the courtyard. He said he had been there less than a minute. We stayed at the hotel long enough for Elvis to take a few snapshots with the girls. When we got in the car, we hugged and kissed like we hadn't seen each other in ages. It was a good feeling, having him as excited to see me as I was to see him.

'Will it be okay with you, baby, if we just hang around the house again today? I'm still expecting that important phone call.' His tone was somewhat apologetic.

'I don't care what we do, Elvis, as long as I'm with you.'

When we pulled in the driveway, Mr Presley was sitting in the car waiting to take Mrs Presley grocery shopping. They were babysitting the telephone until Elvis got home. I felt a little strange, being in the house alone with Elvis, even though Mrs Presley had said they'd be right back.

Elvis put some soft music on the hi-fi and took some throw pillows from the couch and placed them in the floor, in front of the speaker. Compared to his hyper-activity yesterday, he now appeared to be moving in slow motion. It was a pleasant change of pace. He laid his head in my lap, closed his eyes, and enjoyed having my fingers running through his hair. We were still in the same position when the Presleys returned. Mrs Presley smiled when she came in and saw Elvis's head in my lap.

'You better watch it, June, he'll stay there forever, if you play with his hair.' I hated to disturb him, but my rear-end was going to sleep. I was glad when Mrs Presley brought in two bowls of ice-cream; at last I could get up and stretch. As soon as we finished the ice-cream Mr Presley came in.

'Telephone for you, son.'

Elvis jumped up and ran to his bedroom. He was gone about five minutes, and came back smiling.

'Come with me, June.' He pulled me to my feet and hugged me tight.

'Baby, you've got to go with me.'

'Okay, let's go! Where to?'

'To pick up my new car.' He lifted my feet off the floor and spun me around and around. Then he put me down and put both hands on my shoulders.

'Now, let me see. This is what we've got to do. You go call the motel and see if Marie is there. Ask her if she'll pack a few things for you and bring them over here.'

'Pack a few things? Why? Where are we going?'

'We're flying to Houston, Texas. We'll be staying overnight. Go ahead, baby, call them; ask them to come over and visit for a while. Hurry up, I have to use the phone. I've got to call the airport, and make reservations, then I have to call and find a hotel near the Cadillac company.'

'The girls won't like this, Elvis.'

'Sure they will, June, they had a good time over here.'

'I'm not talking about that, I'm talking about me going out of town with you.'

'They're not gonna say anything, June. Go call 'em.'

'There's something you don't understand, Elvis. The only reason I'm here is because Marie wanted to take her vacation in Memphis. I didn't realize until after we were here that the only reason we came to Memphis was to see you.'

'June, if I was you, I wouldn't worry about it. When I was in Biloxi, doing a show, I was asking around whether anyone knew June Juanico, and Marie told me she was your best friend. I asked her if she would go out after the show, and she and some of her friends went with us to a nightclub. Marie's a nice girl, June, she won't be mad with you. If she gets mad with anyone, it'll be me. Anyway, she's the one who told me you were engaged.'

'She did?'

'Yeah, that's why I was so surprised to see you. What's with this guy she told me about?'

'What guy? I'm seeing several guys. I'm not engaged. I'm not even going steady.' He took my face in his hands and looked me in the eyes.

'No one special in your life?'

'Yes, my mother is the one special person in my life.'

'No special guys?' he asked.

'Only you,' I answered, smiling. He smiled back, and kissed me gently on the lips.

'Go make that call, June.'

I called the room and Marie answered the phone. I told her I was going out of town with Elvis, and asked her if she'd pack a few things for me and come over to his house. She asked what I was going to do about Edval, the guy I'd been dating most back in Biloxi.

'What about Edval? I'm not engaged to Edval, we're not even going steady, Marie.'

'I know, June, but if he finds out about this, it'll break his heart.'

'Marie, I'm not about to go home and rub it in his face. If you don't want to come over here, I'll get Elvis to take me to get my clothes.'

'No, it's okay, I'll pack a few things for you and we'll be there in a little while. I just want you to be sure you know what you're doing.'

'I'm not doing anything wrong, Marie, I promise. Thanks Marie, and don't forget my PJs.'

Marie was the oldest in the group, and for some unknown reason I thought I should have her permission. I hung up the phone, knowing Marie wasn't too crazy about the idea of me going out of town with Elvis, but I told myself that I was a big girl and didn't have to answer to anyone but my mother.

When the girls arrived, about thirty minutes later, Elvis and I both answered the door. I took the overnight case from Marie, thanked her, and sat it in the foyer. We all followed Elvis to the den, where he was the perfect host, making sure his attention was spread equally.

I felt like the girls were being a little cool to me, but I wasn't going to let it bother me. I didn't plan to take Elvis away from anyone; he was the one who chose me, and I was having the time of my life. I hadn't even wanted to come to Memphis in the first place.

They all played King of the Mountain on a big round ottoman in the middle of the floor. I didn't want to get mussed, so I just watched. With the girls double-teaming Elvis, he didn't stand a chance. They laughed as hard as they played, until Elvis had to go get cleaned up for the trip. We had to be at the airport in an hour. I still looked good; I'd made sure of that before I left the motel.

Elvis came back to the den, smelling great, looking his usual gorgeous self, and said it was time for us to leave. The girls got up off the floor, said their goodbyes to me, kissed Elvis and left. We were still standing at the front door, waving to the girls, when Mrs Presley walked up behind us and put her arms around us both.

'You two have a good time, be careful, and call me as soon as you land. Elvis, you be sure and mind your manners.' She kissed Elvis on the cheek, took me by the hand and led me to the living room. I looked around. Elvis was nowhere in sight.

'June, I need to talk to you for a minute. How old are you?'

'I'm eighteen, Mrs Presley.'

'Are you sure, June?' she asked, doubting me.

'Yes ma'am, I'm sure. Actually, I'm eighteen and a half.'

'I just wanted to be sure, June. You know, Elvis could get in lots of trouble if you was under age, 'cause he's taking you across the state line.'

'I promise you, Mrs Presley, Elvis could take me anywhere in the world and he'd never get in any trouble. And, about Elvis's manners, Mrs Presley, I wouldn't worry one bit. Elvis took me around town the other day, and introduced me to all his friends. What impressed me the most about him was his impeccable manners. You've done a great job, Mrs Presley.'

'Well, thank you June, I tried to do right.'

'You did right, Mrs Presley, believe me. My mother always said, "You can tell how a person was raised by his manners," and that good manners are a gift of love from your parents.' She lightly brushed my face with the back of her fingers, the same way she did with Elvis when she called him her 'Satnin'.

'I guess I'll have to call you my little Satnin, 'cause your face is soft and smooth like satin too.'

'Thank you, Mrs Presley.'

'It's the truth, June. You're very special to Elvis. I know. Not only because he told me so. I could tell by the way he looks at you.'

'Elvis is very special to me too, Mrs Presley.'

'I know that too, June. Well now, you two go along, and have a good time. Make sure he calls me as soon as you land.'

'Not to worry, Mrs Presley, I'll make sure he calls.' Elvis was just hanging up the phone when we went back to the den.

'I know Elvis will take good care of you, June, and I want you to take good care of him.'

'Did my two favorite girls have a good talk?' Elvis said, hugging his mother and giving me a wink.

'Don't worry, Mama, I'll take good care of June.'

'Elvis, I think we should keep June around, what do you think?' she said, winking at me.

She walked us out to the car, where Mr Presley was sitting in the driver's seat with the motor running. The three of us rode in the front seat of Mrs Presley's big pink Cadillac. The drive to the airport was very quiet. Mr Presley didn't say a world until we were getting out of the car.

'Son, don't forget to call your mama.'

'Okay, Daddy, I won't forget,' Elvis answered.

We walked in the Air Terminal, over to the ticket counter, picked up our tickets, and went straight to the plane. Unlike our modern airports today, we had to walk outside in the roaring noise and climb the portable stairway to the plane. Elvis never let go of my hand. I thought it was because he didn't want to lose me, but I realized after we were buckled up and ready for take off that he was afraid. It was only last month that his airplane had developed engine trouble and almost crashed somewhere in Texas. He had promised his mother he would never fly again, only to break that promise for this trip: his 'last one', he promised again.

His grip was getting tighter and tighter. I finally had to take my hand from his and massage it to get the circulation back.

'Oh, baby, I'm sorry, I didn't realize I was hurting you. I hate flying; it makes me a nervous wreck. Aren't you nervous?'

'I don't know; this is my first time on a plane. I don't know if I'm nervous or excited. I guess I'd be nervous if I wasn't sitting here next to you.'

'What difference does that make, June?'

'Well, it's like when we were going real fast on the motorcycle; I was scared at first, and then I thought – nothing can happen to me when I'm with you. You're special and loved by thousands of people, and I think God has a special plan for you.'

'C'mon June, be serious.'

'I *am* serious. You have lots of good things yet to come. You have already touched a lot of people and made them

happy for just knowing you. God knows all this; do you think
he would let anything bad happen to you? I don't!' About that
time the engines started to rev up, and he looked at me and
smiled.

'You're not afraid, June?'

'No, I'm not afraid.'

We started down the runway, both of us looking through
the tiny window, watching the ground go by faster and faster.
His left hand was holding my right, my left hand was on top
of his left hand, and his right hand was on top of my left. We
were in the air and starting to level off when we began pulling
our hands apart, just like in a child's game when you take
your hands from the bottom and move them to the top of a
baseball bat. We both laughed; his tension was easing. Then I
heard and felt a thud under my feet.

'What was that?' I shrieked.

'That's only the landing gear. I thought you weren't afraid,'
he laughed.

'Are we going to land?' I asked, trying to sound calm.

'No silly, the wheels are going back up under the plane.
Have you ever seen a plane flying around with its wheels
hanging down?' We both laughed. Even today I smile when
I'm flying and feel the thud of the landing gear.

'I love you, June Juanico.'

'I love you too, Elvis Presley. You're the most fun person
I've ever known.'

The cloud formations, off in a distance, all looked like car-
toon characters. We found Mickey Mouse, Donald Duck, and
even Popeye, with a pipe in his mouth. We had a snack of
cheese and crackers while we searched the clouds for characters. We talked of our families, and doing funny things when
we were kids. He asked if I had any precious memories, but I
couldn't think of any memory I considered precious.

'I have one precious memory, June, and it just happened
recently. It was the look on my mother's face when I gave her
my gold record of "Heartbreak Hotel". It's a memory I'll
cherish for the rest of my life.'

The stewardess came down the aisle with a notebook in her

hand, asking all the passengers their name and destination. I wanted to know why, because they already had our name and all that at the ticket counter. Elvis said he didn't know why. It was probably in case we crashed or something, making sure we were really aboard.

The captain's voice came over the scratchy PA system, announcing the time of day and the current temperature. We would be landing in approximately fifteen minutes, and were advised to buckle our seat belts. The plane landed smoothly on the runway. My first flight, and one which I would never forget.

We collected our luggage and took a taxi to the hotel. Elvis signed the register and then passed it to me. As I signed, I noticed we had different room numbers. I was relieved, yet disappointed at the same time. The desk clerk rang and motioned for a bell-boy, but Elvis stopped him.

'That's okay, don't bother, we only have these two bags and I'm sure we can find the rooms. Thank you very much.'

We went to my room first, long enough to close the door behind us and steal a quick kiss. He picked up both suitcases again.

'Now let's go see my room.' We got back in the elevator and went up one floor.

'They could have put us on the same floor,' I complained. We found Elvis's room, but it wasn't a room at all, it was a big beautiful suite.

'This is better, don't you think? We'll stay here.' He could tell I was nervous, so he pulled me close to him.

'June, I love you. I would never hurt you. Trust me, baby.' Somehow I knew I could, but it didn't stop me from being nervous.

'I requested two rooms, so no one would think we were shackin' up.'

'Shackin' up? That's an ugly way of putting it.'

'Well, whatever you want to call it. Relax, baby, I have too much respect for you to have anyone say or write anything ugly about you.'

'Does this have anything to do with your mother asking me my age, and the state line, and all that?'

'No silly, this is for my protection as well as yours. Reporters can get real nasty sometimes, and lately I've been making lots of headlines. Stay in this room with me tonight, June, I promise I won't do anything but hold you next to me.' How could I possibly not trust this beautiful, soft-spoken, gentle man? He sat on the side of the bed, motioned for me to sit next to him, picked up the phone, and called the Cadillac company.

We went down to the front of the hotel to await the arrival of Elvis's new love . . . His white Cadillac Eldorado convertible. (No, it wasn't trimmed in twenty-four carat gold, like some erroneous reports.) He wouldn't tell me anything about the car, he wanted it to be a surprise. I wanted to see if I could pick it out, so I asked him not to tell me when he saw it coming. He just laughed at me.

'I'll bet you can't, not in all this traffic.'

'I'll bet I can! You turn around and face me, and I'll let you know when I see it.'

The one-way three-lane street was full of fancy cars. He figured I'd never know one from the other. We stood there, me looking at the on-coming traffic, and him looking at the expression on my face. I smiled and opened my eyes real wide.

'You see it?' His voice filled with anticipation.

'I think so, don't turn around yet, it's not close enough.'

'Now!' I shouted, turning him around just in time to see a beat-up old green clunker. He laughed, picked me up, and twirled me around.

'June, you're crazy! I'm gonna keep you with me forever.' The Cadillac pulled up and we both saw it at the same time. The top was down, and it was gorgeous!

The driver got out of the car, and without hesitation handed the keys to the easily recognizable new owner.

'Congratulations Mr Presley, she's a beauty!' he exclaimed, as he walked behind the Eldorado to his waiting car. Elvis opened the passenger side for me, and ran around to the driver's side. I couldn't decide what was more beautiful, the car or the smile on Elvis's face. I had experienced a teenage crush before, but the feelings I had for Elvis, at this time, were much deeper than anything I'd felt before.

After hours and hours of riding all over Houston, listening to the radio, and singing along at the tops of our voices, Elvis checked the gas gauge and discovered a near-empty tank. While we were at the service station, he put the top up, and we took off again with another full tank of gas.

'It's a lot more fun with the top down, ain't it, June. Are you getting hungry, baby?'

'Yes, to both questions. I'm always hungry,' I answered eagerly. The cheese snack on the plane was long gone by now. We pulled into a drive-in restaurant and parked at the end, away from all the other cars. We placed our order through little speakers, like the ones at drive-in theaters. Ten minutes later, a cute little carhop, dressed in the shortest of shorts, brought our sandwiches and drinks.

'I hope this little girl don't know who I am,' he said, not really meaning it. At that time he loved having people recognize him. When she got close, I turned his face to me, so all she could see was the back of his head. I handed her a twenty-dollar bill and she put the change on the tray.

'Thank you very much,' I said politely. She smiled and said, 'Nice car!' We dove into the cheeseburgers and fries. I couldn't eat all of mine, so Elvis finished it for me in just a few gulps.

In our many hours together we had discussed every subject under the sun, and found out just about all there was to know about each other. Our conversations then turned to the future.

'What do you wanna be when you grow up, June?'

'I don't ever want to grow up, Elvis. Grown-ups don't have as much fun,' I answered, feeling like a happy child.

'Good idea, June, I don't think I'll grow up either. You can always be my little PP britches,' he said, in baby-talk.

'What kind of britches?' I said, remembering he'd said something about PP britches a few days ago, when we were on Mudd Island. Actually, I wanted him to baby-talk again.

'You know, June, when little kids wet their pants. I remember Mama calling me her little PP britches.'

'Gee, Elvis, you remember that far back?'

'It wasn't that long ago, June. I can remember lots of things I did when I was young.'

'Oh, now I get it. You were ten years old, and still wetting your pants, right?' I said, laughing.

'What am I gonna do with you, June?' All of a sudden he stopped laughing, and got real serious.

'June, I love you.'

'I love you too, Elvis.'

'No, June, I don't mean I love you like I love everybody, I mean, I really *love* you.' I didn't know what to say. This was the first time he had been serious talking about love.

'You don't believe me, do you, June?'

'I'll bet you say that to all the girls, Elvis.'

'No I don't. Only the pretty ones,' he said, back to his joking again. 'No, baby, I'm just kidding. I don't say it to all the girls. I never have. I've never really felt this way about a girl before.'

'You don't even know me, Elvis, we've only been together four days.'

'No, June, it's been longer than that. We've been together eighteen to twenty hours a day for the past four days. It's like we've had . . . Let me see . . . Four goes into eighty twenty times. It's like we've had at least twenty dates so far. Anyway, I think I loved you last summer, when we first met. After all that time had passed, I couldn't believe my eyes the other day when I drove in the driveway and there you were. Couldn't you tell how glad I was to see you?'

'I was glad to see you too, Elvis. Surprised, too! You were supposed to be on tour.'

'I know, June, we were supposed to be together. It was fate. Everything we do in life is all part of God's plan. It was fate!'

I too believed in fate, but I was at a loss for words. He kept going on and on about never knowing what fate had in store for us, and the mysteries of fate.

'Speaking of fate, that reminds me of a song . . . *Fate had me play in love with you, as my sweetheart. Act One was where we met. You read your lines so cleverly* . . . You've heard that song before, haven't you, Elvis?'

'Yes, it's one of my favorites. "Are You Lonesome Tonight", by the Ink Spots.' He started singing a few lines, remembering it well, especially the bass voice that does the talking.

'I think you should record that song, Elvis.'

'Maybe I will someday.'

'Good, you can dedicate it to me and to Houston, Texas.'

'I wouldn't dedicate it to you, June, it's a sad song. *Are you sorry we drifted apart?* Don't ever drift away from me, baby.'

'I'm not going anywhere, Elvis.'

'You promise?'

'Yes, I promise!' (Elvis recorded 'Are You Lonesome Tonight' in 1960. I can't say who he had in mind at the time.)

I snuggled up on his shoulder and closed my eyes. We looked at each other and smiled when 'I Want You, I Need You, I Love You' came on the car radio. He sang softly along with the record. When the song was over, he kissed my forehead, and whispered, 'Is my little PP britches tired?'

He started the car and flashed the headlights to signal the carhop to pick up the tray. When she got to the car, Elvis looked at her and smiled. She smiled back and started to stare.

'I know you, you're Elvis Presley! I think you're wonderful!' she screamed with excitement.

'You're not so bad yourself, honey,' he answered, in his Ink Spot bass voice. I didn't mind Elvis calling other girls honey, just as long as he didn't say it to me. My father's pet name for my mother was honey, and it had unpleasant memories. I playfully hit him on the arm as we were driving away.

'You're nothing but a big flirt, Elvis Presley. You had some nerve calling me a flirt the other day.'

'I didn't call you a flirt, honey.'

'You did too, and please don't ever call me honey. Remember when those sailors were crossing in front of us? You accused me of flirting.'

'Oh that, I was just mad, that's all. I didn't mean it. You was flirting with me last summer, in Biloxi.'

'I beg your pardon, it was you doing all the flirting. I was just giving you my smile of approval, because I liked your singing.'

'Yeah, uh-huh, looked like flirting to me. Let's be honest, June. We were both flirting with each other. You wanted to be with me as much as I wanted to be with you. Right?'

'Right,' I answered truthfully, snuggling up to him.

'It's been a long day, baby, I know you've got to be tired.'

'I'm not tired, my love, I'm exhausted!'

'What was that? Did I hear you say "my love"?'

'It must have been a slip of the tongue,' I joked.

'It was a nice slip, baby. Do you mind me calling you baby?'

'Not at all. As a matter of fact, I love it.'

'You'll be going back to Biloxi in a few days. I'm gonna miss you, baby.'

'I hate to think about going back to Biloxi. I'm going to miss you too, my love.'

When we got back to the hotel, Elvis picked me up and carried me into the room. He laid me across the bed and went to shower. He came out of the bathroom, naked from the waist up. He had put his pants back on. I guess he was a little shy, and I was glad. He sat on the side of the bed and telephoned his mother again, this time to tell her about the car. I picked up my overnight case and went to the bathroom. When I opened it I discovered I had no toothbrush and no make-up, so I picked up Elvis's wet toothbrush and started scrubbing my teeth real fast. I was always humming a tune to go along with the rhythm of the toothbrush. In the back of my mind, I was wondering – did Marie just forget my toothbrush and make-up, or was it an attempted sabotage? I decided it was a genuine mistake. She was my friend, she wouldn't do that to me. She was probably in such a hurry to get to Elvis's house she forgot about everything else.

I had received several pairs of baby-doll PJs for graduation, and was glad I'd packed them for our trip to Memphis. I did a quick inventory and found everything else neatly packed. Half-way through my shower, I started feeling a little nervous. I mean, let's face it – there I was, eighteen years old, and getting ready to go out and let Elvis Presley see me in my next-to-nothing baby-doll PJs. I remember backing away from the vanity mirror, as far as I could, and standing on my tip-toes, trying to get an overall view of myself. I took a deep breath and walked out of the bathroom.

Elvis was sitting up in bed with the covers pulled up to his waist. I couldn't help but notice his black pants, folded neatly, hanging over the back of a chair. He put down the room service menu and looked at me. I was frozen in my tracks, still standing by the bathroom door.

'Thank you,' he said over the phone, and, without taking his eyes off of me, he placed the receiver back on the cradle.

'Come over here by me, baby, I'm not gonna bite you.' I walked to his side of the bed and sat down.

'Oh, before you get in, June, get my watch on the dresser.' I got up, walked across the room, and he started to whistle.

'I don't care what time it is, June, I just wanted to watch you walk. Did I ever tell you that I was strictly an ass-and-leg man?' he said, laughing. I laughed, ran to the bed and jumped on top of him. We wrestled, with him still under the covers, until we were both out of breath. My nervousness was gone. I got under the covers with him and we cuddled so close we were like one. We both fell asleep on the same pillow; I had my back to him and he was snuggled up to me. We fit together like spoons. My pillow wasn't being used, so I put it between my legs, a habit I had picked up as a child to keep my bony knees apart.

Early the next morning the phone started to ring. Elvis came out of the bathroom, already dressed, and answered his wake-up call. He said his usual 'thank you very much' and hung up.

'We did have two pillows on this bed, didn't we? We both slept on the same pillow all night long. What happened to the other pillow?' he asked, confused.

'I have it between my legs,' I answered.

'*Lucky pillow*!' he said, with a silly grin.

I ran to the bathroom, unzipped his black leather shaving kit and borrowed his toothbrush again. When I finished getting dressed, I gave myself one last glance in the mirror. Without make-up I looked like a sixth-grader, but there wasn't a thing I could do.

'Thanks for the use of your toothbrush,' I said.

'My toothbrush? Didn't you bring your own?'

'I didn't pack, remember?'

'Oh, that's right, Marie packed for you. What else did she forget?'

'Just my make-up!'

'You don't need all that junk on your face anyway, you're beautiful just the way you are,' he said, stroking my face with the back of his fingers. 'My beautiful little satnin.'

'That's the same thing your mother called me, right before we left. What does it mean, anyway?'

'She used to sing it to me when I was little. You remember the song, "Mamie's Little Baby Loves Shortnin' Bread"? Well, she used to sing *mama's little baby has satnin skin*. You know, June, skin soft as satin.'

Elvis was in the bathroom when I heard a knock on the door. I opened the door to find a waiter standing behind a huge cart of food. He rolled the cart, stacked high with stainless steel-covered dishes, into the room.

'How many will be dining?' he politely asked.

'Just two, thank you,' I replied.

He began setting the table, complete with table-cloth and candles. With all that food, I assumed he was making several deliveries, but he unloaded everything on the cart and placed it on the table. He said 'enjoy' and left. Elvis came out of the bathroom and we started uncovering dishes.

'When did you order all this food? There's enough here to feed an army!'

'Last night, while you were in the shower. I wanted to make sure and get what you liked, so I ordered lots of everything. Actually, June, it was an accident. I picked up the phone, while I was reading the room service menu out loud, and a voice came on the phone and asked, "Will there be anything else, sir?" I said, "I don't know, what have I ordered so far?" He read the menu back to me and I said, "No, I think that will do just fine."'

We began laughing and uncovering dishes, and uncovering more dishes and laughing. We had white milk, chocolate milk, coffee and orange juice; sausage, ham, and bacon, well done, but not burned; potato pancakes, as well as hash brown potatoes; eggs, both fried and scrambled; sliced tomatoes, canteloupe, toast, biscuits and assorted jellies and marmalade; a tall stack of pancakes, hot maple syrup and tons of butter. Elvis and I both agreed that being in Houston was one of the most fun times we'd ever had.

Elvis had called the hotel garage earlier and requested that his Eldorado be brought to the front of the hotel with the top down. The doorman was standing next to the car, waiting to hand Elvis the keys.

As we drove away I turned to look back at the hotel. We were both a little sad, because yesterday was gone. While Elvis was busy driving through the heavy traffic, I was sitting over on my side of the car, watching him, and wondering what he was thinking. When we reached the highway that would take us across Texas and back to Tennessee, he looked back at the Houston skyline and smiled.

'It was fun, wasn't it, baby? Why are you so quiet, June? And why are you sitting way over there? Come over here and sit next to me,' he said, his voice sounding a little sad. He patted the seat next to him, and I quickly slid over.

'Now, ain't that better? My widdle-bitty girl looks sad. What's on your mind, baby?'

'I just wish we didn't have to go back. Not yet, anyway.'

'Me too, baby. I wish I could make time stand still.'

8

ℬE MY GIRL

THE TWO-LANE highway, divided by a broken white line, appeared to be much too narrow for the Eldorado. The white line seemed to be putting Elvis in a hypnotic trance. An occasional double yellow line, signifying a hill, or school bus loading zone, would break the spell. Passing through farmland we could see parallel rows of corn and other vegetables that seemed to go on for ever. Every ranch had a different style fence, bordering acres and acres of land. Each one had a different name, posted above the driveway's main entrance to the beautiful, sprawling, ranch-style homes.

'This is the way to live!' Elvis said, admiring the vast openness, and I had to agree with him.

One of the ranches was named Circle J, and I called it mine. For miles and miles, we searched for a ranch with the letters E or P, never finding one.

'I guess I'll just have to buy one of my own, huh, June? It would be nice to have a ranch, with horses, and cows, and chickens,' he said, daydreaming.

'Yeah, and lots of chicken shit too!' I said, laughing.

'What do you know about chicken shit, June? I thought you were a city girl.'

'I am a city girl, but I know all about chicken shit. My

grandfather raised chickens, when I was a little girl, and I used to help him gather eggs. The first time I followed him inside the chicken yard, barefoot, I learned all about chicken shit real fast. He had to come get me out of the middle of the yard. I was crying, afraid to move, with chicken shit between every toe.'

'Well, you won't have to worry, baby. When we have our own ranch, I'll gather all the eggs. How many kids do you want, June?'

'I don't know. Maybe four: two boys and two girls.'

'Maybe someday we'll get married and live on a ranch. We'll raise horses and cows and a house full of kids. How does that sound to you, June?'

'Sounds good to me, especially the part where you traded the chickens for the kids.' Both of us laughing, Elvis started singing a song. It seemed everything reminded one of us of a song. 'We'll build a little nest, somewhere out in the west, and let the rest of the world go by . . .'

The gas stations were few and far between. Even though we still had gas, Elvis decided we better get some more while we could. We pulled into a service station, and I immediately ran to find the ladies' room. The station had only one rest-room, with a big sign on the door saying WHITE ONLY! I was washing my hands when Elvis knocked on the door.

'June, you want a Coke? Room service, hurry up, it's my turn, I gotta go!' He wasn't kidding, either. When I opened the door, he handed me the two Cokes and ran in as fast as he could. I went back and waited in the car. I noticed the station attendant talking on the pay phone mounted on the back wall of the station. He kept turning to look at the car, through the front window. I had no problem, reading his lips, when he said the name Elvis Presley. Elvis finally came out of the rest-room, and went inside to pay for the gas. The attendant quickly hung up the phone and ran behind the counter. I could see Elvis smiling and nodding his head, as he gave the man a handshake. Before he could get to the car, several pick-up trucks and a few cars were driving into the station. The attendant had made a few calls and the word was out. It was a gathering of teenage boys and girls, all nice kids. It was funny how girls always behaved better when boys were around. While Elvis was signing autographs, more trucks and cars pulled in. When we left the station, we had a motorcade of trucks and cars following behind. They gradually fell off, one by one, as we drove away from the quaint rural town.

Further down the road we passed a big beautiful pond in the middle of nowhere. It was so picturesque Elvis decided to turn and go back. We sat in the car, admiring the scenery, and then decided, why not? We climbed through the fence and walked to the water's edge. Under a stately oak tree, in the tranquil surroundings, we found the perfect place to sit. We talked about him being so easily recognized, and not having any privacy. I wondered if it would ever be any different. He took my hand, pulled me to my feet, and held me close.

'Be my girl, June!' he said, out of the blue.

'Okay, Elvis, I'll be your girl. Will you be my boy?'

'You don't understand, June. I want you to be *mine all mine*, not anyone else's!'

'You mean, you don't want me to go out with anyone else?'

'That's exactly what I mean!'

'Okay, Elvis, I won't go out with any other boys, if you don't go out with any other girls!'

'I can't be with you all the time, June, I have a busy schedule to contend with. It was hectic enough with just concerts and television appearances, but now I'll be doing movies, too. My time is not my own, but when I do have time off, I want to spend it with you and nobody else.'

He was making promises that would soon prove impossible to keep.

He took my face in his hands, kissed my forehead, my nose, and my mouth. The same way he did the first time we met. Always saving my mouth for last.

We walked hand in hand back to the fence, climbed through and continued our long drive to Memphis.

Elvis was so easy to be with, I felt as though I'd known him for a very long time. He said he felt the same way about me.

We took turns trying to find a radio station without a lot of static. Being in the middle of the boonies didn't help matters.

It looked like rain up ahead, so we pulled over to the side of the road and put the top up. Lucky thing, too, because within a matter of minutes the whole sky had opened up on us. It was raining so hard Elvis couldn't see where we were going. He pulled over and parked on the side of the road, and we waited for the rain to ease. We made ourselves as comfortable as possible, on the front seat of the car, and smooched until all the car windows were fogged. The heavy rain lasted about thirty minutes, and I loved every romantic minute. As soon as the windshield was clear, both inside and out, we saw a beautiful Texas-size rainbow. Elvis sang 'Over The Rainbow' like I'd never heard it sung before. Maybe the acoustics in the car had something to do with it, but his voice sounded much better than it ever did on records. I applauded when he finished the song.

'You like that song, June?'

'It's not the song, it's your voice. It's so rich and smooth and powerful it gives me goose-bumps. Maybe someday, someone will write some music for you that you can really sink your teeth into. The songs you're doing are good, but they don't show off your real talent.'

'Maybe it's not the songs, June, maybe it's me. Maybe I should change my style.'

'I'm not talking about your style, Elvis, I'm talking about your beautiful voice. I want everyone to hear you sing like you sing for me. No one has really heard you sing. Not yet, anyway.'

'The next recording session I have, I think I'll play around with some different arrangements, and see what they think.'

'Good idea!' I agreed. He sang 'Over The Rainbow' again. After he'd finished, I showed him the goose-bumps and the hair sticking straight up on my arm.

'That good, huh?'

'Yep, that good!' I said, rubbing my arms.

A light drizzle of rain stayed with us, off and on, until we got to Memphis. Elvis knew his mother was going to be a nervous wreck when we got home. She worried about him driving in the rain. He tooted the horn when we turned in the driveway. Mrs Presley ran out of the house and hugged him like he'd been gone for weeks. Mrs Presley definitely had her priorities in order. She was so happy to see Elvis she forgot to look at the new car.

'Thank the Lord, you're home! It's been raining here all day,' she said with relief, her arms still tight around Elvis.

'Don't worry Mama, you've got to have rain in order to have a rainbow. Ain't that right, June?' he said, leaning down and kissing me in front of his mother.

We walked arm in arm straight to the kitchen. We hadn't eaten anything since the huge breakfast early that morning, and we were both famished. Mrs Presley fixed us bacon and tomato sandwiches and hot coffee. The bacon on Elvis's sandwich was burned to a crisp, just the way he liked it. Mrs Presley asked me if Elvis had taken good care of me, and I assured her he had.

'June took good care of me too, Mama, even on the airplane. It's the first time since I've been flying that I wasn't scared to death,' he said, giving my hand a squeeze.

Elvis was leaving Memphis the next day, and I wouldn't be seeing him for a while. I hugged Mrs Presley goodbye, and told her she had good reasons to be proud of Elvis. He was indeed a gentleman, and very special to me.

'I have a feeling I'll be seeing more of you, June.'

'I hope so.'

'You take care of yourself, and have a safe trip home,' she said, kissing me on the forehead.

Elvis drove me back to the Holiday Inn, and we sat alone in the courtyard, talking.

'I have to be in Hollywood the first week in June, but after that I'm coming to Biloxi. I'll have some time to myself, and I want to spend it all with you,' he said, kissing me tenderly.

'That sounds wonderful to me. Call and let me know when you're coming, so I can take time off from work,' I said, knowing in my heart that being with Elvis was more important to me than any job.

'I will, baby. I love you. I'm not going to let you get away.'

'I'm not going anywhere, Elvis, I'll be there,' I said, missing him already.

Saying goodbye to Elvis was hard. I couldn't help thinking that I might never see him again. I was about to cry when I finally tore myself from his arms and ran to the room, without stopping to look back.

9

I WANT YOU, I NEED YOU, I LOVE YOU

W<small>E HAD ONE</small> day left of our vacation in Memphis. Knowing Elvis was gone, I was ready to go too. The girls wanted to do something exciting on our last night in town, so we drove across the state line to West Memphis, Arkansas. While I was in Houston with Elvis they had discovered a nightclub which featured a live band. It wasn't long before our table of five was surrounded by local yokels, all wanting to dance. My heart wasn't in it, but I pretended to have a good time.

The next morning we loaded up the pink Ford and said goodbye to Memphis. We were speeding down the highway, somewhere in north Mississippi, when one of the girls spotted a police car. Someone yelled, 'Don't look now!' but naturally we all turned and looked at the same time. Marie slowed the car, but it was too late. A Sheriff's deputy pulled us over, took Marie's driver's license, and made us follow him to the station. Marie had been employed at the City Hall in Biloxi for several years, so she knew all about police proceedings. We all marched, single file, into the small Sheriff's sub-station they called the 'jail'. The arresting officer was talking about locking us up unless we paid a big fine. At this point in our vacation we were scraping our money together, making sure we had enough for food and gasoline. A big fine was not in our budget.

Within ten minutes the station was filled with every cop in the county, but by that time we had it all figured out. The redneck who stopped us was wanting to show off his catch. Marie finally got aggravated with all the small-talk and flirting.

'Where is your phone? I'm calling my father!' she said, figuring it was time to bring this farce to a halt. The deputy said it wouldn't be necessary, we could leave as soon as he wrote up a ticket. He was stalling for time, waiting for a few more of his cronies to get to the station. One of the cops said he'd never seen so many beautiful ladies in one place. He thought he had died and gone to heaven.

They finally handed Marie her driver's license and said we were free to go. They all paraded out to the car to say goodbye. The arresting officer took the ticket from Marie, tore it in half, and told her to slow down. We had wasted a good hour of travel time, but it did give us something to laugh and joke about the rest of the way home.

We arrived in Biloxi later that night. Everyone but me was glad to be back home.

The next morning, after unpacking and putting my suitcase in the back of my closet, I came across my little pink diary, a graduation gift from Pat. I hadn't written in it yet, I didn't think anything was interesting enough; but all of a sudden my head was full of interesting things.

I talked to my mother about Elvis constantly. Apparently I painted a good picture of him, because she wanted to know all about my trip and was anxious to meet my new boyfriend. Even though Pat was in Memphis at the same time, she didn't know anything about my times with Elvis either. I was telling everything to Mom, when she got home from work, and to Pat, whenever we got together. I was forgetting what I had told to whom, and would end up repeating myself.

'You told me that already, what happened after that?' Pat was always saying. I went to my room and brought back my little pink diary.

'Well, I'm glad to see you finally got around to using it! It's about time! It's over a year old already,' Pat said. She had written a little note on the inside cover: 'For your Treasured Memories . . . Love, Pat'. I hadn't had any treasured memories to write about until now. Pat wanted to read it; I told her definitely not.

'I don't want to tell you the same thing over and over, so I'm using it as a reference. Now, where was I?' I said, raising my eyebrows, leading her to believe it was full of juicy parts.

'You were telling me about going to Mudd Island after dark,' she said anxiously. I began flipping through the pages.

'My God, you're writing a book!' Pat exclaimed.

'No I'm not, the pages are so small, I'm only making notes. Only I will be able to read between the lines . . .' After telling her all the highlights, I put the diary away, hoping it wouldn't be long before I could write something exciting again.

Elvis had promised he'd see me the first week in June, as soon as he finished his television engagement. I was at Pat's house, to see him on the *Milton Berle Show*, when he sang one of my all-time favorites, 'I Want You, I Need You, I Love You.' I felt he was singing it just for me, like he had when we were in Houston.

My mother too, had called a friend with a television set, and made arrangements to see Elvis for the first time. She just had to see this person I couldn't quit talking about. She found him to be every bit as handsome as I'd said he was.

As I was watching the TV program, I felt a little twinge of jealousy when Debra Paget was introduced on the same show. Elvis and I had been talking about our favorite movie stars one day, and he thought she was one of the prettiest girls in Hollywood. I had agreed with him, at the time, but only because an old boyfriend had insisted Debra and I looked a lot alike. Now I wasn't so sure. After reading several magazine stories about starlet, Debra Paget, and her relationship with her over-protective mother, I wasn't too concerned. Men, all men, including Elvis Presley, were strictly off-limits to Debra Paget.

A few days after the *Milton Berle Show*, Pat and I walked a few short blocks to Duran's Café, a local teen hangout, to have a Coke and some fries. I put a couple of nickels in the jukebox and played 'Heartbreak Hotel' and 'I Was The One'. I sat listening to the songs, with my face resting in my hands, looking like a typical star-struck teenager.

As we were walking back to my house, a car load of teenagers passed by yelling at me.

'Hey June, Elvis Presley's at your house!' At first, we began walking fast, but soon ended up running full speed. It had taken a moment for the news to sink in. When we turned the corner all we could see were cars and people everywhere. We made our way through the crowd, and found my mother standing in the doorway, looking shocked.

'June, where did all these people come from? Elvis was here, but he was so mad about the crowd, he left. He thinks you told everybody he was coming. He said he was going to Florida, where he could have some privacy,' she said, all in one breath.

'I've got to see if I can find him, Mama. What kind of car was he driving?' I asked in a panic.

'He was driving a fancy white convertible.'

I was disappointed about missing him, but mad at the same time. The nerve of him, driving into the small town of Biloxi in a white Cadillac convertible, with a Tennessee tag, and thinking it was my fault that a crowd had gathered.

Pat and I jumped in her father's car and drove to Ocean Springs. We parked the car on top of a hill, in the Red Drake's Restaurant and Lounge parking lot. From this point we could see all traffic leaving the city heading east. We sat on top of that hill for over an hour. Thinking we must have missed him, we went back to my house. My mother was still frantic.

'June, where have you been? This phone is driving me crazy! Elvis has called here three times. He finally left a number for you to call,' she said, handing me a piece of paper.

The paper had a phone number and a name, Arthur Hooton. When I dialed the number I kept getting a busy signal. I found later that the switchboard was jammed from all the calls coming in asking if Elvis Presley was registered there. When I finally got through to him, he wasn't in a very good mood.

'June, I asked you not to tell anyone I was coming to Biloxi. And where have you been for the past hour?'

He laughed when I told him about parking on top of the hill, and he really laughed when I told him that I hadn't said a word to anyone about him coming. Instead, I put up posters on every corner saying ELVIS IS COMING! ELVIS IS COMING!

He and the boys – Red West, his bodyguard; Gene and Junior Smith, his first cousins; and Arthur Hooton, a friend – had checked in at the Sun 'N' Sand Motel, one of Biloxi's finest, located right on the beach. When Pat and I got to the Sun 'N' Sand, a small crowd was still hanging around trying to catch a glimpse of Elvis. The radio stations were announcing that Elvis Presley was in town for a short visit, before going to Florida for a long vacation. As soon as I walked in Elvis grabbed me. We hugged and kissed for a few minutes, and finally I couldn't take the suspense any longer.

'When are you leaving?' I asked, disappointed.

'I just got here, baby, I'm not going anywhere!'

'I heard on the radio you were going to Florida.'

'Yeah, I lied to the press. I sure hope it works, so I can have a little privacy. I don't have to be in Florida until the third of August. I have a few singing dates, in between, but I can take care of those in two or three days at the most.' I was so excited – we had the rest of June and all of July to be together.

Elvis drove me home later that evening and came in to meet my mother – this time under less stressful conditions. She knew right away I hadn't been exaggerating. There was nothing pretentious about Elvis: he charmed people without even trying. Mama made a pot of coffee, and Elvis felt right at home, sitting with us at the kitchen table.

Elvis parked the convertible out of sight, so we walked whenever possible. We spent the next few days in and out of the Sun 'N' Sand's beautiful clover-leaf pool, when the crowds would allow. Our nights were spent at the Ko-Ko Restaurant and Lounge, across the street from the motel.

Princess Whitecloud, a native American Indian, was featured at the organ in the Ko-Ko Lounge every weekend. Very few people went out on weekdays, so we usually had the place to ourselves. We tried to talk Elvis into playing the organ, but he didn't want to, saying it was the personal property of Princess Whitecloud, and he had respect for other people's property. Both the lounge manager and bartender carefully uncovered the giant organ, encouraging Elvis to play. I told him that Princess Whitecloud would be honored to have him sit at her keyboard. After a little coaxing, he finally agreed. A few older customers were there, and joined in a sing-along.

Everyone treated Elvis like he was just one of the guys. No hounding for autographs, no pulling at his clothes, and no screaming. He had room to breathe and he loved it. This was to be our hangout for the next few days. Even my mother, and Eddie Bellman, Mom's steady date for the past several years, came to the Ko-Ko to join in the fun.

After getting to know Elvis, Eddie was so impressed with his impeccable manners and down-to-earth personality that he wanted to do something nice for him. Before the night was over, he asked Elvis if he would like to go on a deep-sea fishing trip while he was in Biloxi. Elvis said, 'Yes, sir!' He couldn't wait. They would get together later and discuss a date.

The next morning, Pat and I drove to the Sun 'N' Sand to meet Elvis and the boys for breakfast. The Ko-Ko had a great chef who prepared seafood specialities. He must have really raised his eyebrows when he read the order for hard fried eggs and burned bacon, but the breakfast was served exactly as ordered.

Elvis rarely carried money with him. He insisted he had important things on his mind and couldn't be bothered digging in his pocket for petty cash, so he would assign one of the boys to take care of what he called the 'minor details'. On this particular outing, Arthur was in charge of paying the check and leaving a tip.

There was no such thing as the recommended ten to fifteen

per cent of the total bill. A gratuity was freely given as a token of appreciation for good service, so waitresses in the 1950s depended strictly on the generosity of their customers.

Elvis respected the working class and believed in leaving a big tip. It wasn't that long ago that he worked for wages himself, and he remembered it well.

'How much did you leave the waitress, Arthur?'

'I put five dollars on the table, chief.'

'Next time make it ten, she was good!' Elvis said, completely satisfied with the food as well as the service. Five dollars was a very generous tip in the fifties, especially for a check that came to less than twenty dollars.

On the way back to the room, Elvis noticed the swimming pool was deserted, and decided this would be a good time to go for a swim. Red, Elvis and me were the only ones in the pool. The rest of the gang, too full from the big breakfast, were sitting pool-side, relaxing under an umbrella. We had been in the water less than thirty minutes when the parking lot next to the pool started filling up. At first, people were just sitting in their cars, looking in our direction, but then a group of teenagers got out of their cars and came to the pool. It started a chain reaction, with everyone, adults included, piling out of cars and slamming doors. It was slam bang slam bang all over the parking lot. Elvis yelled for Arthur, sound asleep in the lounge chair, to go across the street and get the car. As people were lining the edge of the pool, we were moving to the center. Arthur pulled up and tooted the horn, but we couldn't see the car for all the people. We went to the pool steps, where Pat was standing with our beach towels. A few fans were calling Elvis's name, and some were whistling, as we ran to the car. We drove around for a while until, thinking the crowd had thinned, we went back to the motel.

Red, Gene, and Junior were still at the pool, talking to some of the fans. When they left, to return to the room, a few fans followed from a distance. Looking through the suite's picture window, we could see an occasional head pop up from behind the shrubbery. Elvis was feeling trapped.

'Maybe if I go out and talk to them, they'll go home.'

With all the heat and humidity on the coast, Elvis was constantly changing clothes. He picked up the shirt he'd been wearing earlier that morning, and gave it a sniff.

'Phew, this smells like a pole-cat.' He threw the shirt in the corner and took a clean one from his suitcase. He went in the bathroom, leaving the door open, so I followed. When we were in the pool I'd noticed black smudge marks around his deep-set eyes, so I wasn't at all surprised when he took a little flat box of cake mascara from his shaving kit and carefully applied it to his thick brows and long lashes. He had started using eye make-up after his Hollywood screen test. He liked the look, and kept it. He tucked the clean shirt in his pants, combed his thick mop of hair and, looking in the mirror, gave himself a nod of approval. Now he was ready to face his fans.

I recognised a few friends of mine in the small gathering. One of them, Sal Taranto, known to his friends as Penu, was standing way in the back, away from the crowd.

'Hey June, where ya at, baby?' Sal yelled. This was Sal's usual greeting; he called all the girls 'baby'. I could tell it didn't sit too well with Elvis; he gave me that look he was so famous for.

'Who's the cat in black, June?' he said, hardly moving his lips.

'Only a friend, Elvis, only a friend,' I said, waving to Sal. Sal, all dressed in black, had his collar turned up and his jet-black hair – a flat-top with duck tails – slicked back with Vitalis hair tonic. Standing like the cock of the walk, he had both hands in his pockets. To describe Sal in a few words, he was an original version of the Fonz in *Happy Days*. Every town had a Fonz; my town had Sal. Sal was close friends with Norbie, probably the reason he was being so standoff-ish to Elvis.

Because of all the handsome young airmen stationed at Keesler, the local boys didn't take too well to outsiders. Elvis talked to the small gathering and signed a few autographs. We went back in the room and they gradually left, one by one.

Later, a reporter from the *Daily Herald*, our local newspaper, knocked on the door. Elvis graciously went outside for an interview and some pictures. He reminded the reporter that he was here for one night before leaving for Florida. Then he came back in the room and pulled the drapes closed.

'I guess there's no such thing as privacy any more. I can't stay locked in this room forever; let's go somewhere and do something, anything! June, do ya'll have an amusement park around here, other than the little one down the street?'

'Nope, I'm afraid that's it! But New Orleans has one of the world's largest,' I bragged, acting as though New Orleans was my second home.

'Are you talking about Pontchartrain Beach, June? I've been there before, and you're right, it is big! That's what I want, baby. The bigger, the better. Let's go! I can't get away from 'em, so I might as well join 'em,' he said, shrugging his shoulders. We all piled in the convertible and headed for Pontchartrain Beach – so named because of its location on Lake Pontchartrain.

This beautiful lake of brackish water is forty miles long and twenty-five miles wide. A long section of the shoreline, in front of the amusement park, was cordoned off for swimming and sunbathing on the white sand beach. Lifeguards, in their towering chairs, were strategically located to keep swimmers from venturing outside the cordoned area. It was a great family picnic playground, as well as an amusement park. It was a sad day for the city of New Orleans, and for me, when Pontchartrain Beach closed its gates permanently in the fall of 1982.

As we neared the Beach, just after dark, we could see the bright lights outlining the huge roller-coaster named The Zephyr. The Zephyr, located just inside the main entrance, was our first stop. When Elvis found a ride he liked, he stayed on until the newness wore off. We rode so many times I finally lost count. While walking the midway, checking everything out, several people recognized Elvis and said hello, but no one bothered him. They were all there for the same reason we were, and that was to have a good time.

Everyone riding the bumper cars was dying to get a shot at Elvis, including me. The muscles in my face hurt from laughing so much, and at one point I almost wet my pants. We were just getting started good when the attendant announced, 'Time's up, everyone clear the floor, and exit through the rear.' Elvis had purchased ten tickets for each of us, but we had only used two.

'What am I suppose to do with these?' Elvis said, holding up nearly forty tickets.

'Sorry, sir, on weekends we only allow two consecutive rides per person. You'll have to go stand in line again,' he said, pointing to the long line out front.

'I didn't want another ride anyway,' Elvis said, handing the left-over tickets to a group of young boys standing at the end of the line. 'Gee, thanks, mister!' they yelled, having no idea who their benefactor was.

We stopped playing long enough to get something to eat, at the Terrace, an open-air restaurant on the midway. The Beach's manager, a Mr Batts, came to our table, introduced himself, and told Elvis he would be happy to open the park to Elvis and his friends any weekday after hours without charge, if the crowds got to be too much for him. Elvis thanked him and told him he might take him up on his offer someday soon.

Without even looking at the menu, we all ordered cheeseburgers and french fries. Elvis also ordered a large platter of sliced tomatoes and sliced dill pickles. Between bites of his cheeseburger, Elvis was constantly being handed pieces of paper, even paper napkins, for him to autograph. The teenage fans didn't care if he had a mouthful. Some of them came back to the table two or three times, requesting autographs for little sisters or sick friends who had to stay home. These inconsiderate people were jerking my last nerve, but Elvis took it all in stride.

Leaving the restaurant, Elvis and I took refuge on the Ferris Wheel. Unlike the bumper cars, you could ride as long as your tickets lasted. From the top of the Ferris Wheel, Elvis showed me the outdoor theater where he had performed in early 1955 with a close friend of mine. Ann Raye, better known to me as Martha Ann Barhonovich, was a petite teenage singer with a husky voice, similar to that of the recording star Brenda Lee. Coincidentally, it was Martha Ann's father, 'Yankee', who had arranged for Elvis to make his first appearance in Biloxi.

We left the Ferris Wheel to join Pat, Gene and Red, who were waiting patiently on a park bench. When Elvis and the boys went to throw baseballs, another crowd began to gather around, making it impossible for him to throw, so we left the park and headed back to Biloxi. Elvis and I were the only ones still awake when we got home in the wee hours of the morning. He couldn't wait to go back and do it all over again.

10
WHO IS THIS COLONEL PARKER?

*E*LVIS HAD BEEN in town for two days when I started getting phone calls from magazine and newspaper reporters from all parts of the United States. Even radio disc jockeys were calling for an interview. I got a taste of what it was like having questions thrown at me, left and right. Silly questions, such as 'Did he kiss you goodnight, by the garden gate?' My response didn't seem to matter; they chose to write whatever they had on their minds that particular day.

One day Red, Gene, Pat, Elvis and me were riding down the beach, looking for something to do, with the radio blaring out as usual. The disc jockey on my favorite radio station, WNOE, in New Orleans, made an announcement; he was going to try to interview Elvis Presley's girlfriend, live by telephone, on the five o'clock show.

'Rumor has it, folks, that the eighteen-year-old beauty from Biloxi, Mississippi, and the gyrating Elvis Presley, are engaged to be married. The next song goes out to you, June, from you know who!'

'I Want You, I Need You, I Love You' followed the announcement. Elvis lowered the volume on the radio.

'Oh, shit! If the Colonel hears this, I'm dead! Where's this DJ coming from, June?' he said, looking straight at me.

'I have no idea, Elvis! Don't look at me! I don't know what he's talking about!' I answered defensively, misinterpreting his question.

'No, I don't mean it like that, baby. Where is this radio station? What city?'

'Oh, I see what you mean. It's in New Orleans.'

'Well, if this dude wants an interview; let's go give him an interview!' Elvis said, making a U-turn and heading west. Ninety minutes later we were in New Orleans. Elvis stopped at a pay phone, and I called to get the station's address.

We drove to the front of the St Charles Hotel, the radio station's home, but couldn't find a parking place. After going around the block several times, Elvis impatiently pulled right up front and double-parked on the one-way street.

'The hell with it! Let 'em give me a ticket!' he said, getting out of the car.

We rode the elevator one flight up, laughing all the way to the mezannine floor, and found radio station WNOE. I kept thinking, 'Boy, is this guy in for a surprise!' We stood in front of the glass window, separating us from the disc jockey. Elvis was standing in his usual 'Elvis Position', his arms folded across his chest. The five of us filled the window. The DJ was busy doing something at first, then he looked up. He saw me first, I was closer to his eye level, and then he looked at Red. I was smiling, but Red wasn't – he had assumed Elvis's position too. When his eyes went to Elvis, the man almost fainted. He knew immediately who it was. He stopped the music and announced to his listening audience:

'You folks out there in WNOE land, I'm not dreaming! Mr Rock'n'Roll himself, Elvis Presley, is right here in the studio with me.' He put the music back on, and came to the door to welcome us. He was thrilled to learn that Elvis always listened to WNOE when he was on the Gulf coast. He said he was going to talk to his listeners and put a stop to the ugly rumors.

'Wait a minute: they're just rumors, not ugly rumors. Personally, I think they're kinda cute,' I said, laughing.

'You must be June! You're a real beauty, June. I can see

now why Elvis "likes" you so much,' the DJ said, making little quote marks with his fingers when he said the word 'likes'. I just smiled, blushing a little with embarrassment. He had a quick live interview with Elvis and made one on tape for future use. Elvis denied the engagement rumors on the air, and everything seemed to be okay with him after that. He was so cute, stuttering a little, whenever he got nervous. He was really worried about having to deal with his new manager, Colonel Tom Parker. I hadn't even met the man, but already I didn't like him very much.

The radio station quickly began filling up with fans. One reporter stated that the St Charles Hotel was so full of Presley fans that when one girl fainted she had to walk two blocks to fall down.

Elvis signed a few autographs on the way to the car. The fans were screaming and closing in fast. We piled in the car, still double-parked and blocking traffic, and made our way through the screaming fans. If Elvis's car hadn't been blocking traffic, the St Charles Hotel would have been completely overtaken by hysterical teenage girls trying to get to their idol.

'Phew, I'm glad that's taken care of,' Elvis said, still a little nervous about the interview.

The DJ was playing one Elvis song after another, stopping in between songs to talk about his famous drop-in visitor. He even pronounced my name correctly, while complimenting Elvis's taste in women.

Elvis's long slender fingers dangled nervously from the top of the steering wheel as he listened to the recently taped radio announcement.

'Hi, this is Elvis Presley, and you're listening to my favorite radio station . . . WNOE in New Orleans.'

'Damn! I sound like a hick!' he said, hitting the steering wheel with the palm of his hand.

'No, you don't! You sound wonderful,' I said, trying to soothe his frazzled nerves.

Elvis, not too familiar with the downtown area of New Orleans, was driving aimlessly toward home. When we came to Chef Menteur Highway, a big smile came across his face.

'Now that we're here, we might as well go to Pontchartrain Beach.' No wonder my poor mother worried about me. I didn't know half the time where I was going to be; how could I possibly let her know?

It wasn't long before Mr Batts, the park manager, knew we were back, and insisted we go have something to eat – this time it would be his treat. Elvis ordered fried chicken, and I ordered soft-shell crabs. Elvis was finishing his last piece when the waitress came with another half fried chicken and another soft-shell crab for me. I'd already eaten two and couldn't hold another bite, but it didn't go to waste as Red and Gene polished it off real quick. They had never eaten crabs before, and they loved them.

The *Times Picayune*, one of New Orleans' largest newspapers, reported the next day that Elvis Presley was heavy on the appetite: they said he polished off three halves of fried chicken. And me, his girlfriend, had taken three soft-shell crabs. By reading the paper you would have thought we were a bunch of hogs or something.

Mr Batts made sure we weren't disturbed during our meal. We were having an after-dinner cup of coffee when he brought several friends to the table to meet Elvis. One that I vividly recall was professional fighter and lightweight contender Ralph Dupas. Ralph was a local guy, and a celebrity in his own right. His handsome face didn't appear to have suffered any damage. When Mr Batts introduced Elvis to the young fighter, Elvis stood to shake his hand. Elvis, slightly taller and a few pounds heavier, gave the fighter the once-over.

'Man, I'll bet I could take you,' Elvis joked with the well-built Dupas. They clowned around sparring and posed for a few pictures. The local people loved it.

Out on the midway, we got acquainted with Gayle Higgins, a local girl and frequent visitor to the park. Gayle and her friends, all girls, were out having a good time. Everywhere we went we ran into Gayle and her crowd, so we invited them to join us. Gayle wasn't your average seventeen-year-old. She had bleached platinum blonde hair, and was very attractive. When Elvis commented about how striking she was, I was glad to remember he preferred dark hair. With her smooth, shoulder-length page-boy haircut, she appeared to be from a wealthy family. She complained that most of her summer vacation was spent studying art, in the French Quarter, and that she would much rather be having fun like the other teenagers in the city. We stayed and played until the park closed at midnight, then Gayle invited us to follow her home and have something to drink.

'It's too early to go home. My parents are out of town, so we'll have the place all to ourselves,' Gayle said.

As we waited in the parking lot for Gayle to take the lead, I knew my first impression of her was right. She pulled alongside of us, in a new sports convertible, and led us through town. Where the élite meet, as they say in New Orleans, on the wealthy side of town.

The 'place' Gayle was referring to turned out to be a mansion in the middle of a luxurious residential area in the Garden District of New Orleans, so named for its many fragrant gardens shaded by magnolias, oaks, and other graceful trees. The homes, built in a combination of Greek and other classic styles, are known for their wide porches and spacious rooms. I had only seen pictures of places like these in movie magazines. I couldn't imagine what it would be like to actually live in a place like this. Elvis was impressed, too.

'What does your old man do, Gayle, own the city?' Elvis said, looking around the lavishly decorated home. Gayle just laughed. She was very unaffected by all her family's wealth. We stayed for a while; Gayle and I exchanged phone numbers and promised to stay in touch.

By the time we got back to Biloxi, Elvis and I were both worn to a frazzle.

11
UMMER FUN

*E*LVIS HAD A message waiting for him at the front desk of the hotel: Mr Bellman had called to say he had arranged a deep-sea fishing trip for the whole gang. We were to be at the dock at seven o'clock in the morning.

My hair still damp, and in pin curls, Pat and I went to meet the gang at the Ko-Ko to have breakfast before going to the boat. I walked in the restaurant, sleepy-eyed, with a red bandanna wrapped around my head. Elvis pretended not to know me.

'Aunt Jemima, you can sit next to me if you like,' he said, pulling out my chair.

'Puts me in the mood for a pancake or two,' Gene mumbled drily.

The waitress came to the table with her pad and pencil ready. Elvis was always the last one to order. He had trouble making up his mind, but always ended up ordering the same thing.

'Tell the chef I'll have my bacon and eggs the exact same way I had them yesterday,' Elvis said, smiling at the waitress.

'And how was that sir? I wasn't here yesterday, and I don't think the chef was either,' the waitress answered sarcastically, her tone of voice showing a distinct attitude problem.

'I'll have two eggs fried hard, and I'd like my bacon burned, please.'

She stood there, with her pad and pencil, giving Elvis a disbelieving look.

'I'm serious, ma'am,' he said, smiling. 'Please don't bring me runny eggs.'

When she returned with the food, everyone got exactly what they ordered; everyone apart from Elvis, that is. His eggs were sunny side up, with the yolks jiggling, and his bacon was limp. The smart-ass waitress had a smirk on her face when she put his plate in front of him. She was trying to show Elvis that she wasn't impressed with him or his fame.

'I don't know what it is, but something tells me this waitress don't like me. Arthur, are you sure you've been leaving a tip when you pay the check?' Arthur had a mouthful, so he nodded yes.

'Please ma'am, would you ask them to cook the eggs hard and burn the bacon,' Elvis said, still smiling. She snatched his plate and went back to the kitchen. Everyone else was busy eating. I was feeding Elvis some of my hash browns when the waitress returned with his plate. It looked almost the same as it had before. He picked up a piece of toast and stuck it in the runny egg yolk.

'I'm sorry ma'am, I just can't eat this,' he said politely.

'Do you think you're supposed to get special treatment, just because you're Elvis Presley?' she said, glaring at him.

'No ma'am, I'd like to be treated just like a regular customer.' This time there was no politeness in his voice. He stood up, picked up his plate and tilted it, letting the eggs drop and splatter yolk at her feet. I felt like cheering, but I didn't. Elvis was very cool when he told Arthur to pay the check, and not to forget the tip.

'Maybe she'll use it to buy a book on good manners,' he said, putting his plate back on the table. It was evident we weren't staying, so Pat started putting all the toast in a napkin.

'Leave it! We'll eat somewhere else,' Elvis told her.

'But El, we don't have time; we have to be at the boat in twenty minutes,' Pat pleaded.

Arthur walked over to the cashier, and Red, following Pat's lead, put all the ham steaks and bacon in a napkin too. We divided the ham, bacon and toast, and everyone had a sandwich on the way to the boat.

'That stupid bitch! That stupid bitch!' Gene mumbled between bites.

A small group had gathered at Bariciv's pier to see us off. Eddie Bellman handed Elvis a bag of warm glazed doughnuts. The incident at the restaurant was quickly forgotten, and we were stuffing our faces with doughnuts before the boat left the dock.

Captain Thornton, owner of the boat, the *Aunt Jennie*, shook hands with Elvis. Watching us devour the doughnuts, Captain Thornton commented about how being on the water sure stimulates a person's appetite.

'I hope we got plenty of food; you know we got Arthur with us,' Gene said, putting in his two cents' worth. Someone was always teasing Arthur, the only one in the group a little overweight. Arthur just smiled, taking it all in his stride. Eddie told us not to worry about food, opening the ice chest and showing us enough food for at least fifty people.

'The best way to prevent sea sickness is to keep your stomach full at all times. I wanted to make sure we had enough,' Eddie said, smiling.

About ten miles out in the Gulf, we dropped the lines over to troll. The heavy rods and reels used artificial bait called spoons or spinners. When a fish hit your line, you yelled strike, so the Captain could slow the boat. All other lines should be reeled in at this time to avoid tangles. We had as many as three people fighting a fish at the same time. It was all very fast-paced and exciting. We caught our share of king mackerel, bonita, and Jack Cravelle, all weighing between twelve and sixty pounds.

Elvis expressed an interest in sharks, so Captain Thornton pulled up to a shrimp boat to pick up a bucket of chum. Chum is trash fish shrimpers clean from their nets and usually throw back in the water. You can tell when a shrimper is cleaning his nets by the flocks of seagulls following behind the boat, plucking the small dead fish from the water. Nothing is wasted: what the seagulls don't eat, the larger fish do.

It's traditional for a fisherman to trade a six-pack of beer for a bucket of chum, but we didn't have any beer on board. When Eddie asked Elvis what kind of beer he liked, Elvis replied, 'Barq's root-beer!' Elvis bought it by the case to take back to Memphis. Barq's, now nationally known, was then only available on the Mississippi coast. Eddie mistakenly thought Elvis was against having alcoholic beverages, so he didn't buy beer for anyone. He ended up paying cash for the bucket of chum.

The Captain dropped the anchor and hung a sack of chum from the back of the boat. It wasn't long before the chum was attracting ravenous sharks of all sizes. Elvis and Red did most of the fishing, landing some very impressive-sized sharks. I watched from a safe distance, not wanting anything to do with all those rows and rows of razor-sharp teeth.

The fishing trip was so much fun, Elvis asked Eddie if he could arrange another trip, when his parents came to visit him in Biloxi.

'My daddy loves to fish. I can't wait for him to get a load of this,' he said, beaming.

'Sure I can, Elvis, my boy, just let me know when you're ready to go again,' Eddie said, happy to oblige.

When we returned to the dock that evening, we found the white convertible top of Elvis's Cadillac completely covered with girl's names, addresses, phone numbers and love notes. It didn't seem to bother Elvis, but it really bothered me. I was embarrassed that this had happened in my home town, but I was soon to learn that it happened everywhere he went.

When we arrived at the Sun 'N' Sand, the parking lot was filled with people waiting to see Elvis. Exhausted from the long day on the water, he made his way to the room and col-lapsed on the sofa. He was so annoyed he felt like going somewhere where no one could find him.

'I'd leave tonight if I knew where I could get some privacy,' he said, shaking his head in disbelief.

When I got home that night I told my mother and Eddie

about the crowds and how aggravating it all was for Elvis. Eddie called Elvis the next morning, at the motel, and offered him his house on Porter Avenue. It was a furnished rental house that happened to be vacant at the time, so Elvis and the boys loaded up the car and moved in. Unfortunately some of the same crowd arrived at the same time as Elvis. We knew he wouldn't have any privacy here either. We stayed at the house long enough for Eddie to call the Gulf Hills Dude Ranch and Country Club, to see if they had a vacant villa. Elvis quickly handed Eddie a note saying Arthur Hooton, party of five. With high hopes for privacy, we left Biloxi and headed east, making the crowd think he was going to Florida.

Gulf Hills catered mainly to golf enthusiasts, and their early morning tee-off schedule fit in perfectly with ours. The majority of hotel guests were already in the middle of their golf game by the time we were up and around. We usually had the hotel dining room, the hotel lounge, The Pink Pony, as well as the hotel swimming pool, all to ourselves.

Also, the miles and miles of winding roads around the hotel usually had newcomers going around in circles, which proved to be a great deterrent for over-anxious autograph-seekers. Gulf Hills became Elvis's home away from home for the rest of the summer.

Now that he had some privacy, he was a totally different person. He was free to come and go as he pleased. His only concern now was finding some fun activities for the whole gang to enjoy. The hotel social director came to the villa with a list of possible activities. Golf was at the top of the list, but Elvis didn't play golf, and square-dancing was out of the question – I couldn't see Elvis and his friends doing the 'Promenade'. Horseback-riding and water-skiing, however, got everyone's attention. Elvis got directions to the stable, and we made arrangements to go horseback-riding the following day.

Our villa, walking distance from the hotel, was located on Fort Bayou, a few feet from the water's edge. That evening Elvis and I went for a walk along the bayou, and watched the beautiful sunset from the end of the hotel pier. The Ski Dock, also located at the end of the pier, had posted a schedule for water-skiing for beginners and advanced skiers. Elvis couldn't have been more pleased with his new-found paradise.

'Do you like to ski, baby?' he said, his voice filled with excitement.

'I don't know, I've never tried.'

'You've been raised on the water and you've never been on water-skis? You've got to be kidding!'

'No, I'm not kidding. I don't know anyone with a boat, much less water-skis.'

'You'd be good at it, baby, I can tell. We'll get you some ski lessons while I'm here. You're gonna love it, June.' The thought of water-skiing for the first time had me a little nervous, until he told me he himself had only been skiing for a few months. I figured if he could do it, I could do it too.

With my head resting on his shoulder, we sat quietly, watching the red sky slowly fade into darkness. Suddenly it was so dark we had to inch our way back to the villa, laughing every step of the way. We had so many different activities to look forward to, now he was worried about how to fit everything in.

The boys were all laying around the big living room, smoking long, skinny, wooden-tipped cigars and drinking root-beer. The place smelled awful! Elvis told them to open the windows and doors and get some fresh air in. Coughing and fanning his face, he snatched up the car keys, grabbed me by the hand, and we ran outside. Riding down the beach, several cars started tooting their horns. Elvis pulled the convertible over and put the top up, thinking he would have more privacy. He had forgotten about all the names and phone numbers, most of them written in lipstick, on the convertible top. It only made matters worse. We managed to get out of the traffic without anyone following, and parked in an alley behind my house. Elvis had no idea where we were, until I pointed to the garage apartment in my back yard.

'This is great, June, even your mother wouldn't think to look for us back here.'

My mother had been standing by the stove, and noticed the

headlights coming down the alley. When the headlights stopped, and then went out, she decided to see who was parked behind her garage. The street light on the corner had the area lit up enough for her to see the white convertible with its newly decorated top. We both laughed when we saw her coming round the corner.

'Just checking to see who's out here,' she said, smiling.

'Hi, Mrs Juanico, I was just talking about you,' Elvis said, still laughing.

Mama had just finished icing a banana cake, and still had the knife in her hand. It took Elvis two seconds to get out of the car when she invited us in to have a piece of warm cake and a glass of cold milk.

Mama, anxious to find out all she could about the young singing idol her daughter was involved with, had been buying any and all magazines featuring articles on Elvis. Now that he was sitting at her kitchen table, she had a chance to find out, first-hand, what his life was all about. Without meaning to pry, she was asking question after question, mostly about his singing career. She seemed to know more about his public life than I did. I know he had to feel a little like I felt the first time I met his mother.

When Mama looked at her watch and excused herself, saying she was going to go and have a bath, Elvis announced he was leaving too.

'Thanks for the cake, Mrs Juanico, it was delicious. My mother makes the same cake for me all the time,' he said, running his finger along the edge of the cake plate, having one last taste of chocolate icing.

I walked him to his car, gave him a sweet, chocolate-tasting goodnight kiss, and watched him back slowly down the narrow alley. He blinked his headlights three times before driving away. Smiling inside, I knew he was using the car lights to say I-LOVE-YOU.

12
THE PROPHET

P AT AND I arrived at the villa at exactly 10 A.M. Elvis and the boys were sitting in the living room, ready to go.

'You're not going horseback-riding dressed like that, are you, June?' Elvis asked, knowing shorts and sandals wouldn't mix well with horses and bridle-paths in the woods.

'No way! I've got other clothes in the car,' I said, spinning around, running to the car and changing into long pants and loafers. I was ready in a matter of seconds, but we still had to wait for Arthur, lingering in the bathroom.

It had rained during the night, and the road leading to the stable was muddy. Our seven horses were saddled up and ready to ride. Elvis didn't like the idea of having a guide, but unless you knew the correct route, one wrong turn and the lead horse would make a run back to the stable, with the rest of the horses following. The next time out, our guide promised, we could go it alone.

We left the stable in single file. Our guide was first, Elvis was behind him, I was behind Elvis, and so on down the line. We started off walking, then a little trot, and then a nice canter. The guide's horse was slinging mud in Elvis's face, and Elvis's horse was slinging mud in my face – everyone was getting their share. One can only eat so much mud.

The canter was soon a fully-fledged gallop, with everyone racing for the front. It was like a mad day at the race track, with seven inexperienced jockeys going for pole position. Finally we slowed to a walk, and were all side by side. Everyone apart from the guide was covered in mud. We were laughing at each other, and Elvis, wiping his mouth on his shirt-sleeve, started singing.

'*Oh, we ain't got a barrel of money, maybe we're muddy and funny, but we'll travel along, singing our song, side by side . . .*' We all joined in, singing the familiar tune. Once we were off the road and on the trail through the woods, the ground, covered with pine straw, was nice and dry. We stopped singing and started swaying to the rhythmic squeak of the leather saddles. Next came Gene Autry's 'Back In The Saddle Again', and finally my favorite, reminding me of our trip to Houston, 'Let The Rest Of The World Go By'. I had sung a little harmony in school, and this song was perfect for harmonizing. With the whole gang singing, I didn't mind making a fool of myself. Elvis and I had done a little harmonizing to one of his favorite hymns, 'In The Garden', but I was so intimidated by his beautiful voice, I had held back. Now it didn't make any difference, I was singing as loud as I could. Red was singing the melody, Elvis switched to baritone, and sometimes bass, when he could go that low, and I was singing tenor, the only part I knew. We had quite a trio – even Elvis was impressed. The gang applauded when we finished, and we took a little bow.

'Thank you very much,' Elvis said, exactly the same way he did on stage.

We didn't run the horses any more; we were happy just to walk through the tall pines, singing. Elvis loved singing harmony; he would have been perfectly content being one of the Jordanaires.

Climbing down from the horses and walking back to the car, we all laughed: we walked like we'd been in the saddle for at least a week.

We passed a fireworks stand, on the way back to the villa, and Elvis made a quick U-turn. Soon we not only had seven people crammed in the convertible, we also had two giant boxes of assorted firecrackers. We dumped the boxes in the middle of the floor and divided them into two separate stacks. We chose up sides and had two teams armed, ready, and waiting for nightfall. The eighteen-hole golf course, with wooded areas on both sides, was a perfect battleground. There were only two rules to follow. Number one – you get hit, you're out. Number two – keep a distance of at least fifteen feet between you and your target.

We went to the hotel and planned our strategy while having lunch. I had fired Roman Candles before, but never at another person.

'I can picture the headlines now,' I said, laughing. '"Elvis Presley's girlfriend: last seen running down the fairway, at Gulf Hills, her long dark hair now a flaming red. 'It was all in fun,' the rock'n'roll singer had assured her."'

Everyone laughed hysterically. The louder the laughter, the more vivid the picture my mind was painting. I could always take my share of Roman Candles and run and hide in the woods. When Elvis reached over to take my hand, I almost jumped out of my seat.

'It really is just all in fun, June, I promise,' he said, kissing my hand – then laughing as hard as he could.

'Hell, we got at least six hours before dark; let's go for a swim,' Elvis said, glancing at his watch. We raced down the hill to the villa to get our swimsuits on.

'Last one in's a rotten egg,' Pat yelled, running back to the swimming pool.

We left Gene, Junior and Arthur back at the villa – they had decided they would rather take a little snooze – so Pat, Red, Elvis and I had the big pool all to ourselves. We played King of the Mountain, with Pat on Red's shoulders, and me on Elvis's. We were pretty evenly matched, but I couldn't take another scratch from Pat's hard-as-steel fingernails.

I tried unsuccessfully to teach Elvis the basics of swimming. He did just fine as long as his face was in the water, but as soon as he lifted his face to take a breath he went straight to the bottom. He was happy with what little he did learn, though, and promised he would practice and be swimming as well as me by next summer.

The dreaded darkness was here. We gathered our ammunition and headed for a secluded area of the golf course. Using matches to light the Roman Candles was out of the question. Elvis handed us each a little wooden-tipped cigar. Before doing battle, we lit a few of the candles just to test their power.

'Sometimes you get a hold of a batch that would blow off the side of your head. These seem to be working perfect,' Elvis said, strictly for my benefit.

We lit our cigars, grabbed a stack of Roman Candles, and ran off all in different directions. I tried to find a big fat tree, but we were surrounded by tall skinny pines. So there we were, running around with little cigars clenched between our teeth, shooting fire-balls at each other. To say we were a strange group is putting it mildly. We did have a few close calls, almost setting the woods on fire, but – thank God – no one was injured. Luckily, no one called the police either; we would surely all have been arrested.

The following morning the hotel manager sent a message to Elvis. 'The fireworks were beautiful, but also hazardous to our golf course. In the future, please feel free to use our beautiful sand beach. Thank you, the management.' Evidently we weren't as secluded as we thought. Elvis sent his humble apologies, and promised it wouldn't happen again.

'How do you suppose he knew it was us? We cleaned up all the empty shells,' Elvis said, wondering out loud.

There was never a dull moment with Elvis around. Walking to the ski dock, I was headed for another brand-new experience: I was going to learn how to water-ski. While Elvis was showing off his skills I was at the dock getting lessons from the instructor, Dickie Waters. Needless to say, having never been on skis before I was a nervous wreck. After a few words of advice at the dock, however, I was ready to get in the water. I felt confident with Dickie at my side. The boat pulled away, tightening the slack in the rope, and Dickie raised his hand and yelled, '*Hit it!*' Before I had time to even think about it I was on top of the water and doing great. We went down and around the bayou before heading back to the dock. I was proud of myself for making it the entire way, without one fall, and I had proof: my hair was still dry. Dickie, still at my side, told me to get ready to drop the ski rope, and we let go at the same time. We were going so fast I thought I was going to crash into the dock for sure. I didn't know how to stop, and I started to scream. About ten feet from the pier, though, Dickie grabbed my arm and pulled me down. My hair was no longer dry.

Everyone standing on the pier was clapping and yelling, 'Way to go!' – everyone but Elvis, that is. He was standing there, his arms folded, giving me that look. Dickie apologized for not teaching me how to stop, and for wetting my hair. He told Elvis I was a natural, and would do great with a few more lessons.

'We don't have time for any more lessons. We have to go,' Elvis said, without even looking at me. He was quiet for the rest of the afternoon.

We had supper at the hotel and then walked over to the hotel lounge, The Pink Pony. A small group of tourists were there, having a nightcap. We all ordered Cokes and gathered around the upright piano. We usually started with a sing-along, but most people were a little reluctant to sing with Elvis – they were happy just to sit and listen. He entertained us with all his favorites, including some boogie-woogie. We took turns playing the bongo drums. A hush came over the room when Elvis ended the night with a spiritual song, sung with great feeling.

We normally walked hand in hand, but on the way back to the villa that night Elvis walked a few steps ahead of me. When we got there, Pat gathered her wet bathing suit and her car keys. It was past time for her to have her dad's car home. I grabbed my wet suit, and my purse, and went to kiss Elvis goodnight.

'Where do you think you're going, June? It's not even nine o'clock yet,' he said, holding me around the waist.

'I was going to save you a trip, Elvis,' I said, without show-ing any emotion.

'I don't want you to save me a trip. I'll take you home later,' he said, telling me what to do rather than asking. He took me by the arm and we walked Pat to her car, watching in silence until she was out of sight. Now that my only means of transport was gone, he released my arm and stood silently for a few seconds. He took my hand and walked me through the villa, past the guys and into his bedroom. Still acting a little strange, he let go of my hand and sat down on the side of the bed.

'I want you next to me,' he said, looking up at me.

'Okay, Elvis, I'm here!' I answered, sitting by his side.

'That's not what I'm talking about, June,' he said, being somewhat mysterious.

'Well, what are you talking about, Elvis? I can't read your mind. If something is bothering you, tell me, maybe I can help.' Caring for Elvis, the way I did, my normal assertive reaction was suddenly passive: a side of me I hadn't experi-enced before.

'I don't know how to say that I'm trying to say,' he began, still brooding.

'Don't worry about *how* to say it; just say it. Tell me what's bothering you.'

'What's gonna happen to me, June? What's gonna happen to us? I keep thinking you don't care. You're never next to me when I need you. You're always off somewhere, talking to someone else. I'm constantly calling you to come by me. Whenever a crowd is around, you back off and stand on the outside. I'm always looking around to see where you are. I don't wanna have to look for you, June, I want you next to me. Do you know what I'm trying to say?'

'I understand what you're saying, but you always have peo-ple crowding around you. I don't want to crowd you too. I'm only trying to give you room to breathe.'

'Other girls I've dated are always right next to me. They act like they're proud to be with me. If I say something, they lis-ten. If I want to say something to you, I have to find you first.'

I knew exactly what he was talking about, and I felt a little guilty. But it had nothing to do with my feelings for Elvis. I had made up my mind not to compete with his fans for his attention. I would back away, letting him flirt or whatever with all the pretty girls constantly trying to get close to him. I promised myself I would never cramp his style. I knew he loved all the attention, and I wanted him to feel free to do or say anything he wanted. And even more than that, I didn't particularly care to see him smiling as he accepted a folded piece of paper with the name and phone number of some beauty queen, place it in his top pocket, giving it a pat, and saying, 'It's right here next to my heart, honey.' Jealousy, the green-eyed monster, could eat your heart out, and I wanted no part of it. So I was living by the old cliché – what you don't know can't hurt you.

'I'm not like your other girlfriends, Elvis. I'm not going to hang on your every word, or hang all over you, either. That's not who I am. When we first met, you said, "I like you, June, you're different." Now, all of a sudden, you want me to change and be like everybody else. Why?'

'I don't want you to be like everybody else, June! I just want you next to me and not off talking to someone else. I want you to be mine.'

'I am yours, my love, but I can't live in your shadow. I need room to breathe too. I'm sorry if you're not happy with the way I am, but I don't think that's the real problem. You've been in a bad mood ever since we left the ski dock this afternoon. Why don't you tell me what's really bothering you? Please? Talk to me, Elvis, I love you.'

'When we went water-skiing today, you paid more attention to the ski instructor than you did to me. I wanted you to ride in the boat while I was skiing, but you were too busy taking lessons. I wanted you to watch me ski.'

'I *was* watching you ski. Every time you passed the dock I waved, but you never even looked my way. I watched you until you were out of sight. I've never been on water-skis before, and I was nervous. I was paying close attention to Dickie so I could get it right.'

'Dickie? You even know his name?'

'Yes, I know his name! He's been the ski instructor at Gulf Hills for the past two summers.'

'Have you ever been out with him?'

'No! I've never been out with him! Okay, okay, now I know what this is all about. You're wondering just how many guys have made out with me, and when one of them will show up to brag about it. Right?' I knew I'd hit the nail on the head when he didn't answer.

'Elvis, I told you when we first met that I've been out with lots of different guys, but I've never been serious about any of them. I've been waiting for the right one to come along. And, believe it or not, you're it! I love *you*, Elvis Presley!'

'You'd better love me, June Juanico. You better!' He pulled me down on the bed and kissed me. 'Stay here with me tonight, June. I'll take you home first thing in the morning,' he said, between kisses.

'I can't stay all night, my mother will be worried.'

'No she won't, she knows you're with me.'

'She also knows I need to be home.'

'Okay, baby, I'll take you home. In a little while.'

Lying in his arms, I remembered a book I had received for a graduation present. *The Prophet*, by Kahlil Gibran, always had a soothing effect on me. Maybe reading something other than the newspaper would do him good. It might even calm him down. I was confused by his new possessive attitude. All of a sudden he wanted me under his thumb. He didn't seem to trust me anymore, if he ever had. My guess was he'd been exposed to more than his share of loose women. He'd always shy away from this type, but some of his companions, his entourage, didn't. Getting a piece of ass in every different city was fast becoming the norm. Was he thinking that all females were the same?

As soon as we pulled up in front of my house I ran inside, grabbed the book, and brought it out to him.

'Here, read a little of this. It might make you see things a little differently. Who knows, it might even make you a little wiser,' I said, leaning in the car, kissing him goodnight.

'June, I love you! More than you'll ever know. I'll call you in the morning, before I leave for Memphis.'

'You're leaving in the morning? Are you coming back?' I asked, crushed by the sudden news.

'I'll be back before you realize I'm gone,' he said, reassuring me.

And he was, too. This time, driving a new car. He'd decided that the convertible, especially with the autographed top, was too noticeable for any privacy. The new car, a lavender Lincoln, was much more conservative, and less likely to attract attention. Wearing a hat and sunglasses, I didn't realize it was Elvis parked in front of my house until he stepped out of the car.

'You must be making a shit-sack full of money,' I laughed, rubbing the smooth upholstery.

'I'm doing okay for a country boy,' he said, leaning over to open the glove compartment and show me the copy of *The Prophet*.

'June, I love the book! Can I keep it?'

'It's yours, my love. I knew you'd like it.' I could tell by the way he was talking he'd had a chance to do a little reading while he was gone.

When we got to Gulf Hills, Elvis passed the villas and drove into the driveway of a two-storey house at the end of the road.

'How do you like it?' he said, grinning. I didn't realize he was talking about the house until I saw the boys walking out to meet us.

'I've rented it for the rest of the summer. I might even buy it later, who knows?' he said, still grinning.

The house was owned by a family named Hack, so the boys nicknamed it the Hack house. Elvis showed me around, saving his bedroom for last. The upstairs bedroom had a balcony overlooking the living room. Not only was it private, it was also very romantic.

Elvis's parents were suppose to arrive in Biloxi that night.

'I need to get in touch with Mr Bellman, June. Do you know where I can find him?' he said, anxious about his parents' arrival.

'No, but my mother is home, I'm sure she knows where he is.' We drove to the back of my house and parked the Lincoln in the alley. Mama had the day off and was cooking red beans and rice.

'Hi, Mrs Juanico,' he said, inhaling the aroma. 'Sure smells good in here. Will you do me a favor? Will you get Mr Bellman on the phone? I'd like to talk to him about taking my parents deep-sea fishing.'

'Eddie's on his way over now to eat some red beans. Have you ever had red beans and rice, Elvis?' Mama asked.

'No ma'am, I can't say I have.'

When Eddie arrived, Elvis went to meet him at the door.

'Mr Bellman, it's good to see you, sir. I've talked to my parents and they're all excited about going fishing. They'll be here tonight. Do you think you can arrange another trip?'

Eddie went straight to the phone, but got a busy signal. Dishing out a big plate of beans and smoked sausage, I suggested we eat now and phone later. Elvis and Eddie dove into their plates.

'I've never tasted anything quite like this before, Mrs Juanico. This is delicious. You'll have to teach my mother how to fix this when she gets here.'

'May's a great cook, Elvis. That's why I'm over here so much.' Eddie went back to the phone and got through to Captain Thornton.

'Will tomorrow morning be okay, Elvis?'

'Yes sir! What time should we be there?'

'Same time, same place. I'll take care of everything else.'

'Thanks, Mr Bellman, I sure appreciate this. My parents are gonna love it, and I can't wait to do it again. It was the best time I've ever had!' Elvis said, shaking Eddie's hand the entire time he was talking.

Mr and Mrs Presley checked into the Sun 'N' Sand motel as soon as they arrived in Biloxi. They called my house and talked to Elvis on the phone. We were to pick them up at 6 A.M. the next morning. My mother even made arrangements to take the day off, something she had never done, to go fishing with us. She was anxious to meet the Presleys too.

Mom and the Presleys hit it off right from the start. Mama thought Vernon was one of the most handsome men she had ever seen. She told them that Elvis got his good looks from both his mother and his father. In her opinion, Elvis had his father's strong features, and his mother's deep-set eyes. Mrs Presley was complimenting Mama for raising such a fine daughter, and Mama was saying the same thing about Elvis being such a fine young man. By the end of the day, they were teasing us about having little blue-eyed grandbabies.

Red, Vernon, Elvis and I were the first ones to try our luck fishing. Sitting in chairs across the back of the boat, Elvis was showing his dad how to let the line out and set the drag. Elvis had only done it once before, but by this time he was doing it like a pro. Mrs Presley busied herself making Elvis peanut butter and banana sandwiches. When he started catching fish and had to keep both hands on the rod, she held his sandwich for him, giving him a bite every now and then. Mama had made some deviled eggs, and the boys were eating them whole. I yelled 'Save one for me!', and Elvis took one from the box and shoved the whole thing in my mouth.

It wasn't long before Mr Presley was letting his line out and setting the drag like a champ. He wasn't about to stop and eat. The deviled eggs were only an appetizer for Red, so when he got up to fix himself a sandwich, he gave his chair to Mrs Presley. She didn't want to fish at first, but after pulling in a few she was loving it too.

In the beginning we'd been catching bonita, but then we got into a school of big Jack Cravelle. Mrs Presley, relaxing between fish, her line still over, suddenly got a strike. The fishing-line was resting on the side of her wrist. When the fish struck out the line went *zing*, cutting her right across her arm and wrist. Sitting next to her, I saw the cut, still white, just before it started to bleed. The same thing had happened to me, once before, and I remembered the burning pain. I took her rod and yelled for Elvis, standing only a few feet away. The big fish was taking the line out fast. I gave the rod and reel to Red, and took Mrs Presley to the Captain's quarters to find the first-aid kit. Elvis sat down on the bunk next to his mother and put his arms around her. I was on my knees, trying to be careful not to hurt her as I put on a bandage. When I finished she kissed me on the top of the head.

'Thank you, little satnin, it'll be all better now,' she said, trying to ignore the pain.

The boat was rocking from side to side, and Mrs Presley began looking a little pale. I told Elvis to take her outside in the fresh air, and I sat with her until she was feeling better. I remembered moaning and groaning when the same thing happened to me, but she never once complained. Red finally landed the big Jack fish responsible for the accident. Elvis picked up the gaff, hooked in the fifty-pound Jack, and showed it to his mother.

'Look at the size of this thing! There's no way you could have landed him by yourself, Mama.'

'I would have if he hadn't gotten me first. Just give me a minute, I'll get another one!' she yelled. Still looking a little pale, I asked her if she had eaten anything yet, but she said she wasn't hungry. I fixed her a sandwich and insisted she eat, telling her what Eddie had told us about keeping a full stomach on the water. Within thirty minutes, her color was back and she was fishing again. It took her a while, but she did manage to land another big one, and all by herself too. Elvis kept trying to help her but she kept pushing him away.

'If I'm strong enough to handle you, I can certainly handle this fish.'

We were at least two hours from shore by then, so at three o'clock in the afternoon the Captain turned the boat and headed for the coast. We watched a school of porpoise swimming along with the boat. Even though everyone was tired and sunburned, it had been a great trip, landing over fifty fish.

About five miles from shore, another boat signalled us to stop. The Captain, thinking they had engine trouble, pulled up next to them, and two members of the press jumped on board, as their boat pulled away. Elvis was so mad about the intrusion he refused to talk to them. We stayed on the front of the boat, with Red and Arthur standing in each walkway, making sure they couldn't squeeze in.

We pulled in the dock to find hundreds of fans waiting. We stayed at the dock long enough to have a few pictures taken from the pier. The reporters then got off the boat, thinking everyone was getting off as well, but when the boat pulled out, Mr and Mrs Presley, Elvis and me, along with the Captain, were still on board. The fans all ran to their cars and followed the boat all the way down the coastline. We managed to lose them on the east end of Biloxi, as the boat went behind the seafood factories lining the shore. Eddie was waiting for us at one of the factories, with both his car and Elvis's car too. Elvis couldn't figure out how he'd managed it.

'The fans were following the boat. They didn't know where you were going, but I did. I'll drive your mother and father back to the hotel, you wait here for ten or fifteen minutes, then you shouldn't have any problems getting back to Gulf Hills.'

'Thanks, Mr Bellman, you're a hell of a nice guy. If I can ever do anything for you, I hope you let me know.'

'It was my pleasure, Elvis, my boy. I'm one of your biggest fans,' Eddie said, proudly extending his hand to Elvis.

During all the excitement, Elvis had forgotten to tell his parents he'd reserved them a villa at Gulf Hills. Instead of going there he drove to my house and parked in the alley out back. He called his daddy and told them to check out of the hotel: he was going to meet them so they could follow us to Gulf Hills, but Mrs Presley got on the phone and told him not to come.

'The parking lot is filled with people. They think you're here in my pink Cadillac. It's so crowded, I'm afraid to go out.'

'Stay right there, Mama, I'll think of something and call you back.'

Elvis came in the kitchen and told us what was going on. Eddie came to the rescue again.

'Don't worry about a thing, Elvis. I'll make sure they get to Gulf Hills, and take care of the fans, too.'

Within twenty minutes Eddie was in the parking lot talking to the fans. He explained the Presleys were just passing

through, on their way to Florida to spend some time with
Elvis, and that Mrs Presley was fearful of crowds. They all
backed away from the pink Cadillac, and Eddie went to the
Presleys' room to help them with their luggage. The crowd
waved from a distance. Several fans were shouting, 'We love
Elvis! We love Elvis!'

The Presleys waved back to the fans and drove off behind
Eddie, arriving at Gulf Hills without one single fan following.
Elvis and I helped them get settled in their villa and the four of
us went to the hotel dining room. Elvis's parents had both
missed their afternoon caffeine break and were dying to have
a cup of coffee.

'Maybe this coffee will help me stop rocking back and
forth. I feel like a newborn calf trying to find his legs,' Mrs
Presley said, still swaying from the long day on the boat.

13

*T*HE TENDER SIDE

*E*LVIS HAD MENTIONED his love for water skiing to Eddie, and wanted to hire a boat for the day. He didn't care to go on a specified route, with a ski instructor, for a ten-minute ride. He wanted to go it alone for as long as he pleased.

Eddie, along with a friend, drove in the driveway pulling a boat behind the car. They launched the boat across the bayou with Elvis, extremely sunburned from the fishing trip, wearing a long-sleeve shirt and long pants to protect his tender skin from the sun. I sat on the bank with his mom and dad, and we watched the boys skiing up and down the bayou. Eddie, riding in the boat, took some shaky, out-of-focus movies for us to laugh about later.

After skiing, Eddie joined us for a pool-side lunch, along with Elvis's mom and dad and the rest of the gang. Elvis kept insisting he wanted to do something nice for 'Mr Bellman', and finally Eddie – insisting Elvis call him 'Eddie' – came up with the idea of Elvis making a personal appearance at his downtown Biloxi shoe store.

'I'd be happy to, Mr Bellman, I mean, Eddie. Just let me know when.'

'I'll talk to my partners, Elvis. How about tomorrow?'

'Sounds good to me, Mr, er, Eddie. I don't have any other plans.'

The store owner, Dave Rosenblum, together with Eddie and partner, Lew Sonnier, alerted the radio stations in the area, as well as those in Mobile, New Orleans, Jackson and Hattiesburg. Eddie drove to Gulf Hills and picked up Elvis the next morning. He was planning to sneak Elvis through the back door, but when they arrived, the streets and sidewalks were so packed with people they had to get a police escort to take them inside. The police stayed at the front door, allowing the crowd to come inside in shifts. Elvis stayed at the shoe store, signing autographs for well over an hour.

In appreciation for his time, the three businessmen bought Elvis a 410-gauge Winchester pump-action shotgun. Eddie brought the gun to Elvis later that day, along with a handtrap and some skeet targets. This was the first time Elvis had ever shot at flying targets. Later that same day, Elvis sent the boys to a hardware store in Ocean Springs, and bought all the BB guns the store had in stock. My brother, Jerry, came out to Gulf Hills with a broom handle stuck through the middle of some old 45 records. Jerry sailed the records in the air while we took turns shooting at them: we had our own BB skeet-shoot.

Elvis and I had a quiet dinner with his mom and dad that evening. Elvis checked his schedule and realized he had to be in Memphis for a personal appearance the following night. He decided to leave early the next morning. The Presleys were leaving too. Elvis was coming back in a few days, but I didn't know when I'd see the Presleys again, so I said my goodbyes to them and Elvis took me home. I kissed him goodnight, thinking he was going to turn in early.

'Are you trying to run me off, June?' he said, following me in the house.

'I'd never run you off, but you do need to get some sleep.'

'I couldn't go to sleep early if I tried. I'd just like to stay here for a few hours, and not say a word.'

I turned on the radio, found some soft music, and he put his head in my lap: a sure sign he wanted me to run my fingers through his hair. He was almost asleep when the phone rang.

'Don't answer it, June, let it ring.'

'It might be important. It might be for you,' I said, running to catch the phone. The phone call *was* important, and it did concern Elvis.

Bea Manuel, a friend of my family, had an eight-year-old daughter suffering from leukemia. Little Carole, now seriously ill, was a big Elvis fan – she'd seen all his television appearances and had all of his records. They had passed my house one day, while Elvis was out signing autographs in the yard, but Carole was too ill to get out of the car. I had mentioned this to Elvis a few weeks ago, but with all the excitement constantly going on we had both forgotten all about it. I had promised to call Mrs Manuel the next time Elvis was in town. She had heard about Elvis being at the shoe store, but by the time she and Carole got there Elvis had already gone. Elvis said he was going to stay at my house for a few hours, so I took it upon myself to invite them over. They were going to be at my house within the next thirty minutes. Now all I had to do was tell Elvis we were expecting company.

I told him who was on the phone, and before I had a chance to tell him anything else, he said, 'Go call her back, June, tell her I'll be here for a while.'

'You're not too tired?' I asked.

'No, I'm not too tired, go call.'

'I don't have to call, I've already invited them,' I confessed, smiling.

'I should have known,' he said, smiling too.

Elvis greeted them at the door when they arrived, and I made the introductions. Carole's eyes were as big as saucers; she was speechless. Elvis took her tiny hand and sat next to her on the couch. To break the silence, Mrs Manuel and I were talking about how cute the hound-dog was on the *Steve Allen Show*.* Carole said she liked the part where Elvis had to turn the dog to face him because it wasn't paying attention.

* Elvis recorded his performance on the show on 1 July 1956. The show's organizers had arranged a female basset hound named Sherlock to accompany him on stage during his rendition of 'Hound Dog'.

Carole quickly got over her nervousness, and was talking up
a storm. She liked 'Hound Dog' the best, and her next best
was 'I Want You, I Need You, I Love You'. Elvis picked her
up, put her in his lap, and started singing her second favorite
song. She would look in his face, and then look down at her
hands, folded in her lap. He put his hand under her chin, and
lifted her face up. She would look at him a few seconds, and
then back to her folded hands. He lifted her face one more
time and she smiled, unable to take her eyes from his face.

'That's better. For a minute I thought you were going to be
just like that hound-dog,' Elvis said, giving her a hug. I felt a
lump coming in my throat when Mrs Manuel, her eyes filling
with tears, whispered thank you to Elvis. He gave her a nod,
letting her know that, somehow, he realized a little of her
pain.

'Well, it was very nice meeting you, Elvis. I do hope we get
to see you again,' Mrs Manuel said, clearing her throat.

'Do we have to go, Mama?' Carole whispered.

'Yes, we have to go. Elvis is very busy, and if we don't get
home soon, Daddy will be worried about us.'

Elvis carried the little girl out to the car, and kissed her on
the forehead.

'I'll see you when I come to Biloxi again, I promise.'

Elvis was back in my lap, relaxing, but this time his eyes were
wide open. I asked him what he was thinking about.

'I'm thinking about that beautiful child, and the pain her
mother must be feeling.'

'You're a sensitive person, Elvis. I think that's one of the
things I love most about you.'

'June, did you see the look in Mrs Manuel's eyes when I
was singing to her little girl?'

'No, I was busy looking at you and Carole.'

'It was the same way my mother used to look at me when
I was a little boy. She would tuck me in bed at night, and
kneel down by my side to pray. She would look toward the
heavens, and ask God to watch over me. When she looked
down at me again her eyes would open wide. It was like her

eyes were opening wide enough for me to come in, where I'd be safe. I saw that same look tonight, in Mrs Manuel's eyes. Your eyes do the same thing, June. I knew you loved me, the first time we met.'

He lifted his head from my lap and kissed me for a long time. We lay face to face, holding each other, until he fell asleep. I finally had to wake him and send him on his way. We kissed goodnight and he promised to see me in a few days.

14

MY BUDDY

SCHEDULING MY LIFE to coincide with Elvis's was next to impossible. I never knew when he was coming back, if indeed he was coming back at all, or if he was going to spend a week or a day. He knew his schedule, but for some unknown reason he couldn't or wouldn't let me know a thing. In retrospect, I think he preferred to keep me guessing when and where he would show up. His way of testing me. If I had no other plans, then I should be at his beck and call.

I had promised not to date other boys, when Elvis and I were in Houston, but I had made my promise very clear: only as long as he didn't date other girls! And so far, according to all the press reports, he wasn't seeing anyone but me.

Our local newspaper did a story on me, along with a picture of me holding Pelvis, the black-and-white Panda bear, in my lap. Pelvis was wearing my motorcycle hat, and I was wearing the white dress I'd worn on our very first date. Overnight I was a celebrity in my home town, getting phone calls from friends I hadn't heard from in months.

Buddy Conrad, a lifelong friend, called to say he had been keeping up with me in the news. Buddy, an ardent fan of Elvis's from the very beginning of his career, had inherited a large sum of money and had been living the life of a playboy.

A long-time fan of country music, Buddy had seen Elvis many times on the 'Louisiana Hayride', in Shreveport, long before he ever appeared in Biloxi.

Twenty minutes after our phone conversation, Buddy was knocking at my front door. He invited me and Pat to go for a ride in his tiny MG convertible. Buddy had a new toy, a portable record player, the latest thing on the market. Now he wouldn't have to wait for the radio station to play his favorite Elvis records.

Pulling over at the first available parking bay on Highway 90, he opened a brand-new copy of Elvis's first long-play album, *Elvis Presley*, which at the time was number one on the *Billboard* chart, and placed it on his new machine. Emulating his idol, Buddy would stand tall, spread his legs in an Elvis position, strum his imaginary guitar and sing to the top of his lungs. He had all the Elvis moves down pat.

Buddy was tall and slender with bright orange-red hair. His mouth was wide and filled with beautiful, white, even teeth. He was not what you'd call handsome, but what he lacked in looks he made up for in personality. A real-life clown, he was always making people laugh. I always thought he'd missed his calling; he should have been a stand-up comic.

After listening to both sides of the album, Buddy decided to take us to the local amusement park. He wanted to win me a teddy bear, like Elvis had. We played several throw games, winning no prizes. Pat and I left Buddy, still throwing base-balls, and went for a ride on the Ferris Wheel, constantly stopping to let people off and on. We were near the top, and all of a sudden, a little boy, riding just above us, got sick. Vomit hit Pat in the back of the head and she started scream-ing and gagging.

'Get me down! Get me down!' she yelled.

I was following behind her as she ran wildly over to the floating duck game. She was pushing the ducks out of the way and splashing water all over her face and head, while the attendant was yelling for her to stop.

'Get out of here, you can't do that!' he screamed, outraged. Looking around, I spotted a faucet near by, and she stuck her head under the running water. If anything bad was going to happen, it always happened to Pat.

Buddy finally won a little stuffed tiger, and gave it to Pat, when he saw the state she was in. Buddy, holding his breath, couldn't get us home fast enough. Poor Pat, reeking from the stench of vomit, needed more than running water. She jumped in the shower, clothes and all.

I promised Buddy I'd give him a call next time Elvis came to town, but I wasn't sure when that would be. Coincidentally Elvis called later that same day – he was leaving Memphis and planned to be in Biloxi that night.

'Don't wait up for me, baby, I'm going to be late. I should have left you a key to the Hack house, but I didn't think about it. It would have been nice to have you sleeping in my bed,' he said, softly. I had chills of excitement when I hung up the phone.

I happily called Buddy and told him to be at my house in the morning, no later than nine o'clock. He was all excited; he had gone car-shopping after taking me and Pat home, and couldn't wait to show us another surprise. He was there at nine on the dot, driving a beautiful 1956 mint-green Continental Mark 2. Elvis was expecting Pat and me at ten o'clock. When I saw the new car, my first thought was, 'Boy-oh-boy, wouldn't Elvis be surprised to see me drive up in this?'

'June, why don't you and Pat take the Mark 2, and I'll drive out later in the Sarge's car,' Buddy suggested, apparently reading my mind. Buddy thought it was a great idea: Elvis would meet his car before he met him.

'He might not be impressed with me, but I know this car will get his attention,' Buddy said, knowing it was a sure thing.

I was, by no means, an expert behind the wheel, and was just a tad nervous about driving Buddy's new car. The only practice I'd ever had was driving someone else's. I drove my grandmother's car sometimes, when she came for a visit. My brother didn't trust me with his truck, and my mother didn't own one. I got most of my practice driving Pat's dad's car. The

Sarge, as we called him, didn't know about me getting behind the wheel of his car, but Pat trusted me. I had driven to Gulf Hills a few times before, with no problem, but this time I was a bundle of nerves. I was having second thoughts about driving Buddy's beautiful new Mark 2 across a narrow two-lane bridge, but Buddy assured me the car had plenty of insurance.

It was almost ten o'clock, and, as luck would have it, Elvis and the boys were standing in the Hack house driveway. They were all staring at the gorgeous car coming down the winding road. They had no idea it was Pat and me. I pulled in the driveway, and stopped right at Elvis's feet. When he recognised me, he got that *look* on his face, and folded his arms across his chest.

'Where'd you get the car?' he said, through clenched teeth.

'Ain't she a beauty? She drives like a dream, too,' I said, proudly showing off.

'*Where'd you get the car*?' he asked again, only louder.

'The car belongs to a very good friend. You'll get to meet him, he's coming over later,' I answered with a smile.

'*I don't care who you fuck, June!*' he said, looking at me as cold as ice. He turned on his heels and went in the house. I looked at Pat and the boys, but they didn't seem to be the least bit shocked.

'Oh well, so much for that little surprise!' Pat said, as she was getting out of the car.

'Get back in the car, Pat. Let's go!'

'C'mon June, he'll get over it. You haven't seen him in three days, and look at you, you're all sun-tanned and gorgeous, and you're driving another man's car. What's he supposed to think? You can straighten him out,' she said, defending him.

'I can straighten him out okay, but I don't have to take his shit,' I said, now angry as well as hurt.

She got out of the car, came to my side and opened my door. I walked in to find Elvis, sitting in an easy chair, his arms still folded across his chest. I stood in front of him, folded my arms, spread my legs apart, and put a sullen look on my face. I had assumed my *Elvis position*. Now I was ready to do battle with the King.

'I don't appreciate you talking to me like that, Elvis Presley!' I said, looking him in the eye.

He looked at me with the same sullen look, and didn't say a word. Finally, a little grin came on his face. He stood up, took me by the hand, and pulled me in the bathroom, closing the door behind us. Elvis would never settle any disagreement in front of the boys. He didn't want anyone to see him apologize or show any sign of being a tender, understanding human being. It wasn't considered 'manly'.

'I'm sorry baby, it's just when I think of you with someone else, I go crazy. Now, who the hell owns the car?'

'I told you when I drove up. You'll get to meet him, he's coming over later. His name is Buddy Conrad and he's a good friend of ours.'

'Ours?' he said, emphasizing the word.

'Yes, *ours*! Mine and Pat's. He's also the biggest Elvis Presley fan in the whole world.'

'Really?' he said, lightening up a bit.

'Yes, really! He'll be here in a few minutes, so stop acting like this.'

'Like what?' he said, pouting.

'Like this!' I said, assuming my Elvis position again. He picked me up and kissed me; his little fit of jealousy was over. 'I'm so glad you're here, June, I've been missing you real bad, baby.'

We were still in the bathroom when I heard a car door slam.

'Hey, you guys, quit that smooching and get out here,' Pat yelled. Buddy was giving his car a going over, making sure there were no scratches. Elvis reached out his hand to Buddy.

'Great-looking car, man! You'll have to let me take it for a spin. I'm Elvis Presley; you must be Buddy,' Elvis said, as if Buddy didn't know who he was.

I handed the car keys to Buddy and he threw them to Elvis. Pat, Buddy, Elvis and I jumped in the car, leaving the boys standing in the driveway. It was the beginning of a great friendship.

'Man, I've got to have one of these!' Elvis said. Buddy just smiled. He had met his idol, and Elvis, in turn, had made a friend for life. From that day on, Elvis made sure Buddy was included in everything we did.

In the ten years that followed, Buddy spent money at an alarming rate. He had nothing saved, and had no investments. I tried to get him to put some away for the future, but he laughed, saying he still had plenty. One day I told him I needed five hundred dollars, and he didn't even ask why. He only had two hundred on him at the time, but he reached in his pocket and gave it to me. I took the money to First Federal, and opened a savings account for him. I had him sign the papers the next time I saw him. I didn't see much of Buddy, but when I did see him, he would give me twenty dollars or more to add to his savings.

One day, Buddy and a friend came to my house wearing overalls splattered with paint. My dear friend, Buddy, was painting houses for a living. He needed money, so I gave him his bank book. The next time I heard from Buddy he was in hospital, in quarantine. They thought he had infectious hepatitis, usually characterized by jaundice. Further tests proved it to be cancer of the pancreas. I visited Buddy often after the quarantine was lifted. We would talk for hours on the phone, always about Elvis and the good old days. Buddy died within a few months of his diagnosis. He was flat broke.

Buddy had a great time, living it up and spending close to half a million dollars. I'm glad now that he didn't save for the future; he didn't have one. He was only thirty-three.

15

*I*S IT SO STRANGE?

*E*LVIS PULLED INTO a service station to replace the tank of gas we had burned in Buddy's new car. Reaching in his pocket, he realized he didn't have any money on him and quickly apologized to Buddy for being caught without cash.

'Hey, don't worry about it E.P., I've got a few bucks on me,' Buddy said, pulling a roll of bills big enough to choke a mule from the glove compartment.

On the way back to the Hack house, Buddy yelled for Elvis to pull over and get some firecrackers. Buddy, not interested in Roman Candles, bought a large bag of every other kind. We had only used half the Roman Candles in our first battle, and still had a full box left.

We walked in to find the boys dividing up the candles in the middle of the floor. They were getting ready to do battle again that night.

'What a coincidence! Show 'em what you got in the bag, Buddy,' Elvis said, as Buddy dumped the bag in the floor.

'Man, this is boot-leg shit!' Red said, scooping up a handful of cherry bombs. 'You can't find these in Tennessee, man, too many kids have had their hands blown off.'

'They're not supposed to sell them to kids, Red. You're

supposed to be a responsible person, like me,' Buddy said, placing his thumbs under his arms, like a big kid bragging.

To me, fireworks were only enjoyable visually. I had no desire to hear a loud *boom* that made me turn my face and cover my ears. I let it be known that I wanted nothing to do with the dangerous cherry bombs. Buddy gathered all the little red bombs and put them in the trunk of his car.

He was in for a real surprise that night, thinking Roman Candles were just for girls. Elvis asked Buddy if he knew of a good place where we could shoot the fireworks, other than on the beach. Buddy, knowing most of the beach was a residential area, suggested a secluded section further away called the Second Seawall. The Second Seawall was known as a lovers' paradise. The cool breeze coming off the water made it an ideal 'parking' spot for young couples. I myself had never parked there before, but I had been there in the daytime, out of curiosity, to see the place that was so popular with some of my peers. Buddy let Elvis know that this was the place where he had lost his 'cherry'.

The infamous parking spot was secluded, but it was mostly seawall, with only a small patch of white sand. The woods had thick underbrush, so hiding behind a tree was out of the question. Instead of having our battle, we fired the Roman Candles and bottle rockets out over the water. Elvis occasionally fired a candle in Buddy's direction, giving him a taste of what our war had been like, and keeping him on his toes. The boys wanted to go back to Gulf Hills and find a more secluded spot, but Elvis refused, saying his reputation was at stake.

The gang all piled in Buddy's car, leaving Elvis and me to ride alone. I was expecting Elvis to follow Buddy out of the secluded area, but he drove only a few yards before stopping the car.

'How many times have you parked here, June?' he said, in what I thought was a light-hearted way. Joking back, I held up my fingers and started counting.

'Let me see; there was Joe, John, Bobby, Bill, Frank—'

'Stop it, June! I'm serious! How many times?'

'Zero times, Elvis Presley, and I don't care if you believe me or not. Where's *your* favorite parking spot? Mudd Island?'

'I'm only teasing, baby, I believe you.'

'Good! And besides, this is too far from home. We have lots of parking places that are closer to my house,' I said, trying to sound serious but failing completely.

We made several wrong turns as we left the unfamiliar area, and laughed at every dead-end and double-back. The gang was beginning to wonder about us, we heard later, and were debating whether or not to go back and see if we were okay.

'Uh huh! Ya'll got lost, didn't ya?' Buddy said, nodding his head up and down as we pulled in the driveway.

'Naw, man, I never get lost. I almost lost my "cherry", though!' Elvis said, joking.

Later, as we were driving past Biloxi Hospital, I suddenly remembered Mrs Manuel calling the house and leaving a message to say that Carole had been admitted. We were always so busy, it's a wonder I ever remembered anything. I told Elvis about her call.

'Is there any way we can sneak in for a few minutes, just to say hello?' Elvis asked.

'It's late, and visiting hours are over, but we can try.' We parked by the emergency room entrance, and I went in to find out where she was. All the doors were open in the pediatric wing. I found Carole's room and ran back to the car to get Elvis. He opened the trunk of his car, took out an album, and we tiptoed down the hall. We made it to the room without seeing anyone. Carole was having a blood transfusion, and appeared to be sleeping through it all. Her arm was strapped tightly to a board, partially cutting off the circulation to her tiny hand. She blinked when Elvis gently touched her little swollen fingers, but quickly opened them real wide when she realized who it was.

'I knew you would come,' she said, in her weak little voice. Her eyes were glued to Elvis's face. She didn't even know I was in the room.

'I told you I'd see you again,' Elvis said, bending down and kissing her on the cheek. She smiled up at him, closed her eyes, and then fell sound asleep. Elvis put the album in the drawer of her night-table, bent down again, kissing her good-night, and we tiptoed out of the room.

'Look around, and count your blessings, June,' he whispered as we walked quietly through the halls of the hospital. We drove down the beach in silence.

Elvis pulled over in front of the White House Hotel, and parked the car.

'This is where I fell in love, June. Wanna go for a walk?' he said, remembering our first evening together as he looked out at the long pier. Hand in hand, we walked to the end of the pier, talking about the night we had met. Elvis was great for remembering details, even reminding me that he never did get to go floundering. Standing behind me, with his arms around my waist, he lifted my hair and started kissing me on the neck.

'Everything's the same as it was then, June. We're even looking at the same full moon.' He was right. Everything was the same, even the chills I had felt when he kissed me.

Elvis wasn't wearing a watch, but pretended to check the time by looking at his left wrist.

'I guess I'd better take you home, June, it's either 1:15 or 3:05, I can't tell,' he laughed, remembering my panic that first night. He was just kidding – it was still early. Early, that is, for Elvis's way of life.

I had no objections when he drove past my street and headed for Ocean Springs. The boys had already retired for the night, and the Hack house was in darkness. Without turning on the lights, we sneaked up the stairway to his balcony bedroom. Fully dressed, except for our shoes, we lay on the bed snuggled in each other's arms and fell asleep.

Later, thinking I had been sleeping a long time, I sat straight up in the bed.

'I have to go home!' I said, in a panic.

'Relax, baby, it's early!' he said, pulling me back down and looking at his glow-in-the-dark travel clock on the bedside table. One thirty in the morning may have been early for Elvis, but it wasn't early for my mother. I dozed off, waking ten minutes later, and sat straight up again. Cat-napping, waking, and sitting up every five minutes, I was up and down like a yo-yo. Elvis finally agreed to take me home. We walked outside and looked up at the moon.

'This night is too beautiful to waste. Wait here, I'll be right back,' he said, running back inside. I had no idea what he was up to. I could only think about my mother killing me for being out so late. Even though she was getting used to it, it still bothered me that she might be worried, but looking up at the moon I had to agree with Elvis. The night was too beautiful to waste.

He came back with a blanket, and spread it in the middle of the yard. Lying on the blanket next to Elvis, and looking up at the moon and stars, my worries disappeared.

'Keep your eyes on the moon, June, and let's spoon.' He laughed. 'Seriously, baby, keep your eyes on the moon, and you'll see a glowing blue ring appear.'

After staring at the moon for about two minutes, I could see the bright blue ring. It seemed to pulse with the beat of my heart. I was fascinated, unable to speak.

'Do you see it? Now, let yourself totally relax, and just focus on the space between the moon and the stars. Don't think about anything! Just let yourself float. If you can relax enough, you can go right up there with them.'

Elvis was always playing little tricks on me, but this time he sounded very sincere. Still mesmerized by the blue ring, I tried to do exactly as he said. Feeling a little strange, I stopped looking at the moon, and looked at Elvis.

'How long have you been doing this?' I whispered.

'Since I was a little boy,' he whispered back, his eyes still on the moon. 'You don't believe me, do you, June?' he said, now looking at me. 'I promise you, June, I'm serious. People think you're crazy if you talk about things they don't understand. My mama knows. She's the only one I know that really understands.'

He was acting strange, but he wasn't drinking or using

drugs. At that time, the only pill Elvis ever took – other than an aspirin – was a No-Doze tablet when he was on the road at night, and his strongest drink was a Coke.

It was peaceful and quiet, except for an occasional 'riv-itt' from the bullfrogs near the bayou. I tried relaxing as much as possible, and was about to fall asleep when Elvis's voice brought me back to reality.

'It's okay if you fall asleep, baby, then you can dream your way up to the sky. It takes a little practice, but you can do it if you really want to. All you have to do is make up your mind. You think I'm crazy, don't you, June?'

'No, Elvis, I don't think you're crazy. I think you're wonderful!' I whispered, feeling very content.

'I think you're wonderful too, baby. I love you, June! I want you for my very own. I can't get married for at least three years. Wait for me, June, I want you to be my wife. I want you to be the mother of my children.'

'Do you really mean it? Are you serious?'

'I've never been more serious in my life. I promised the Colonel I'd never do anything detrimental to my career. He insists marriage would be the end of me. I'd marry you now, if I could, but we're both young, we have plenty time. Hopefully in a few years I'll be able to have a life of my own.'

'You *are* serious, aren't you?'

'I'm very serious, June. I'm talking about our lives, our future. But you haven't answered me yet . . .'

'Yes! Yes! Yes! I want to marry you too. I love you, Elvis, I love you!'

A few years is a long, long time, however, and I wondered, as I often did with Elvis, whether he'd still feel the same in a few years' time.

'We can't be sure of what the future holds for us. I only know what I'm feeling now, and that's that I want to be with you for the rest of my life. It would be a sin to waste a love like ours.'

He started singing a song I'd never heard before. He wasn't real sure of the words.

If you tell a lie, you know that I'll forgive you,
though you say our love is just a game.
And when you hear my name,
you'll say I'm from a strange world,
but is it so strange to be in love with you?
Is it so strange that I love you, more than all the world?
Is it so strange I have no eyes for any other girl?
Won't you take me back, and say that you still love me?
To waste a love like ours would be a sin.
Let us kiss again, let me hold you near,
and take me from this strange world that I'm living in.

I was so touched by the song that tears came to my eyes. I held him close, not saying a world. The words to the song kept going over and over in my mind.

'What's the name of that song, Elvis?'

'"Is It So Strange?" You like it?'

'I love it! I love the words.'

'I thought of you, baby, the first time I heard it. God knows, I do live in a strange world. God also knows I have no eyes for any other girl. Do you believe me, June?'

Hundreds of girls, some young, some old, and some the perfect age, threw themselves at his feet every day of his life. He said he had no eyes for any other girl. Could it be the right face hadn't come along yet? I could tell at a glance if Elvis was going to single out a face in the crowd. She had to have the required dark hair, and blue eyes, framed in thick dark lashes, before she ever got a second look. But even with the hair and eyes, she also had to have the rest to go with it. Do you believe me, June? was his question. Was he doubting my love too, or did he just require constant affirmation? Even at my young age I could understand his dilemma. Does she love me for who I am, or does she love me for *me*? But then I had a dilemma of my own. He loves me now, but what happens when a prettier face comes along? It wasn't a lack of self-confidence; I had more than my share of that. It was Elvis himself, and the circumstances of our surroundings, his strange world, that kept me wondering: when will it all come to an end?

'I believe you, my love,' I answered, knowing that's what he wanted to hear – but in my heart, I still wondered.

'Will you record that song for me one of these days?'

'It's not what I'd call a million-seller, June.'

'I don't care about that. I want you to record it just for me.'

'One of these days I will, June. Just for you.'

16
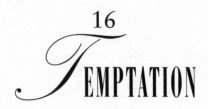TEMPTATION

W HILE MAMA WAS getting ready for work, I was following her from room to room telling her bits and pieces of my night.

'Sounds like things are getting pretty serious between the two of you.'

'They are, Mama. Elvis asked me to marry him last night.'

'He did? Anytime soon?'

'In about three years.'

'Good, that will give you time enough to get to know each other better.'

I never did understand why she showed so little enthusiasm. Maybe she too had her doubts. She gave me a big hug and left for work. I then called Pat to tell her the news. She wasn't the least bit surprised.

'He's crazy about you, June. Everybody can see that! When's the big day?'

'Not for at least three years.'

'Good! That will give you enough time to know if that's what you really want.'

'I feel like I'm talking to my mother, Pat. She said the same thing. Damn! Am I the only one that's excited, or what?'

'No, June, I'm happy for you. It's just that you're all caught up in this love thing, and you've only known Elvis for a short time . . .'

'That's true. Well, anyway, he's coming to pick me up in a few minutes. We don't have any plans, I guess we'll just hang around the Hack house, so come on over after a while. And Pat, don't mention this to another person, okay?'

'My lips are sealed, June – and about the engagement, congrats! I knew you'd be the one.'

As soon as I hung up the phone Mrs Manuel called. Her little girl kept telling her that Elvis came to see her last night.

'June, that's all she's been talking about. I thought she'd been dreaming for sure. I was only out of her room long enough to go to the nurse's station and get a cup of coffee. I was just humoring her until I opened the drawer in the nightstand and saw the record.'

'Carole wasn't dreaming, Mrs Manuel. We did go to see her last night. She talked to Elvis for a moment, then fell asleep.' There was a period of silence, and then I heard her whimpering.

'Hug him for me, June. Tell him I think he's a great person, and Carole and I both love him.'

'I think he's great too, Mrs Manuel, I'll tell him you called. Kiss Carole for us.' When I got in the car I kissed Elvis on both cheeks.

'One's from Mrs Manuel, and the other one's from Carole. And this one is from me,' I said, kissing him softly on the lips. 'Because I love you.'

'I love you too, June.'

When we arrived at the Hack house, the boys were all out front, loading the BB guns and getting ready to shoot the leftover records. We left the gang throwing darts in the living room, and went upstairs for what he called 'quiet time'. It was early afternoon when we stretched out across the bed. Neither of us had had much sleep the night before, and we were both exhausted. We fell asleep and didn't wake up until well after dark.

While we were sleeping Buddy had picked up a portable

barbecue grill, and all the makings for hot dogs. We didn't
have any pots, so Buddy had the opened can of chili on the
grill along with the foot-long weiners. When we went down to
join the gang, Elvis naturally picked the one that was charred
the blackest. With mustard and chili running down our chins
we looked like a pack of ravenous wolves.

Buddy had also picked up a giant-size, ice-cold watermelon,
but we had no knife to cut it with, so he raised the big melon
over his head and dropped it on the concrete driveway, bursting it to pieces. Elvis and I stayed in the background, watching
as they dug out the heart and battled with the rest. When the
watermelon fight was over, they peeled off their sticky shirts
and ran up to the hotel pool.

Wide awake now, after our five-hour nap, and wanting to
get away from the boys' antics, Elvis ran in the house to get
the car keys.

'Let's get the hell out of here, baby, before they get back.'

I didn't pay much attention to where we were going until
Elvis rounded the curve and pulled up at the Second Seawall.
Elvis turned off the engine and wound the windows down.

'Now you can tell your friends you've parked at Second
Seawall,' he said, moving over towards me from the driver's
side. There wasn't much of a breeze, and it was getting hot in
the car – in more ways than one – so we decided to get out.
When I opened the car door to get out, though, I came within
inches of stepping on a used rubber.

'*Yuk*! Let's get out of here,' I said, pointing to the condom.

Elvis just laughed; he thought it was funny. We stayed in
the car and drove for a while before stopping again, but by
this time the mosquitoes had found us and were about to eat
us alive.

'Something tells me we're not going to park here after all,'
he said, swatting what he called the 'buzzing little bastards'.
Even today when I get a mosquito bite, as unpleasant as it is,
I laugh, remembering that night and the 'buzzing little bastards.'

Elvis suggested we go back to the hotel, and go for a swim,
but I had a better idea.

'You want to go for a swim? I know the perfect place.' We drove to the west side of Biloxi, on the outskirts of town, to the Sunkist Country Club. The pool behind the club house wasn't fenced in, and a gang of us teenagers used to sneak in all the time. We stripped down to our underwear and quietly slipped in the cool water. The club house had a few lights across the back; just enough for us to see each other.

'What happens if someone catches us?' he whispered nervously.

'Nothing! They'll just make us leave, that's all. The night-watchman must be hard of hearing; he's never caught us yet, and we always made noise. Relax, there's nothing to worry about,' I whispered, giving him a long passionate kiss.

'I need you desperately, June. Do you wanna make love in the water?' he whispered between kisses.

'Only if you do,' I answered, leaving the decision up to him. I was so aroused I couldn't have said no if I tried.

'You're no help at all, June. We can't both lose control, one of us has to know when to stop,' he said, putting both hands on top of my head and dunking me under the water. When the dunking was over I couldn't resist getting my own back. I grabbed the back of his underwear and, with an upward yank, gave him a wedgie – or what we girls call a 'PIC' (Panties In Crack)! I swam like crazy to the deep end, treading water until he promised he wouldn't drown me if I came back. Hoping he would keep his promise, I swam back to his arms.

Playing in the water until our fingers were all shriveled, we kept a sensible distance between our almost nude bodies, stealing a kiss every now and then.

He took me home and we sat in the car talking for a long time. He didn't tell me he was leaving the next morning until we were on the porch, kissing goodnight.

'Why didn't you tell me you were leaving?'

'It's bad enough *me* knowing; I didn't want to spoil your night too. I won't be gone long, baby, I promise,' he said, giving me a quick kiss and leaving me standing on the porch.

Disappointed, I went straight to the bathroom, washed the

chlorine from my hair, and started putting it in pin curls. Realizing I had no reason to look good, I quickly took the bobbie pins out. I hadn't had a haircut in over a year. I was either wearing a pony-tail or sleeping every night in pin curls, and it was getting to be a royal pain. The sun and chlorine had damaged the ends of my hair, so I decided to surprise Elvis with a new hairdo. I was one for changing my hairstyle as often as I changed my mind, so it was no big deal for me. I went to bed planning to make an appointment the next day.

In the morning I had to explain to my mother why my panties and bra were hanging in the bathroom. When I told her about sneaking in the pool, she just laughed. She was probably relieved to know I'd kept them on.

With my new haircut, closely resembling that of actress Gina Lollobrigida, I left the beauty salon with a smile, knowing Elvis was going to approve of the new me.

17

ℐHE SUNSHINE STATE

THE THREE LONG days Elvis was gone seemed like an eternity, but I did manage to catch up on some much-needed sleep. The only time I wasn't missing Elvis was when I was sleeping, so I was going to bed early and staying in bed late. I'd also been neglecting my duties around the house, so I tried to make the time pass by keeping busy. I was doing everything that needed to be done, including the cooking and cleaning. My mother, happy to have me back, was enjoying a mini-vacation of her own.

I was so excited to hear the familiar toot of the lavender Lincoln's horn that I ran out forgetting all about my new haircut. After a big hug, Elvis held me at arm's length, checking out my hair.

'When did you do that?' he said, running his fingers through it.

'Well?' I said, waiting for a response.

'Well what?'

'Whaddya think?' I asked.

'Think about what?' he said, grinning.

'About my hair!'

'It'll grow back, baby, don't worry,' he said, being very serious, kissing my pouting lips and then laughing. 'I'm only kidding, baby, I love it! You look exactly the same as you did the first night we met. I love it, I really do!'

Before coming to pick me up he'd gone by the riding stable and reserved horses for all of us. I ran inside and changed into some long pants, bringing a change of clothes with me. The gang was already there waiting when we arrived. The same two horses Elvis and I rode the first time were saddled and ready for us again. Elvis's horse was sometimes used as a lead horse, so they were going to let us go it alone this time.

Before we had a chance to leave the stable, a car pulled up, and a man carrying a camera stepped out. He introduced himself and asked Elvis if he could spare a minute of his precious time. Elvis was impressed. He was used to cameras clicking without anyone ever asking if it was okay or not. We stayed for a few pictures, and a short interview, before hitting the trail.

Singing our harmony songs we were Roy Rogers and Dale Evans in the Wild West. I was on top of the world when Elvis told me he didn't have to leave again for two whole weeks.

'I reckon you'll be putting up with me for the next few weeks, Dale. We gotta lotta hard work ahead, gettin' these here cattle to market, and fightin' off them there cattle rustlers,' Elvis said, sounding more like Roy's sidekick.

'Don't fret none, Roy. Me and Trigger'll be right here by your side ever' step of the way,' I said, sounding absolutely nothing like Dale Evans.

Singing and slowly walking the horses through the woods, we stretched the forty-five-minute ride to ninety minutes. Thinking we were lost, one of the guides came to look for us, and we bumped into him as we rounded the curve heading back to the stable.

'That's enough action for today, gang. Let's go home and relax,' Elvis said, thanking the horse with a pat on the neck. Knowing he had time to call his own, Elvis was content to sit around and do nothing for days at a time.

In the beginning he had been excited about his upcoming Florida tour. I tried not to let my feelings show, but I had been dreading the arrival of August all summer long. As our time together grew shorter, Elvis grew less anxious to leave.

'I'm gonna miss you, baby. I hate to think about being away from you for so long,' he said, holding me close. I didn't know exactly how long 'so long' was – I only knew it was going to be a long time. His tour of Florida was due to last ten days, and after that he had to report to Hollywood to work on his first movie. Florida didn't seem to be all that far, but California was on the other side of the world as far as I was concerned.

'I'll miss you too, Elvis. I don't know what I'll do without you,' I said, close to tears.

'If I could only figure out a way to hide you from Colonel Parker, you could go with me. Let me see what I can work out. Do you think your mother would let you go?' he said, apparently thinking out loud.

'Me? Go to Florida with you? I'd love to, but I doubt if my mother would let me.'

'I'm not worried about your mother, baby, I'm sure I could convince her. It's the Colonel – he's already told me about seeing too much of you. He'll shit a brick if he sees you in Florida. I'll think of something. I'll figure out a way,' he said, assuring me with a kiss.

Colonel Parker was supposed to be Elvis's business manager, but apparently he had control over his personal life too. Elvis was twenty-two, and, in my opinion, old enough to make his own decisions. I was also of legal age, but I felt that I had to have my mother's approval, so I guess it was the same thing. His relationship with his manager was more like father and son, so, at that time, I respected his feelings of loyalty.

Within the next few days Elvis had convinced Buddy to go on the Florida tour and to take me and Pat with him. It didn't take much convincing; Buddy would have gone to the ends of the earth for his idol. I discussed making the trip with my mother, but she gave me a definite 'No!' Elvis was disappointed when I told him I couldn't go.

'Did you tell her you'd be going with Buddy? She trusts

Buddy, don't she? You'd have me and Buddy both looking out
for you. Do you think she'd agree to that?'

'I doubt it, Elvis. It's when I said "ten days" that she hit the
ceiling. She still considers me her little girl, and she worries
about me.'

'We still have time to work on changing her mind. I know
what I'll do. I'll have my mother talk to your mother. I'm call-
ing home tomorrow, to invite Mama and Daddy back to
Biloxi so I can spend some time with them before I leave for
Florida. Just leave everything to me baby, I can fix it! I know
I can!'

With just a flash of his smile, my feeling of doubt was
turned around. Elvis had a power of persuasion unlike anything I had ever seen. If he said he could fix it, I knew he
could.

He brought me home earlier than usual that night, for two
reasons: he wanted me to get a good night's sleep, and he
wanted me to spend some time with my mother. She wasn't
even home. She didn't have to get up early, so she and Eddie
had gone out for the evening. They used to go out at least
three times a week, so I couldn't understand what the big
deal was about me going out so much.

Elvis, assuming I'd had a nice long visit with my mother,
called early the next morning to see if anything had changed.

'Is your mother home, June? Good! I'll be there in a few
minutes,' he said, not giving me a chance to say anything. Pat
was coming over, so I called and told her to meet us at Gulf
Hills later. Elvis walked in with a big smile on his face.

'Good morning, Mrs Juanico, how are you?'

Mama smiled back at him but was with quick with an
answer.

'I'm just fine, Elvis! I was just asking my daughter the same
thing. I haven't seen much of her lately,' she said, looking at
me instead of Elvis.

'Don't be mad with June, Mrs Juanico, it's all my fault. I
can't go anywhere or do anything until late at night, when the
rest of the world is sleeping. My vacation is almost over; I'll
be leaving for Florida in a few days. It will probably be two or

three months before I get to see June again.' Mama looked at him, shook her head, and smiled. She was beginning to soften just a little.

'Would you like some breakfast, Elvis? I know how to burn bacon without even trying,' she laughed.

'No, thank you very much, Mrs Juanico, I've already eaten. Has June been making fun of the way I eat?'

'She wasn't making fun, she told me about the breakfast you had at the Ko-Ko. I thought it was funny. I wish I could have been there.'

'Will it be okay if I use your phone, Mrs Juanico? I have to call my parents.'

'Sure, hon, just leave your nickel next to the phone,' Mama said, joking. Elvis laughed, and Mama, seemingly in a good mood, laughed too. Things were beginning to look up. He talked to his mother for a few minutes, and then called my mother to the phone. He gave me a wink, but I just shrugged my shoulders. I didn't know what he had up his sleeve.

After talking to Mrs Presley for a good ten minutes, Mama came back to the kitchen smiling, poured herself a cup of coffee and sat down at the table with us.

'Your mother was telling me what a trusting, responsible young man you are, Elvis. She promised me you would take good care of June if I let her go with you to Florida.'

Elvis reached across the table, and held both my hands in his.

'I will too, Mrs Juanico, I promise!'

Mama said she would have to think about it for a while, but that was good enough for me. I knew she wouldn't say no. Before we left, Elvis invited Mama and Eddie to join us at the Pink Pony lounge that night.

'Don't worry about June, Mrs Juanico, I'll have her home early again tonight,' he said, giving Mama a hug. I gave her a big hug too, and we went back to Gulf Hills.

Pat's car was in the driveway, and a motorcycle was parked right next to it. Pat, Buddy and the boys were sitting around doing nothing. They were all lost without Elvis. I grabbed Pat and started jumping up and down.

'We're going to Florida! We're going to Florida!' I sang like a child.

'Did your mother say it was okay?' Buddy asked.

'Not exactly, but I know she will.' I told them all about Mama talking to Mrs Presley on the phone, and I was sure she was going to say yes. Pat was beside herself. Elvis wanted to know who the motorcycle belonged to, but nobody was paying him any attention. Buddy, all excited, was busy hugging me and Pat.

'Now all I have to do is make sure Mom and the Sarge will let me go,' Pat said, crossing her fingers. Elvis was still trying to get someone's attention.

'Who owns the motorcycle parked outside?' he asked again. Buddy suggested we all take a ride to Pat's house, and get her parents' permission. We all sat on the couch and started to make plans. Elvis was standing in the middle of the floor, looking at us. He had assumed his *Elvis position*.

'Is everyone through talking? Will someone please tell me whose motorcycle is parked in the driveway?' he shouted.

'It's mine, E.P. I'm sorry, I wasn't paying attention. The bike is mine. You like it?' Buddy said, jumping up from the couch.

'I have one just like it, Buddy,' Elvis smiled.

'I know, E.P., that's why I brought it over. I thought you might like to go for a ride,' Buddy said, smiling so wide you could see every tooth in his mouth.

'Thanks Buddy! You're too much, man.'

Pat had to get the car back to the Sarge before he hit the roof. Buddy was going to pick her up on the bike, but Elvis suggested we go in the Lincoln and talk to them about Florida.

'You take the bike, E.P.,' Buddy said, throwing him the keys.

Elvis and I were on the motorcycle, revved and ready, before Pat and Buddy could even get in the car. We rode alongside of them whenever the traffic would allow. It was hard to tell who had the biggest grin: Elvis, doing his favorite thing, or Buddy, satisfied just to watch. They were alike in lots of ways; Buddy too loved making others happy.

Pat's three little sisters were playing in the front yard when we arrived. They stopped in their tracks, frozen with their mouths wide open, watching Elvis's every step. We went inside, with Pat leading the way.

Every visit I ever made to the Napier home was an education in itself. Normally the daily newspaper was divided into two sections: news and sport. Mrs Napier, a grade school teacher in the public-school system, was more concerned with the racial segregation problem going on in our neighboring State of Alabama, or with Nikita Khrushchev saying 'We will bury you!' to America, or with nuclear tests in the Pacific.

'What's the world coming to?' she used to say, reading the news section of the paper.

Sergeant Napier, meanwhile, reading the sports section and sipping a beer, would wonder if the New York Yankees or the Brooklyn Dodgers would win the World Series that year.

This time things were different. There was no talk of current events, just smiles on their faces. Elvis's appearance seemed to change the atmosphere completely.

'Mom, Dad,' Pat yelled. 'There's someone here I want you to meet.' The Sarge, looking a little puzzled, wasn't sure if he even knew who Elvis Presley was.

'Sergeant Napier, it's good to meet you, sir,' Elvis said, shaking his hand firmly.

'This is the singer, Daddy – you know, "Heartbreak Hotel"!' Pat said, while one of the little sisters yelled, 'And "Hound Dog"!' Another sister yelled out, 'Don't forget "Blue Suede Shoes"!' Pat's mother, waiting to be introduced, was smiling all the while.

'I know exactly who this is; all I ever hear around this house is Elvis Presley, Elvis Presley, Elvis Presley. It's nice to finally meet you, Elvis,' Pat's mom said.

'It's a pleasure to meet you too, Mrs Napier.' Pat was grinning all over herself; she knew by the smiles on their faces that she was going to Florida, too.

Elvis was telling them about his upcoming tour, and somewhere in the course of the conversation they both gave Pat permission to go along. It was hard to resist Elvis's charm.

Mrs Napier offered everyone something to drink, and handed Pat's sister Beverly some money to buy some Cokes. Elvis took the money and handed it back to Mrs Napier.

'Let's all go, my treat,' Elvis said.

We walked across Race Track Road to Pearl's little country store. Pearl, an Elvis Presley fan, couldn't believe her eyes when she realized he was in her store. Elvis bought us all Cokes and let the little sisters, Beverly, Nancy, and Judy, reach their hands in the candy jar and take all the candy their hands could hold. When Elvis reached in his pocket, though, he realized he didn't have any money. Buddy quickly pulled out some bills, handing them to Elvis. All eyes were on Elvis as they lined up to give him a thank-you kiss. They watched and waved as we drove away on the motorcycle.

'Okay, June, where to? It's your turn to show me your town.' We drove by St Martin School, the little country school, grades one through twelve, where I was one of nineteen graduating seniors. Elvis couldn't believe how small it was compared to his own high school. From there we went to Tchoutacabouffa River, the summer-time weekend hang-out for all my friends. I had him stop the bike in the middle of Lamey's Bridge, overlooking the white sand beach where all my friends had surprised me with a weiner roast for my sixteenth birthday.

'Can you believe I used to dive from here? It's high, ain't it?' I said, knowing what a stupid stunt it was.

'No, I can't! Were you crazy, June?'

'It was during my young and foolish years; the years when you think you're indestructible. I'd never do it again!'

'How deep is the water?' Elvis asked.

'No one knows. They've never been able to find the bottom.'

'Damn, June, you had to be crazy!' he said, dropping a rock over the side of the bridge.

I took him down Biloxi's main drag, Howard Avenue. The Avenue itself was constructed of red bricks, and still had the old street-car tracks running down the center, even though street-cars were way before my time.

Unlike our day-long tour of Memphis, the city of Biloxi, surrounded by water on three sides, could be seen in less than an hour.

When we returned to Gulf Hills, local artist Harry Reeks was waiting to do a charcoal sketch of Elvis and anyone else who wanted to pose. Elvis sat me in the chair, across from the artist, wind-blown hair and all, insisting I go first. Running my fingers through my hair, I asked Mr Reeks if he would be so kind as to comb it with his charcoal as he went along. Elvis, watching his every stroke, thought it was a good likeness, but insisted I was much prettier. I blushed when Mr Reeks apologized, saying it was 'hard to capture that much beauty'. I watched in amazement as Mr Reeks caught perfectly the famous sulking look on Elvis's handsome face. I took both sketches home with me, planning to have them framed someday.

Harry Reeks went on to become famous on the Gulf Coast for his work as a sculptor as well as an artist. It wasn't until after Elvis's death, looking through my scrapbook, that I discovered the charcoal sketches, still in good condition, and took them to be framed. They hang side by side in my home, where everyone can see them.

We spent the evening with my mother and Eddie at the Pink Pony lounge. Red took my mother for a twirl on the dance floor while Eddie took his turn on the bongo drums. It's thanks to Mama, a real shutter-bug, always clicking her camera, that I have most of the pictures reproduced in this book.

After Elvis had done his bit at the piano, and we had sung every song we knew, we left the Pink Pony and went back to the Hack house. Eddie sat around shooting the breeze with the boys while Elvis gave Mama a personal tour of his summer hideaway. Before we all said goodnight, I not only had permission to go to Florida, but a big hug to go along with it.

 OWN SOUTH

ELVIS'S PARENTS WERE due in that afternoon, and the biggest part of our day was spent going through the Hack house with a fine toothcomb making sure we had all our belongings. Elvis had reserved the entire villa to accommodate his parents as well as himself and his entourage. Elvis and I walked hand in hand back to the house for one final check. Standing on the balcony, he held me in his arms, and kissed me gently.

'This place is full of beautiful memories, June. Maybe, by this time next year, I'll own it. Then we'll never have to say goodbye,' he said, kissing me again.

After getting everything put away in the villa, Elvis and I stayed out on the front lawn, so he could see the pink Cadillac as it rounded the curve. He was anxious to see his mother – it was the first time they'd been together in weeks. Tomorrow was his last day before going to Florida, and he wanted the four of us to spend the day together doing something different. My grandmother lived in New Orleans, so I knew lots of interesting places to visit. He liked my idea, and was going to suggest it when they arrived.

Elvis's entire face lit up as he watched the pink Cadillac rounding the curve. After all the hugs and kisses we helped them get settled in the villa, and the four of us walked to the

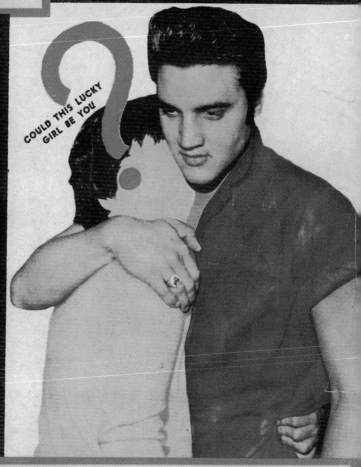

ELVIS

HIS LOVES & MARRIAGE

25c   P.D.C.

ALL NEW!

THE FULL INTIMATE STORY OF THE GIRLS IN HIS LIFE ... NEVER BEFORE PUBLISHED!

25 REVEALING NEW PHOTOS

IS ELVIS READY TO MARRY? **WHO WILL HE WED?**

COULD THIS LUCKY GIRL BE YOU?

SEE... THE FIRST PUBLISHED PICTURE OF ELVIS' "DREAM GIRL"!

The lucky 'dream girl' was me …

Elvis with a not-so-lucky girl: swapping photos with a fan.

Elvis with the Four Coins singing group. Restaurant-owner Gus Stevens is on the left.

*R*iding with Elvis at the Gulf Hills Dude Ranch and Country Club – *before* we got covered in mud! Gulf Hills became Elvis's home away from home throughout the summer of '56.

*E*lvis with C. E. Spearman, director of Gulf Hills. He was happy to have Elvis to stay, but less happy when we set off a load of fireworks on his golf course.

*A*board the *Aunt Jennie*, the charter boat we hired to go fishing.
Left to right: Captain Bull Thornton, Elvis, me, and Elvis's parents, Vernon and Gladys.

*B*y the pool at Gulf Hills.
Left to right: Elvis's friend Arthur Hooton, Gladys, Vernon, Elvis, Red West, and Elvis's cousin, Junior Smith. This is an excellent example of Elvis's *sullen* look.

*E*lvis took this picture of his baby – although I'm not sure who's the baby: me, or his '56 Cadillac convertible.

$\mathcal{W}$ith Elvis at the Sun 'N' Sand Motel. We'd just got out of the swimming pool and Elvis is munching on a plum.

$\mathcal{E}$lvis sitting at Princess Whitecloud's organ at the Ko-Ko Restaurant and Lounge, across the street from the Sun 'N' Sand. Elvis had to be persuaded to play – he wouldn't touch someone else's property.

*E*lvis at the Sun 'N' Sand.

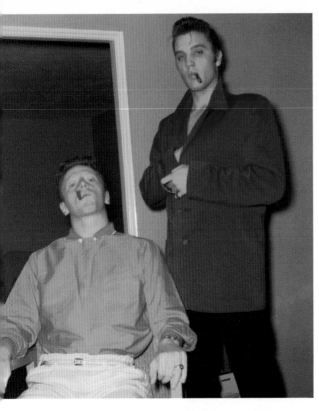

$\mathcal{E}$lvis and Red West:
the gangster look.

$\mathcal{E}$lvis and Eddie Bellman, my
mom's steady date, having
breakfast at the Ko-Ko.

*T*rying to hit a low note under Red's direction.

*W*ith Elvis at my house in Biloxi.

*I*n my bedroom, holding the panda Elvis won at the carnival in Memphis.
The panda, which Elvis named 'Pelvis', is wearing the motorcycle hat Elvis bought me.

*O*ne of my favorites: playing records at my house. Notice how Elvis was peeling from his sunburn.

*D*oing his famous dance
through the doorway.

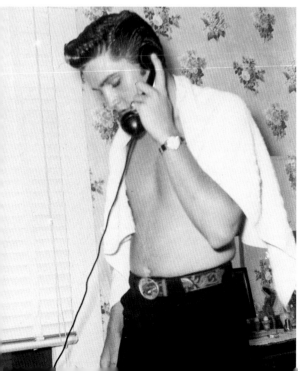

*I*n my bedroom –
checking in with his mom.

*I*n the Pink Pony Lounge at Gulf Hills – jamming with bongo drums and piano.

Eddie Bellman giving Elvis his first shotgun, at the Gulf Hills villa Elvis rented for the summer.

Taking aim.

The portrait I had taken to send to Elvis. Soon after, though, the tears would be for real

hotel restaurant for a bite to eat. They'd had breakfast before leaving Memphis, but Mrs Presley – in a hurry to get to Biloxi – didn't want Vernon to stop even for gas, much less something to eat.

Right away Mrs Presley started teasing me about having some kind of spell over Elvis.

'He used to come home between shows, but now he acts like *this* is his home. What have you done to my little boy, June? He can't wait to get back to Biloxi.'

'It's not me, Mrs Presley, it's the Gulf Coast; it has a way of making people return,' I said, boasting about my beautiful home town.

'You can't fool me, June, I know better,' she said, with a little smile.

When Elvis mentioned our plans to spend the day in New Orleans, Mrs Presley, fatigued from the long drive, didn't seem very enthusiastic. I suggested we cancel our plans and just take it easy, but she wouldn't hear of it. She'd been wanting to visit New Orleans for a long time, and promised to be good as new after a night's sleep.

The pink Cadillac offered more room, but also drew more attention, so Elvis decided we'd take the less conspicuous Lincoln. The ride alone was a new experience for them. I had made the same trip hundreds of times, but this time it was different. I saw, through the eyes of Elvis's mother, the uniqueness and beauty I had always taken for granted as if for the first time. It began with twenty-seven miles of beautiful white sand beach, the longest man-made beach in the world. At that time, the coastline of Mississippi had some of the world's finest homes. Today, only half of these homes still remain: the other half didn't survive the devastating 200mph winds of Hurricane Camille back in 1969. When we got to Pass Christian, Mississippi, the area hit hardest by the storm, Elvis slowed the car so his mother could get a better look at all the antebellum homes. She was ooh-ing and ah-ing over different ones, asking Vernon if he would like to live in a big house like that one day. She was getting no response from Vernon, so she sat on the edge of her seat and leaned forward between me and Elvis. I asked Elvis to stop the car so I could change seats with his mom, but she insisted the view from the back was just as good as the view from the front.

Mr Presley's interest was finally aroused when we reached Bay Saint Louis, Mississippi. He was curious about the signs on several gift shops in the area: BABY ALLIGATORS FOR SALE. Elvis had stopped on one of our previous trips, but stopped again so his dad could see the tiny reptiles for himself. Some of them were no bigger than five inches long.

'They're adorable, but what do you do when they get big?' Mrs Presley asked.

'You run for your life, Mama!' Elvis answered. The alligators later became an endangered species, and were no longer sold as pets.

Travelers on Highway 90, the only route between Biloxi and New Orleans, always made a traditional stop at the White Kitchen Restaurant to have a slice of their famous pie. The menu listed six different varieties of cream pies. Elvis, unable to decide, ordered a slice of each.

Riding through the Rigolet's, Mr Presley perked up again when I told him that most of the baby alligators we had seen were probably born right here. He was straining his eyes trying to catch a glimpse of mama or papa gator. Houses and fishing camps were built on both sides of the highway, running through the bayous and swamplands of Louisiana. Little did we know that Elvis would soon be filming *King Creole* on location right here, and would be using one of these camps in the movie.

Highway 90 became Chef Menteur Highway as we entered the New Orleans city limits. Elvis was now on familiar ground, and decided to make a quick trip to show his parents Pontchartrain Beach. He put on his hat and sunglasses, and we walked the midway without incident. Mrs Presley seemed to be tired, so they rested on a bench overlooking Lake Pontchartrain while Elvis and I went for a quick ride on the Zephyr. He wanted to throw a few baseballs, but I reminded him that the day belonged to his mom and dad, and Pontchartrain Beach was not on the itinerary.

'We can always come back some other time, okay?'

'Okay, June, you're the boss. But only for today!' Mrs Presley and I took Elvis by the hand and had to practically drag him from his favorite playground.

We drove slowly down Bourbon Street, so the Presleys could see a little of the world-famous French Quarter. Mrs Presley wasn't at all impressed with the scantily-clad dancers in every bar, clearly visible from the street. She did enjoy walking through Jackson Square, however, and seeing all the artists displaying their wares.

No trip to the city would be complete without stopping at one of the two open-air coffee shops in the French Market, serving only *café au lait* and *beignets*, little doughnuts dusted with sugar. Once we were settled with our coffee and dough-nuts, we talked about New Orleans.

Miles and miles of levees surround the city and its neigh-boring parishes, protecting them from the waters of the Mississippi River and Lake Pontchartrain. Standing at the base of the levee, when the river is at its highest stage, it's pos-sible to see a gigantic ship steaming down the river right over your head. Elvis's mom found it hard to believe when I told her the river was only a few yards from the coffee shop – she had to climb the many steps up the side of the levee to see for herself. We were all covered with powdered sugar but didn't realize it until we started up the stairs. Laughing and dusting ourselves at every step, we were worn out by the time we made it to the top.

With me on one arm and his mother on the other, Elvis was smiling like he owned the world.

'I don't know what I did to deserve this, but Lord, I'm thankful,' Elvis said, briefly raising his eyes to the heavens, then kissing us both on the tops of our heads.

'Me too,' I whispered, feeling on top of the world myself. Elvis and his dad left us resting on top of the levee and walked back to pick up the car.

Our next stop was the Audubon Park Zoo. Still wearing his hat and sunglasses, we had made it through the day, so far, without one person recognizing Elvis. He was all smiles, watching his parents holding hands and strolling through the park like two young lovers.

'Look at those two. We must be contagious,' he said, giving my hand a squeeze.

We were laughing and watching the antics of the monkeys, baboons, and orang-utans, when a teenage girl tapped Elvis on the shoulder. At first we thought he'd been recognized and she wanted his autograph. She smiled, handed Elvis her camera, and asked if he would mind taking a picture of her with her two friends. Elvis took the camera, listened closely to her instructions about which button to press, and patiently waited for them to pose. They thanked him and went on their merry way, never knowing who had snapped the shutter.

With the humidity near a hundred per cent, and the ninety-degree-plus temperature, we were happy to skip the rest of the attractions and go back to the air-conditioned car. Elvis drove aimlessly around the city, pretending to know exactly where he was going. The Presleys enjoyed seeing the street-cars, an unfamiliar sight, plentiful back then, both on St Charles Avenue and Canal Street. No one bothered to question our whereabouts until we were on the outskirts of New Orleans, in the city of Metairie.

'We've been riding forever. Are we still in the same city?' Mrs Presley asked as we were passing a large cemetery. She was impressed with all the rows and rows of beautiful tombs and statuary, and asked Elvis to drive through. Reluctantly, he turned the car around and drove slowly through the cemetery so his mother could have a closer look. He stopped the car so she could read the dates on some of the more elaborate tombs. Some of the inscriptions dated back to the Civil War. This was not Elvis's idea of a fun place to be, but he had to admit, it was truly beautiful.

'I've never seen so many tombs in all my life – but where are all the graves?' Mrs Presley asked, thinking there must be another section.

'There are no graves, Mrs Presley. New Orleans is four feet below sea level, making underground burial impossible.'

'June, you're amazing. How in the world do you know so

much about so many things?' she said, shaking her head in disbelief. I just smiled proudly, not telling her that the sea-level issue was the major reason my grandmother had recently purchased burial plots in Biloxi rather than in New Orleans. She didn't want to burden the family with the added expense of a tomb.

'Well, no wonder I haven't seen any graves. I don't like the idea of being put in the ground. I'd much rather be put in one of these,' she said, modestly pointing to one of the less expensive, smaller tombs.

'Stop talking foolish, Mama. Let's get out of here,' Elvis said, looking for an exit.

'Death is a part of life, son. It's something we all gotta do, sooner or later. It don't hurt none to talk about it,' she said, touching Elvis on the shoulder.

'Well, I don't wanna talk about it, okay? I've got a lot of living to do, and so do you. We're just getting started. Is anybody hungry? Let's go get something besides doughnuts and pie. I want some real food!' he said, trying to change the subject. Elvis took the nearest exit and was immediately confused about which way to turn. He would never admit to being lost, but we were.

Getting lost in a big city is one thing, but getting lost in a big city during peak traffic had us all on the edge of our seats. New Orleans was, and still is, known for its wild, crazy drivers, and in order to survive one must drive wild and crazy too. Elvis proved himself to be a real champ behind the wheel, even though he had us shutting our eyes on several close calls. Thanks to his driving skill, and a great sense of direction, he had us back on familiar ground an hour after leaving the cemetery. By this time we were all starving. He drove straight to Martin Brother's restaurant, another traditional stop for travelers on Highway 90. As soon as he turned off the car, we all let out a sigh of relief.

Martin Brother's was famous for New Orleans-style 'po-boys', a type of hoagie sandwich made famous in the South. Having stopped there once before, on one of our trips to Pontchartrain Beach, Elvis was anxious for his parents to try one of the delicious sandwiches. Reading the menu, listing six different varieties, Elvis, as usual, couldn't make up his mind, and ordered one of every kind. The waitress, knowing it was a lot of food for four people, took the order and walked away smiling.

'We can always take the left-overs home,' Mrs Presley said when the food came, looking at the table filled with foot-long sandwiches.

'I sure hope so! With six feet of sandwiches, we should have some left over,' I laughed.

Seated in the back corner of the restaurant, with his back to everyone, Elvis, being the perfect gentleman, had removed his hat and sunglasses. When the waitress, an attractive middle-aged lady, came back with our check, she looked at Elvis, did a double take, and smiled. Not because she recognized Elvis, but because the only thing left on the table was a few crumbs of french bread. Elvis and his dad simultaneously unbuckled their belts and groaned.

On the ride home Mrs Presley asked me how I knew so much about New Orleans, and had me dredging up long for-gotten memories of my childhood spent in 'The City That Care Forgot'; so named because the people of New Orleans were always ready to lay aside their business and have a good time. Even though I was born and raised in Biloxi, I probably knew more about the city than most native children. They were raised in residential areas, and didn't get to visit 'Le Vieux Carré' until they were of legal age. Le Vieux Carré or Old Square, the oldest and most famous section of New Orleans, was also known as the 'French Quarter'.

My grandmother was the manager of the Astor Hotel, on Royal Street, smack dab in the middle of the French Quarter. My grandmother, or Maw Maw, as I called her, and step-grandfather were also residents of the old hotel, where I spent most of my summers and every other weekend. As a young child I couldn't wait to visit Maw Maw's big house.

The four-storey hotel had a hand-operated elevator that looked like a big square birdcage. It held four people at a time; or two if they had luggage. By the end of the summer, my brother, Jerry, and I had mastered the trick of stopping the elevator on the same level as the floor. Jerry was sometimes allowed to take up hotel guests all by himself. I used to pitch a fit every time. He was only two years older, but I could drive the elevator just as good as he could.

'I'll bet my widdle-bitty got pissed off good and proper, too,' Elvis said, interrupting me for a second.

Mrs Presley was sitting directly behind Elvis, so I had turned sideways, facing her, so she could hear what I was saying. Elvis was constantly touching the inside of my knee, then walking his fingers up my thigh. He was keeping his eyes on the road, and his arm down, so his mother couldn't see what he was doing. I was stopping his walking fingers and trying to concentrate on what I was saying all at the same time. He was not only distracting me but enjoying every minute of it.

'Elvis, you leave June alone. I'm enjoying what she has to say. I don't know what you're doing, but I have a good idea,' Mrs Presley said, slapping him on the back of his head with a folded magazine.

'The one thing I didn't like about the hotel was the bathroom arrangements,' I said, sliding a little farther away from Elvis, trying to continue my story. Every guest had to share the toilets and showers, located at the end of the halls. My mother used to keep a chamber pot under our bed, in case we had to go in the middle of the night.

One of my favorite things about the hotel was the lighting in the lobby. In a storage room behind the front desk, floor-to-ceiling shelves were filled with kerosene lanterns to be used in case of a power failure. My grandmother loved the warm glow of the lanterns, and always had several burning in the lobby, along with the electric table lamps. One of the lamps had a multi-colored, beaded fringe shade. It would gently sway with the breeze from the ceiling fan. I would sit under the lamp for hours, watching the kaleidoscope of colors dancing on my lap.

Elvis, still behaving like a naughty little boy, reached out his hand for me to hold. As soon as I took his hand, he started scratching my palm with his index finger. I'm sure this well-known gesture needs no explanation. Mrs Presley could see him looking at me with his mischievous little grin, and gave him another whack with the magazine.

'Son, behave yourself, before I take your daddy's belt and give your hide a tanning,' she said. He put both hands on the wheel and pretended to look straight ahead. Still wearing his silly little grin, he would glance at me from the corner of his eye. I had the urge to jump in his lap and smother him with kisses, but I felt I had to behave in front of his mother.

'I'll get you later, Elvis Presley,' I said.

'Is that a promise, June?' he said, raising his eyebrows up and down like Groucho Marx.

'Don't pay him no mind, June, tell me more about your hotel.' Elvis had a way of distracting me without even trying, so if I wanted to finish my story, I had to focus all my attention on his mother. I paused for a moment, and then tried to pick up my train of thought.

My favorite person at the hotel was Addie, one of the hotel maids. Addie knew my name, but always called me Blue Eyes. I used to follow Addie from room to room while she cleaned. She taught me how to fold hospital corners on the bed sheets. My mother always kept our room tidy, so Addie only came in our room once a week, to put fresh sheets on our beds. I knew when Addie had made my bed; it was like crawling into an envelope. The sheets were so tight, when I laid on my back, my toes were pressed down like a ballerina, dancing on *pointes*. I always had to get out of bed and loosen the sheet at the bottom. There were certain rooms I could go in, and others where I wasn't allowed. The rooms that were off limits to me Addie called the 'quickie' rooms, unsafe for little blue-eyed white girls. I didn't learn about these rooms until I was well into my teens.

The hotel was in walking distance of Mississippi River and the port of New Orleans. Longshoremen, in town for the night, couldn't bring their girlfriends aboard ship, so they would rent a room at the hotel. Maw Maw would only rent certain rooms, the ones she called quickies, to the longshoremen.

Because of the subject matter, Elvis was now paying as much attention as his mother was. They both laughed. Mr Presley, full of po-boy sandwiches, had his head tilted back on the seat and was snoring up a storm. I didn't mind, I felt more at ease talking to just Elvis and his mom.

I carried on talking about the Astor, telling them how the hotel didn't have a restaurant, so we had to do most of our cooking and eating in my grandmother's room.

'Wait a minute, June, you were talking about the quickie rooms, now you're talking about eating. What else happened in the quickie rooms?' Elvis said, raising his eyebrows again.

'Don't make me hit you again, Elvis. They had a quick piece, and then they checked out. Now let June finish talking!' Mrs Presley said, shaking the magazine in his face. I was laughing so hard I couldn't remember what I had been talking about. Mrs Presley reminded me about cooking in the room.

My grandmother had two electric hot-plates, but they were on different sides of the room. If you plugged them both in the same outlet, they would blow a fuse. Mama usually planned ahead and brought along pre-cooked frozen meals, but many nights we had chicken noodle soup straight from the can.

Maw Maw always cleaned her own room, but Paw Paw was such a slob the maids cleaned his room daily. One day, when I was helping Addie clean Paw Paw's room, she told me the story of Voodoo Queen, Marie Laveau. I asked Mrs Presley if she would like to hear it.

'You might as well say yes, Mama. June's wound up like an eight-day clock and making no sense at all,' Elvis said, teasing, but meaning every word.

He was right. I wasn't making much sense. I was trying to finish telling the story Mrs Presley had become so involved in.

My grandfather had an ugly carved coconut head hanging from the ceiling fan in his room. Every time Addie walked in his room, she looked up at the coconut head, made the sign of the cross, and mumbled a few words I could never under-stand. It was always while we were in this room that she would talk about Marie Laveau. Marie had lived in New Orleans, just a few miles down the road from the hotel, over a hundred years ago. She would dance once a week in the square with a snake around her neck. Everyone was nice to Marie because they were afraid of her voodoo power. She could put a spell on you and make you turn into a frog, or something worse. She had the power to make you do anything she wanted you to do; even if it was against your will. She would make little cloth pouches and stuff them with all different colored chicken feathers, dog hair, hair from a black cat, ground bones, and herbs. These little pouches were called 'gris-gris'. The gris-gris were placed under the bed of the person you wanted to control. There were two kinds of gris-gris; one was good, the other was evil. My sweet old friend, Addie, said I should always be good. If I was bad, the spirit of Marie Laveau would come after me. For a while I didn't know if I should be good because Santa Claus was coming or because Marie Laveau would get me if I wasn't.

'And then what happened, June?' Mrs Presley said, leaning up on the edge of her seat.

'Well, I found out I didn't have to worry about Santa Claus, he was only make-believe,' I laughed.

'You mean to tell me this Marie was a real person?' she asked.

'Yes ma'am, she was real!' I answered.

Mrs Presley was quiet, waiting for me to continue. By this time Mr Presley was snoring even louder than before.

'Don't pay him no mind, June. He's used to going to bed early,' Mrs Presley said, apologizing.

'Yeah, baby, now you know how much Daddy liked your story,' Elvis said, laughing.

'June, I can't thank you enough for today. I can't ever remember having such a nice time. You've had such an interesting childhood,' Mrs Presley said, leaning forward and putting both hands on my shoulders.

'You don't have to thank me, Mrs Presley; I had a good time too,' I answered.

'Don't you think it's about time you called me something besides Mrs Presley, June? After all, one of these days you're gonna be part of the family.'

I looked at Elvis; he just smiled. He hadn't mentioned anything to me about telling his parents. Mrs Presley kissed me on the cheek as if reading my mind.

'Elvis didn't tell me anything, June. I can tell it's getting serious, just by the way you two love-birds have been looking at each other all day long. I've never seen my boy so taken with a girl. You two are planning to get married one of these days, aren't you?' she asked, directing her question to Elvis.

'One of these days, Mama, not any time real soon. I've got to get my career going good first.'

'You better not let Colonel Parker know how serious you are about June. You know how he feels; especially about marriage.'

'I know, Mama. He don't even like it when I see a girl more than once. Don't worry; when the time comes, I'll handle the Colonel,' Elvis said, completely unaware that the Colonel would not only control his career, but also his personal life – dictating when, where, and to whom, Elvis would finally wed.

'Well, I hope you two make it, June. If I had to choose a wife for my son; it would be you,' Mrs Presley said, putting both hands on my shoulders again.

'Thank you, that's the nicest compliment I've ever had,' I said, turning in my seat and hugging her neck. I knew she liked me from the very first time we met, but to choose me for her daughter-in-law, especially this early in the game, was overwhelming.

'Now, if I could just get you to call me something besides Mrs Presley . . .' she said again.

I had known a girl named Gladys when I was in school, and the name didn't seem to carry enough respect for Elvis's kind, soft-spoken, loving mother. I remembered her telling me her full name, and decided her middle name, Love, was the only name that would fit her perfectly.

'Will it be okay if I call you Lovie, Mrs Presley?'

'I like that, June; I like it a lot. It sounds kinda special,' she said, leaning back in her seat and smiling.

All day long Elvis and I had been sitting on opposite sides

of the car like an old married couple. I hated being so far away from him, but I was concerned about his mother's opinion of me. I was a responsible young lady, capable of controlling my emotions. She was used to seeing ladies, young and old, hanging all over Elvis. I didn't want to be put in the same category. But when Elvis put his arm across the back of his seat, and motioned for me to sit next to him, I didn't hesitate.

'This is where you belong, baby,' Elvis said, pulling me even closer. I looked over my shoulder, smiling at Lovie; she smiled back and gave me a wink.

When we got back to Biloxi, Elvis deliberately passed the street to my house. I didn't mind; it was too early to go home.

'Your mother knows you're in good hands, June; you can call her when we get to Gulf Hills. This is my last night here, and I want you with me.'

When we got to Gulf Hills Elvis stopped at the hotel long enough for me to run inside and call my mother. I told her we were back in town, and I would be staying with the Presleys for a while. I had no idea I was going to spend the night.

The villa had four private bedrooms; two on each side of the central living area. The boys were staying on one side, and Elvis had the room next to his parents. We sat around the living area talking until everyone was ready for bed. I was assuming Elvis was going to take me home, after we all said our goodnights, but instead he took me by the hand and led me to his room. I had wanted to be alone with him all day, so I had no objections. With very little effort, Elvis convinced me to stay the night. We had both been perspiring, off and on, for most of the day, and after a few salty kisses we decided to take a shower; but not together – we were not yet that brave. Elvis loaned me a T-shirt and a pair of his Fruit of the Loom briefs. I showered first, and was almost asleep when he crawled in next to me. A few kisses later, we fell asleep in each other's arms.

Elvis was still sleeping soundly when I woke up early the next morning. I unzipped his black leather shaving kit and borrowed his toothbrush. I'd just finished scrubbing my teeth when he stuck his head around the corner.

'You're not through yet; you have to brush mine too,' he said, so I put some more toothpaste on the brush and stuck it in his mouth. I was doing a terrible job, standing there facing him, so I got behind him and brushed his teeth as if it was it was my own mouth. I thought I was doing a good job until he gagged. I gathered my clothes up as he finished the brushing himself, but Elvis had other ideas.

'It's too early to get up, baby; everybody's still sleeping,' he said, pulling me back to the bed. He started tickling me, and put his hand over my mouth several times because I was making too much noise. We started kissing and, all of a sudden, the laughing stopped. I had, almost without realising, let all my defenses down; but, after all, I *was* going to be his wife someday . . . I raised my hips, making it easy for him to remove my borrowed briefs. Evidently he was feeling the same way as me. All the other times when we'd been in this situation I had stopped him, or he had stopped himself, saying he wanted it to be special. He said he wanted to wait until we were married. So did I, but this time our passion for each other had taken us too far; pushed us both out of control. We had made love, in our own special way, every time we were together, but this was the first time we actually came close to physically having sex. Elvis was slowly and gently beginning to enter me when we heard a 'tap tap tap' at the door.

I was so startled I felt like my heart had stopped. He rolled off me and sat straight up in bed.

'Who is it?' Elvis yelled, after making sure I was covered. The unlocked door opened; it was Lovie.

'I heard all the laughing in here, and then I didn't hear anything but quiet. I just wanted to tell you that maybe we should get June something to keep her from having too many babies,' Lovie said, smiling at us both, but also being very serious.

'Don't worry about June, Mama, she's a virgin and she's gonna stay that way till we get married,' Elvis said, looking like a little boy caught with his hand in the cookie jar.

'I was just making sure you two didn't do anything you might be sorry for later. Ya'll get dressed; your daddy wants to go have breakfast. Oh, and maybe you should check under your bed for "gris gris", Elvis,' she laughed, closing the door.

We dressed quickly and joined Elvis's waiting parents. The four of us walked outside to find several cars parked in front of the villa. Barbara Lawrence, the Social Director at Gulf Hills, was the first one out of her car. She ran as fast as she could over to Elvis and me.

'Some members of the press are here to interview Elvis. June, you don't have to answer any questions; I'll handle it,' Barbara said, completely out of breath. The very first question was not for Elvis, however, but directed at me.

'Did you spend the night with Mr Presley, Miss Juanico?' one reporter asked, with raised brows.

'No, I didn't spend the night with Mr Presley. *Mrs* Presley spent the night with *Mr* Presley,' I answered, raising my eyebrows too.

'Miss Juanico has her own private room next to Mr and Mrs Presley,' Barbara answered, trying not to laugh. Elvis and I just smiled at each other and kept walking to the car, with his mom and dad following close behind. We stopped long enough for Elvis to say he was leaving for Florida that same afternoon.

'If you don't mind, I'd like to spend some time with my parents. Thank you,' Elvis said politely.

Lovie couldn't believe all the reporters gathered in front of the villa, and wanted to know if this sort of thing happened all the time, and so early in the morning.

'I haven't been bothered at all until today. It must be your pink Cadillac, Mama,' Elvis said, kissing her cheek. We drove the short distance to the hotel to have breakfast. Evidently the press got Elvis's message – they didn't follow and left us alone.

Elvis always got a little uptight whenever the press was around, and started fidgeting with his menu. After the waitress took our order, Lovie took Elvis's hand and held it in both of hers while she talked to him.

'Have you been getting enough rest, son? Are you eating right? I know how you are.'

'I'm doing fine, Mama. Don't worry your little head about me. I'm gonna be just fine, I promise. It's just the nerve of some of these bastard reporters, that's all.'

She sweetened his coffee and buttered his biscuits. It was obvious that he was the most important thing in her life, even more so than her husband. Elvis thrived on his mother's attention, and was constantly making her feel needed and appreciated. He would never just say 'Thank you' to her without touching her hand or face. Her presence alone seemed to have a calming effect on him.

Several articles written after his death referred to him as a 'wimp', a 'mama's boy', tied to her apron-strings. Nothing could have been further from the truth. Elvis was a loving, devoted son, trying to make up for the hardships his parents had suffered in their lives. If this makes a man a wimp, then the world should be full of wimps like Elvis Presley.

We drove back to the villa, and I waited by the car with Lovie while Elvis and his dad went in to get their luggage.

'I noticed how he can't keep still, June. Make him slow down a little, if you can,' she said, her voice filled with concern.

'I'll try Lovie. I'll do my best,' I assured her.

'I know you will, June.'

Lovie's eyes were brimmed with tears when she hugged and kissed her son goodbye. Sharing him with the rest of the world wasn't easy.

'Take care of yourself, Daddy, and take good care of Mama,' Elvis said, giving his dad a bear-hug. As his parents drove away he kept his eyes on the pink Cadillac until it was out of sight.

Elvis and the boys were leaving that same afternoon. He had to be in Miami, on the Colonel's orders, the day before his first show. I went back into the villa long enough to help him pack his clothes. He had two suitcases, one with neatly folded clothes and the other for dirty clothes only. I picked up the shirt and briefs I'd slept in, and was going to put them in with the dirty clothes, but he snatched the briefs from my hand and put them in the 'clean' suitcase.

'I'll wear these for my first show. Hopefully they'll bring me better luck than they did this morning,' he said, with a sheepish grin. Slightly embarrassed, I just grinned too. I wasn't exactly sure how I felt about what had almost happened.

He didn't have much to say when he was driving me home; I assumed he was preoccupied with his Florida tour. We both got out on his side of the car, and just stood there for a moment. He took my face in his hands, kissed me tenderly, and got back in the car.

'Be careful on the road, and I'll see you in a few days,' I said, breaking the silence.

'I really don't want to go, June. I want to stay here for ever. Just you and me.'

19

$\mathscr{B}$AD PUBLICITY

W$_{\text{ITH THE}}$ A$_{\text{NTICIPATION}}$ of the trip, and the excitement of it finally arriving, getting a good night's sleep was completely out of the question. I had seen Elvis performing live on stage before, but that had been well over a year ago. Now I was going to be in the middle of it all, watching Elvis do his thing.

My mother, leaving for work, had just given me a hug and a kiss goodbye when the phone rang. It was Buddy, trying his hardest to imitate Elvis.

'*Well it's one for the money, two for the show, three to get ready, let's go cat go! Get your glad rags on, and join me hon, I'm leaving now, so we can have some fun . . .*'

I hung up the phone, dragged my suitcase to the front porch, locked up the house and began pacing back and forth, too excited to sit still. I could hear Buddy's horn blowing a block away. While Buddy was loading my suitcase, Pat and I were hugging and jumping around in circles.

While Elvis always did all his own driving, Buddy decided to split the driving three ways. Unlike the interstate highways today, bypassing all the major cities, highway traveling in 1956 took you through the center of every little city and town. Inching our way across the Florida panhandle, it seemed to be an endless journey. I decided it would be easier if we didn't look at the long distance to Miami, but take it one town at a time. It made the time as well as the miles seem to go much faster. Before long, Pat's 300-mile shift was over and it was my turn at the wheel. When my shift was over, I stopped in the middle of nowhere, in the middle of the night, and woke Buddy. It was a relief not to hear any more of his loud snoring. We arrived in Miami early the following day, and checked into the first available motel in Miami Beach. We had just enough time to get some sleep before Elvis's first show of the day.

I woke up at daylight feeling a little uncomfortable, and went to the bathroom. *Yuk*! I was totally unprepared for what I found. With all the excitement, I'd completely forgotten about my monthly visit from the Red Devil.

'Wake up Pat!' I yelled in desperation.

'Why? What's the matter?' she yelled back.

'You're not going to believe this! I've started my period, and I didn't bring any Kotex,' I said, on the verge of tears.

'Oh, shit! Why now? I didn't bring any either. What should I do?' she said, coming into the bathroom rubbing her eyes.

'I can't move, Pat, I'm bleeding like a stuck hog. I've got to have some pads,' I said, now crying.

'I'll go get the car keys from Buddy, and find a store. Here, put this between your legs and go back to bed,' she said, throwing me a towel. We didn't have a phone in the room, so she put on her clothes and went next door to Buddy's room. I could hear her knocking lightly and then banging on Buddy's door. The entire motel could probably hear it too.

'I can't wake him up. I'm going to the office to get a pass key,' she said, storming back in the room.

'I'm so sorry, Pat, I'd go myself, but I can't go anywhere with this towel between my legs.'

Pat came back in the room a long five minutes later.

'Did you get the car keys?' I asked.

'Hell no! He's got the friggin' chain on the door. I can see him but he won't wake up. He's passed out cold, stark naked, and ain't got the first sign of any covers,' she said in disgust. I got out of bed, traded the towel for a washcloth, and went with her to Buddy's room. We yelled at him through the crack in the door, but couldn't get him to budge. Looking around for something to throw, we saw a drinks machine that dispensed orange juice and milk in little cartons. Next to the drinks machine was a trash-can full of empties. We grabbed a handful and started throwing them through the crack in the door, but the empty cartons were so light they wouldn't reach. We needed something heavier, so we pooled our coins and bought some full cartons. We only had three, so we had to make every shot count. The crack was so small we could barely get our hands through. We missed with the first two, finally hitting him in the chest with the last carton. He shot straight up in the bed, looked all around the room, and tried to figure out what was going on. Garbage was everywhere! He walked to the door like a zombie, tripping on the sheet he was holding in front of himself, and handed Pat the car keys.

'You might as well come with me, June. You can help me look for a drug store,' Pat said, now completely awake.

It was six o'clock in the morning, and everything was closed. Back in the fifties there was no such thing as a 7–Eleven convenience store. By this time, Pat was really getting aggravated. I was trying to be sincere when I said I was sorry, it was all my fault, but when I looked at her, I had to laugh. She was only five feet tall and weighed eighty-seven pounds. The top of her head was at about the same level as the steering wheel of the big Mark 2.

We'd been riding for half an hour and still couldn't find a store. When we stopped for a red light, two men pulled up alongside of us. They looked at us and started to laugh. One of them stuck his head out of the window and yelled.

'Hey little girl, you better take your daddy's car home.' Pat took a deep breath, and turned to face the man.

'*Fuck you, mister!*' she yelled.

The light turned green and she floored it. I was laughing my head off. At least she'd had enough Southern upbringing to include the world 'mister' when she was addressing him.

We finally found a gas station-cum-store, bought what I needed and went back to the motel for a few hours' sleep.

*

We got to the Olympia Theater about twenty minutes after the first show had started. It seemed to take forever for us to find a parking place. Police were surrounding the Theater, and gave us directions to the stage door. After telling the guard that we were with Elvis, he went inside and came back with Red. Red waved for us to come in and we watched the opening act from the wings.

The size of the crowd was unbelievable. When Elvis made his entrance from the opposite side, he saw me and gave me a wink. Screaming girls were being held back from the stage by police. I was caught up in the excitement of it all. I knew the effect he had on me, but seeing this many girls go completely wild was a little frightening.

Two security police positioned on either side of the high stage had the impossible task of keeping the frenzied teenagers under control. Blinding flash-bulbs, exploding from every angle, were not only capturing the image of Elvis but the audience reaction as well. Making matters even worse, Elvis would dance his way to the edge of the stage, step over the stage lights, and reach out to the audience. This had the crowd back on their feet, stampeding to the edge of the stage, wanting to touch his hand.

Members of the press, witnessing this phenomenon for the first time, were compelled to get this news to the public. Within twenty-four hours of his arrival in Miami, Elvis had every parent in the state of Florida scratching their heads, wondering what he was all about and what kind of power he had over their youth. It was the beginning of 'Elvis Mania' – and seeing was believing.

Minding my own business, enjoying the show from the wings, I was soon approached by several members of the press. They not only knew my name, they also knew where I was from and that I was in Florida with Elvis. Elvis was on stage and out of reach, so they were following me. Everywhere I turned, someone was asking me questions. They couldn't get a good story out of me, so some genius of a reporter decided to telephone my mother. Finding the phone number was easy; only two Juanicos were listed in the directory. In retrospect, I realized I should have told my mother never, under any circumstances, to talk to the press, but I had no idea anything like this would ever happen.

The media in New Orleans had already caused a stink earlier that summer, with the erroneous report of our engagement that had put Elvis in a panic. We had managed to squelch that rumor before it reached Colonel Parker's ears, but this time we weren't so lucky. Elvis and I were then completely in the dark about the front-page story in the *Miami Herald* that followed, only to learn later that it was my mother who had spilled the beans.

Fans quickly discovered Elvis was driving the lavender Lincoln Premier, and with anything that would make a mark they had autographed the car from top to bottom. They also formed a constant vigil around the car, making it impossible for Elvis to drive, forcing him to hire a limousine service to take him to and from his performances.

He had a death grip on my hand as we ran the short distance from the stage door to the waiting limo after the show. Crowds had pushed their way past the barricades, and police were having a hard time holding them back. Three motorcycle cops were escorting us back to Elvis's hotel. We were going so fast one of the cops couldn't make the curve; he lost control of his bike and spun out, hitting a fence. Elvis yelled for the limo driver to stop, but we kept on going. As soon as we got to the hotel room, Elvis collapsed on the sofa with his head in my lap.

Emotionally drained, but still wired from his afternoon show, I was running my fingers through his hair, trying to calm him down. He was anxious to find out about the motorcycle cop, but no one could find out anything. Meanwhile, Arthur Hooton, one of the boys, had rear-ended someone in Elvis's Lincoln, and was being held in the Miami jail. Red was off somewhere trying to see how many girls he could make out with, as usual, and Junior was drinking again. I felt so sorry for Elvis that day, he was trying to be granddaddy to us all. (Arthur's car crash later cost Elvis five thousand dollars in an out-of-court settlement.)

Elvis was finally beginning to relax when someone knocked
at the door. He shouted for Gene, in another room, to see who
it was. Before Gene could get to the door, in stormed the
Colonel. He had a folded newspaper in his hand, and his eyes
darted from me to Elvis. Elvis jumped up from the sofa and
went to his side.

'Son, we can't have this kind of publicity!' the Colonel said
in a loud voice, slapping the paper with the back of his hand.

'What is it, Colonel?' Elvis asked, confused.

'Read it yourself, son, and make damn sure you do something about it!' the Colonel ordered, giving me a look and
slamming the door on his way out.

'What was that all about?' I asked.

'I don't know, baby, let's find out,' Elvis said, sitting next to
me and opening the newspaper.

My mother, trying to protect my honor, had told the news
reporter everything she knew about my relationship with
Elvis, as well as our future plans. That afternoon I saw a side
of Elvis I never knew existed. He was realizing he had very little control over his life. The Colonel was on his back because
of me being with him in Miami. He was getting bad press, and
being called vulgar, and he blamed me for not telling my
mother to keep quiet. Everything was getting to him all at
once. He started pacing the floor and taking his anger out on
me.

'If only your mother hadn't talked to that damn reporter!
Call your mother, June, tell her never to talk to anyone else.'
He was yelling at me, but looking out the window.

I went to the phone and made a collect call to my mother,
but she wasn't home. I promised I'd call the next day. He
finally calmed down, sat next to me on the sofa, and wrapped
both arms around me.

'I'm sorry for yelling, baby. You know how much I love
you, but we can't let the whole world know, okay? In a few
years it'll all be different, I promise. I'll be in control of my
life, do what I want to do, and not have to worry about anything but you and me,' he said, kissing his index finger and
touching my lips.

'*We'll build a little nest, somewhere out in the west, and let the rest of the world go by*,' he sang softly, then, picking up the newspaper again, he smiled at the headlines: 'ELVIS IS IN TOWN — WIGGLES AND ALL. The Olympia Theater was filled to capacity yesterday when rock'n'roller Elvis Presley came to town.'

I got my mother on the phone later that night, and we had a nice long talk. I told her about the trouble Elvis had had with his manager because of the newspaper story.

'The reporter was making it sound like there was something wrong with me letting you go all the way to Florida with Elvis. He was doing most of the talking, trying to put words in my mouth. I promise I'll never say another word. From now on it'll just be "no comment". Tell Elvis I'm sorry, and I love him. I love you too,' she said, instead of goodbye, as she always did when hanging up the phone.

20

$\mathcal{T}$HE RENO BROTHERS

ELVIS WAS RESTLESS between shows, so he decided to go car-shopping, taking Colonel Parker with him to do his wheeling and dealing. They drove the lavender Lincoln as a trade-in to downtown Miami and made a fast deal on a new Continental Mark 2. All white, inside and out, it was the same make and model as Buddy's car. The Lincoln dealer parked the lavender car, still sporting all the names, phone numbers and messages to Elvis, along with a small dent in the front bumper, in the middle of his showroom floor. A big picture of the auto-graphed car was in the paper the following day. Nothing escaped the press, not even the car. The Lincoln dealer had crowds he couldn't handle, but they didn't come to buy, they came to see the car that used to belong to Elvis Presley.

While Elvis was car-shopping, Pat and I took the mint-green Continental and went downtown to do some shopping our-selves. We parked the car in a parking lot, and I put the ticket in the pocket of my blouse. We spent several hours going in and out of stores, both buying an identical pair of black pants – identical except that Pat's were two sizes smaller than mine. The two-piece swimsuit was just coming into fashion, and I bought a white one I decided I couldn't live without. Pat was more daring; hers was pink and black, Elvis's favorite colors.

Going in and out of so many stores, we didn't realize we were lost until we tried to find the car. We knew the parking lot was on a side-street, but which one? Walking down the main street and looking down every alley, we were relieved when we finally saw the public parking sign in the middle of the block. We ran to the parking lot, but there was no mint-green car. Thinking the car had been stolen, Pat and I both started to panic, until the parking attendant told us of another lot a few blocks down. We found the parking lot, but again, no mint-green car, and this time no attendant. We were walking back to the main street, completely out of breath, when I remembered the parking ticket in the pocket of my blouse. The address was on the ticket, so now all we had to do was find the street. We asked a couple of directions.

'Sorry, we're not from around here,' they said, shaking their heads. I asked another man and got the same answer, so I then decided to ask people if they were from Miami before asking directions. Some people were standing across the street, so we ran over to them.

'Is anyone here from Memphis?' I asked. They all looked at me and Pat like they didn't understand the question.

'No, we're not,' they answered.

'Are you from Memphis?' we asked another couple. Giving us a strange look, they both said no.

'Well, if this don't beat anything I've ever seen! Nobody in this town is *from* this town,' I said to Pat. Finally it dawned on us at the same time: we were saying Memphis instead of Miami. We'd obviously been around the boys too long; they were always talking Memphis, Memphis, Memphis.

The very next person I asked was from Miami, and at last pointed us in the right direction. We'd wasted an hour trying to find the car, and barely made it in time to shower and change for the afternoon show. Pat and I laughed about that incident for a long time afterwards. Even today, when I go to ask for directions, I hear myself asking, 'Are you from Memphis?'

Buddy dropped Pat and me off at the stage door and went to

park the car. By this time the guard knew our faces, so we had no problem getting in. When we got to Elvis's dressing room, we found him in the middle of a press interview. We stood quietly in the background, listening to some of the dumbest questions I'd ever heard. Now I understood perfectly why Elvis hated any and all dealings with the press. One of the reporters asked him what he thought of the *Andrea Doria*, a ship that had sunk recently and was in the news.

'I haven't had time to read a newspaper, and therefore I have no opinion. Now, if you gentlemen will excuse me, I only have fifteen minutes before show-time. I will be happy to speak with all of you later,' Elvis politely answered.

I could tell he was getting hot under the collar as he shook their hands, one by one, when they left. He leaned against the door, his arms folded across his chest, and just shook his head from side to side.

'I should've asked that son of a bitch if he knew anything about rock'n'roll music. I thought reporters were supposed to be well educated. What kind of asshole would ask me a stupid question like that?' he said, still shaking his head in disbelief.

'*A stupid one!*' we all answered together.

'Being called vulgar is bad enough, but that dumb mother-fucker wants me to look stupid as well. Can you believe that shit?' he said, grinning and giving me a big hello kiss. One good thing about Elvis was that he was able to push annoying things out of his head and get on with his life. Me, I had to stew a while before forgetting about it.

Pat and I were trying to watch the show from the wings, but we couldn't get away from the same group of reporters. They were trying to find out what we were doing in Elvis's dressing room. I wasn't about to talk to them, especially the stupid one. We gave up trying to watch the show and went back to Elvis's dressing room. The alley below was filled with screaming fans who had come to see the show but couldn't get in. Pat was leaning out the window talking to some of them. They were chanting, 'We want Elvis! We want Elvis!'

After his show, Elvis walked in the room, went to the window, leaned out and waved. They went crazy and started yelling, 'Throw me something! Throw me something!', reminding me of the Mardi Gras parades in New Orleans.

Elvis took off his shirt, hung it over the back of a chair, and went to the bathroom to freshen up. Pat picked up the shirt, soaking wet with perspiration, and threw it out the window. The kids in the alley tore the shirt to shreds and were scrambling for bits and pieces. Elvis came back in the room and was looking all over for his shirt. After a few minutes of trying to look innocent, Pat finally confessed.

When it came to Elvis, the press sure got things turned upside down. The press reported that Elvis had thrown his pants out the window to a small gathering of teenage girls. It was another lesson learned about the media.

Colonel Parker, without warning, stopped by Elvis's hotel room later that afternoon, to bring Elvis the script for his first movie. He stayed just inside the door, glanced at me, sitting next to Elvis, and without saying a word handed the script to Gene. Then he turned and left, slamming the door harder than was really necessary.

'I wonder when I'm supposed to find time to read this?' Elvis said, taking the script from Gene.

'He don't care if you read it or not. He just wanted to see if I was here,' I said, knowing damn well I was right.

The title on the cover of the script was *The Reno Brothers*. I immediately thought cowboys and indians, but couldn't picture Elvis in such a role. Reading from the beginning, we learned the movie was set during the Civil War. Elvis insisted on turning to the back to see if it had a happy ending, only to be disappointed to learn his character gets killed in the end.

'June, I don't want to die in my first movie,' he said, pouting like a little boy.

'Why not? I think it's a good idea. I always remember the character who dies. Happy endings you forget, sad endings stay with you longer. At least that's the way it affects me.'

'You know something, June, I think you might have a point. I always remember the one who dies too,' he said, giving it more thought.

Buddy parked the mint-green car at Elvis's hotel and we all

rode to the theater in the limo. It was the final show, and the plan was to leave Miami as soon as it was over. Arthur, trying to make up for wrecking the car, volunteered to stay and pack up the new Mark 2.

'I want everyone to be here in the limousine when I *start* to sing the last song; not when I finish the last song. Did everyone hear me?' Elvis ordered, before the limo came to a stop.

'*Yes sir!*' Pat and I answered with a salute.

'We hear you, Chief,' Red and Gene acknowledged, while Junior stared blankly through the limousine window.

Feeling personally responsible for the boys, Elvis definitely had a heavy burden to carry. They should have been looking out for him, but that's not the way it always happened.

Before leaving his dressing room for the stage, he gave me a quick kiss and reminded me to avoid the Colonel. I needed no reminder, there was never any love lost between me and Colonel Tom. Avoiding him was easy; I just wouldn't go near the theater lobby. There, the Colonel would set up a table and sell photos of Elvis for fifty cents each. The crowds numbered seven thousand per show, and Elvis had four shows in Miami. Over half of all those in attendance bought pictures. According to my figures, that adds up to a lot of pocket change. Having a curious nature, I asked Elvis about the pictures.

'Oh, that's just a side-line to keep him busy. He has to feel like he's doing something,' Elvis said naïvely, never suspecting the Colonel might do anything dishonest.

I felt the Colonel was not only pushing him too hard, but also taking advantage of him financially. I don't know why I felt that way, other than the fact that, to me, the man looked like a crook. I couldn't believe the list of cities and the number of shows scheduled for the next nine days. The past two days had been killers, with Elvis doing everything on the run. He was doing all the work, trying to keep up a good appearance, and busting his ass, while the Colonel puffed his cigar and got richer and richer.

Elvis had nothing but respect for the Colonel and gave him all the credit. Naturally I disagreed, saying it didn't matter who his manager was. It was *Elvis* who was the star, and Elvis would have made it regardless.

'Now, now, June, you're sounding just like my mother.'

I had become curious about the man Elvis called the Colonel earlier that summer, when the radio station had announced our engagement and Elvis had been more concerned about the Colonel hearing the rumor than about the rumor itself. My curiosity became aroused again when Mr and Mrs Presley, Elvis and I were having lunch one day at Gulf Hills, and she boldly announced her opinion about Elvis's manager. She thought the Colonel was treating Elvis like a piece of merchandise, and referred to him as a fast talking bull-shooter. I laughed, thinking she was going to use another word instead of 'shooter'. 'I just don't trust the man,' she went on to say.

'Let the man alone, Gladys, he's doing a good job,' Mr Presley said, taking the Colonel's side. I hadn't met the Colonel, as yet, so I didn't have an opinion one way or the other. In my mind, the title 'Colonel' suggested a proud, honest military man, fighting for his country.

Shortly after the lunch conversation, I was surprised when I learned that the Colonel wasn't a real Colonel, but had been given the honorary title by friends. He was nothing more than a Carney, and had spent most of his time with a traveling carnival show.

Seeing him in action, peddling his Elvis pictures and his Elvis souvenirs, before and after every performance, made one think he had never left the Carnival. He even said 'step right up' like a barker at a carnival side-show, and reminded me of a barker I once saw charging twenty-five cents to see the 'World's Ugliest Human': a sad-looking man sat on a stool wearing only a pair of ragged pants. His face, body, and even his feet were covered with tumors, like some kind of Elephant Man. As the barker used his cane to point out the deformities, I remember being horrified at such exploitation.

Elvis's mom may have been naïve about a lot of things, but as it turned out Gladys Presley was an excellent judge of character. The title 'Colonel' wasn't the only lie about Tom

Parker. Tom Parker wasn't even his real name. He was an
illegal immigrant who had sneaked into this country when he
was nineteen years old; his real name was Andreas van
Kuijk, and he was born in Breda, Holland. Unfortunately,
this information didn't surface until long after the death of
the King.

Elvis played to another full house for his final Miami show.
The screams could still be heard as he climbed into the waiting limousine, before the crowds had even realized he was
gone.

'Everybody here? Where's Arthur?' Elvis said, making a
quick check of everyone.

'Back at the hotel, packing,' I answered.

'Okay, let's go!' he shouted to the driver.

Leaving the theater before the crowd made the ride back to
the hotel much safer and a whole lot easier. From now on, this
was to be Elvis's standard plan of departure. We ran to the
hotel room to make a final check and change into some comfortable clothes for the long ride on the Tamiami Trail, to
Tampa, Florida, the next city on the tour.

On the way to the car, Elvis asked me to ride with Buddy
for a little while. I didn't ask any questions, I figured he
needed some time alone to discuss things with the boys. About
five miles down the road, he pulled the white Mark 2 over
and stopped. Two of the boys came back to Buddy's car and
traded places with me and Pat. I figured his little talk with the
boys was over. Needless to say, I was more than a little upset
when I found out the real reason.

As soon as I got in the car, Elvis began telling me about his
long conversation with the Colonel. He put an unlit cigar in
his mouth and started to mimic his manager.

'You're seeing too much of this girl from Biloxi. She's not
good for you, son. You can't be linked to any one girl; not if
you want to make it in this business. Believe me, son, I know
what I'm talking about. Don't get any ideas about marriage
either. And for God's sake, don't get her pregnant. You do and
you're through, son, that's for sure.'

'He don't even want you riding in the same car with me,

June. That's why I asked you to ride with Buddy,' Elvis said, trying to explain, not realizing I was getting thoroughly pissed off.

'I wish I'd known all that, I wouldn't have let Buddy stop. Pull over Elvis, I'll be glad to ride with Buddy,' I said.

'C'mon baby, don't be mad. I'm just trying to tell you what he said. He thinks it would be bad for me if my fans thought I had a steady girlfriend.'

'And what do *you* think, Elvis, or does it matter? Does he tell you when you can go take a shit?' I said, taking my anger out on Elvis. 'Stop the damn car, and you won't have to worry about the Colonel *or* the fans.'

'I'm not worried about the Colonel or the fans, June, and I'm not stopping the car. Now get your cute ass back over here where you belong,' he said, patting the smooth white leather upholstery. I couldn't resist his gorgeous, smiling face, and slid next to him. Still angry about the Colonel, I sat quietly. As he talked about the events of the day, I noticed his voice was beginning to crack. He noticed it too, and blamed it on the air-conditioning.

'It's too much singing and not enough rest,' I said.

'I'm glad you're still talking to me. Don't be mad with me, baby, I need you, you're the only sane thing in my life. Don't worry about the Colonel; I can take care of him. He don't have to know all my business,' he said, pulling me close.

'Well, I don't like him! I wish he'd go back to the circus and sell tickets to see the Bearded Lady, or the cow with two heads.'

'I love you, June. You know that?' he said, laughing.

Between the constant thump of the highway seams and Junior's snoring, Pat, sitting behind Elvis, couldn't hear a thing. She was on the edge of her seat, her head practically between Elvis and me, waiting for the somewhat heated discussion to continue. When Elvis turned his head sharply to the right, their noses collided.

'Oh! Don't mind me, I'm just trying to get comfortable,' Pat said, slightly embarrassed.

'You could hear a lot better if you come sit in my lap, Pat,'

Elvis said. The three of us started laughing, and the Colonel was quickly forgotten.

The shortest possible route from Miami to Tampa, the Tamiami Trail got its name from a combination of two names; *Tam*pa and M*iami*. I wasn't paying much attention to the long, dark highway running through the Florida Everglades, or the Big Cypress Swamp, until Elvis started teasing about the car breaking down in the middle of the snake-and-alligator-infested swampland.

To avoid shaking a chill every time I looked out the car window, I laid my head in Elvis's lap and tried to get to sleep. When the car came to a stop, I was afraid to open my eyes.

'Wake up, baby, we're gonna get a bite to eat,' Elvis said. Still half asleep, with snakes and alligators in the back of my mind, I was relieved to see the flashing neon lights of a restaurant. Located half-way down the Tamiami Trail, miles from civilization, the restaurant appeared to be deserted. A waitress, wearing a white uniform, suddenly appeared in the picture window. She stood watching as the eight of us piled out of not one, but two of the most expensive cars in the United States.

We raced inside and headed straight to the rest-rooms. Elvis only stopped at gas stations and restaurants; a 'pee' break was out of the question.

The boys pulled two tables together and we finally got seated. Elvis said he wanted one of everything in the house. I laughed, remembering breakfast in Houston, and wondered if he was serious. Buddy was seated across from Elvis, being a clown as usual. It didn't take much to make us laugh; we were tired and all had a case of the 'sillies'.

'Please help me out of this swamp,' Buddy kept saying, over and over, only it wasn't the normal way to say 'swamp': he was making a popping sound on the end of the word by putting his big lips together and forcing the air out. Everyone at the table started trying to do it, but nobody's pop was as loud as Buddy's.

We all settled down and got serious when the waitress brought us our menu.

'What's the best thing in the house?' Elvis asked.

'We have a great Chef salad, and the best fried chicken in the South,' she answered.

'Bring us all a salad, and maybe by that time we'll be ready to order. Okay, honey?' Elvis said, giving her his sexy, crooked smile.

Working so far out in the boonies it was apparent she'd never heard of Elvis Presley. I walked over to the out-of-date jukebox, and sure enough, not one of Elvis's songs was listed.

The waitress brought out eight beautiful salads, topped with feta cheese and capers, and then walked over to the picture window. Everyone but Elvis started digging into their salads.

'What are those little black things on that white stuff?' Elvis asked, looking at his salad, mystified.

'Eat it, E.P., it's good for you. It's swamp-pop bugs,' Buddy said, picking one up with his fingers and dropping it in his mouth. Elvis stabbed a caper with his fork, examined it closely, gave it a sniff, and popped it in his mouth.

'Taste more like ether balls to me,' he said, making a face and pushing the capers to the side of his plate.

'What did you kids do, rob a bank?' The waitress asked, still looking out the window at the two cars.

'Yes ma'am, but we'd appreciate it if you'd wait at least an hour before calling the sheriff,' Elvis said, serious enough to sound convincing.

The waitress was right about the chicken. Except for Elvis's mom's, it was the best I'd tasted.

'If you want some good fried chicken, you should come to Memphis, Tennessee. Nobody does chicken as good as my mama,' Elvis said, unable to resist the opportunity to brag about his mother.

'That's not the only thing she did good,' the waitress said, putting her hand on his shoulder, and raising her brows. Needless to say, she got a good tip.

21
$\mathcal{S}$EX ON TOUR

I WOKE UP IN such a fog it took a while for me to realize we were in Tampa. Pat had already had breakfast and was back in the room, reading a newspaper, and making all kinds of noise.

'Will you please stop that racket? What the hell time is it, anyway?' I asked, trying to get my bearings.

'It's twelve o'clock, lazy bones. Are you gonna sleep all day? I'll let you see what I'm reading if you promise not to get mad,' she said, grinning.

When I came out of the bathroom, she handed me the newspaper, after making me promise not to get mad. The following is written exactly as it appeared in the morning edition of the *Miami News*:

ELVIS DENIES BILOXI BEAUTY IS HIS 'STEADY'

Elvis says no – that she is one of his 25 'regulars'. The teen-ager's mother says – in no uncertain terms – that 'The Pelvis' has asked her daughter to be his 'permanently' in three years.

The girl with the unsettled status is June Juanico, who, it is said, has been stroking Elvis's brow between his hectic shows. It is said – He prefers her to aspirin.

ATTACHMENT PROCLAIMED

June proclaimed her attachment for the teen-idol to a *Miami News* reporter while Presley was performing at the Olympia Theater. Asked about the relationship yesterday, Elvis interrupted buying a $10,800 car to reply:

'Now, this is the way it is. I got about 25 girls I date regular. She's just one of the girls.'

In declaring her feelings for the writhing singer, June said she is going on the Presley tour of six Florida cities and New Orleans.

MOTHER SAYS YES

Her mother, Mrs Mae Juanico of Biloxi, told the *Miami News* by telephone that Elvis 'wanted June to be with him' on the tour. 'I don't object to her making the trip,' Mrs Juanico said. 'He's a nice boy and June's a good girl. I talked to his parents and they said Elvis would take good care of her.'

CLAIMS MADE

Parker took reports of Elvis's 'steady' girlfriend calmly. 'They show up – sometimes eight at a time – in the hotel or theater lobby, all claiming they're his "steadies",' Parker said. 'One girl even claimed she was my daughter, and I don't have a daughter.'

I had to laugh. Pat was relieved, she thought I might take it seriously. I mean twenty-five girls? Give me a break! I couldn't wait to see Elvis and show him the article. I folded the paper and put it in my purse so I wouldn't forget. Elvis called the room, saying he was just getting out of bed, and would meet us in the hotel dining room. When everyone was seated I pulled out the paper and slapped it with the back of my hand.

'Son, you've got to stop this kind of publicity. Pretty soon people will be calling you "Super Pelvis",' I said in my deepest voice.

He read the article with a grin on his face the entire time. The paper was passed around the table so everyone could share the laugh.

'I was trying to say what the Colonel wanted to hear, but I goofed. Boy, you should have seen his face when I said twenty-five. Even the reporter said, "Pardon me, did you say twenty-five?" Without even looking at the Colonel, I knew he was giving me the evil eye. It was on the tip of my tongue to say, "Either twenty-five or thirty, I haven't taken a head count lately," but I decided I'd better keep my mouth shut.'

'Yeah, that's why he takes us along; we take care of the overflow,' Gene said drily.

'Speaking of overflow, will you please make sure the door is locked the next time you take care of it?' I said, speaking directly to Red.

'What are you talking about, June? Is Red up to his old tricks again?' Elvis asked. Red, trying to avoid the issue, kept stuffing his mouth with food and didn't say a word. Pat began ferociously digging her spoon into a half of cantaloupe, her eyes darting from Elvis to Red to me.

'Does he do it all the time?' Pat said, trying not to giggle. Everyone but Elvis started to laugh.

'Okay, okay, somebody better tell me what happened. What did you do this time, Red?' Elvis asked.

'It was nothing, man, Pat and June opened the door on me and this chick, that's all,' Red answered, like it was no big deal.

'Damn it, Red! I've told you about that kind of shit. You're gonna get my ass in trouble just because you can't keep your fuckin' pants zipped,' Elvis said, slamming his empty coffee cup on the table.

You could have heard a pin drop when the waitress ran over and refilled Elvis's empty cup. I'd heard him cuss on occasion, but lately it was getting to be every other word. His patience was wearing thin. Elvis was glaring across the table at Red when Buddy, still half asleep, joined us at the table. He picked up the paper and started reading the article.

'Damn, E.P., twenty-five? I thought I was doing good with three. Do you really have twenty-five?' Buddy asked.

'Naw man, I just pulled that number out my ass. It made

the Colonel happy. It made June happy too, didn't it baby?' he said, patting me on the thigh.

'Yeah, it made me happy, especially for the daughter Colonel Parker didn't have,' I answered sarcastically.

'You don't like him very much, do you baby?' Elvis asked.

'Very much? No, I don't like him at all!' I answered.

As soon as I finished my last bite, Elvis took me by the hand and we left the dining room. I assumed we were going to my room when he pushed the elevator button.

'Now, I want you to tell me everything that happened with Red,' he said, sitting down on the side of the bed.

'Everything? Details and all?' I asked.

'Yes, everything! You don't have to get descriptive, June, but I do need to know what happened.'

'You were on stage and Pat and I were watching from the wings. I was tired of reporters asking questions, so Pat and I decided to go wait in your dressing room. All the doors looked exactly alike. We saw a beam of light coming from under a door and thought it was the right one. We opened the door and went right on in. Red and this girl were on the top of a long table against the wall, and they were doing it,' I said, picturing the awful sight again.

'Doing what, June?' he said, teasing, knowing damn good and well what I was talking about.

'You know what, Elvis! Do you want me to draw you a picture?' I answered, feeling my face turn red.

'Did Red see you when you came in?'

'Yes, he saw us both, and so did the girl. It didn't make any difference to either of them; they just kept on going. It was a disgusting sight! Red didn't have his shirt on, his pants were around his ankles, and he was sweating like a hog. Sweat was dripping from Red's face into the girl's face. It was awful! Pat and I were both so shocked, we just stood there with our mouths open, not believing what we were seeing. I grabbed Pat by the arm and we ran out the door. The very next door was your dressing room. We could still hear the table banging against the wall. The banging must have lasted a good ten minutes.'

'How old a girl would you say she was, June?'

'I don't know, Elvis. Maybe twenty-five, maybe older. I wasn't paying much attention to her appearance; it was her position that caught my eye,' I said, laughing to cover my embarrassment.

'Well, I hope she was at least eighteen. I've had this problem with Red before. Just a few weeks ago I told him I was gonna fire him if he didn't learn to keep his dick under control. It's times like this I wonder why I even have them around. I can't say anything to the Colonel about them; he'd run their asses up the road. They're all good boys, June, and they need me. I need them too; I just haven't figured out what for yet. So, it was her position that caught your eye, huh?' he said, laughing, pulling me to my feet, and giving me a kiss.

It was times like this, and they were often, that made me realize what an unselfish, loving, and forgiving person Elvis Presley was, and why I was growing to love him more and more.

Elvis never did say any more to Red about the incident; he didn't have to. Red got the message when he heard the loud bang of Elvis's coffee cup. Nothing and no one would ever come between Red and his sex drive, however, but on the rest of the tour he was more discreet.

22

ANOTHER SELL-OUT

ELVIS'S FIRST SHOW in Tampa was scheduled for 3:30 P.M. at the Fort Homer Hesterly Armory. The Seratoma Civic Club, sponsors of the show, after hearing about the extra security needed in Miami, had over forty club members, six policemen, and over a dozen National Guardsmen trying to control the 10,000-plus in attendance.

Pat, remembering she had relatives in the Tampa area, suggested we skip the afternoon show and visit three of her cousins. We were on our third day of the tour and I was more than ready to sit and relax. Tom, Sylvia, and Bob Hayes, all close to the same age as Pat and me, would be a welcome change of pace. Elvis wasn't too happy when I called his room to say we were skipping the show, but Colonel Parker was there so he couldn't give me any argument. By the time Pat finally got her cousin Tom on the phone, however, it was too late to visit. Tom apologized, saying they weren't going to be home. They had tickets to see Elvis Presley and wouldn't miss it for the world. They wished we could go with them, but the show had been sold out for weeks and no tickets were available. When Pat told him we didn't need tickets, he just laughed, not believing a word she said. Pat hung up the phone saying, 'We'll see you tonight.'

The huge Armory was all on one level, with the stage built up on a platform. The area surrounding it was roped off and heavily guarded. The screams started when Elvis, wearing white buck shoes, black pants and a maroon jacket, stepped on the platform and joined his three-piece band in the center. There were no wings to watch from, so I stood between Arthur and Red until I knew the Colonel was nowhere in the area. I should have known he'd be up front, making a head count, more concerned with the $1.50 general admission than with Elvis's performance.

I turned to see who was tugging on my shoulders to find Pat, up on her tiptoes, scanning the audience. I moved her up in front of me, knowing it would be impossible to find anyone in a crowd this size; even more impossible with feet stomping, hands clapping, and heads swaying back and forth to the rhythm of 'I Got A Woman'.

'How long has it been since you've seen them?' I asked Pat, referring to her cousins.

'Just a few years ago, why?' she asked.

'I thought maybe they wouldn't recognize you since you've grown up.'

'Are you kidding?' she laughed. 'I stopped growing in the sixth grade.'

The crowd didn't get quiet until Elvis began singing his first slow song of the night. All of a sudden, there was a loud scream coming from the audience.

'*Patsy*!' Tom, Sylvia and Bob screamed, waving their hands. Pat jumped from the platform, made her way through the wall of security men and went to see her cousins. Close to the end of the show, she still wasn't back. She waited for a quiet moment and let out a scream of her own. '*Ellviss*!' She was being held back by the guards, and was in a panic. Elvis saw her and motioned for one of the boys to get her. On the way back to the hotel he chewed her ass out.

'Listen, little lady, you're my responsibility. I'm the one who promised to take care of you. Pull that shit again, I'll put you on a bus and send your ass back to Biloxi,' he threatened. She sat silently in the back seat, her lower lip quivering, and tears running down her cheeks.

Elvis was anxious to get out of his sweaty clothes, and went straight to his room without a word. Pat and I continued down the hall and went to our room too. It was late, and I figured we were in for the night.

Pat's hurt feelings had now turned to anger. She snatched her PJs from the dresser drawer and stormed into the bathroom.

'He don't have to put me on a bus; I can put myself on a bus!' she yelled, taking it out on me.

'Don't yell at me, Pat, you heard him as well as I did when he said no one was to leave the protective circle. The boys are always giving him problems; he certainly don't need any from us,' I said, defending him. She crawled into her bed, faced the wall, and pulled the covers up over her head.

I was just about to get into bed when I heard Elvis's familiar knock on the door. He went to Pat's bed, pulled back the covers, and kissed her on the cheek. She sat up smiling and said, 'It'll never happen again, I promise.'

There was another knock on the door. This time it was Gene, looking for Elvis.

'The Colonel called the room, looking for you, Elvis. I told him you were in the shower,' Gene proudly announced, letting Elvis know he wasn't about to betray his secret rendezvous.

Leaning back on the twin bed like a chaise longue for two, he waited a few minutes, picked up the phone, and told us both to be very quiet. After talking to the Colonel a few minutes, he hung up the phone, smiling.

'Guess what? The two shows today had over ten thousand people in attendance, and they turned away over a thousand at the door. Shit, baby, that's a lot of people, you know that?'

My first thought was to wonder how many pictures the old fart sold, but I didn't say anything.

'I hope the Colonel still has some of your pictures left. I need another black-and-white glossy, but I refuse to buy it from him,' I said.

'Didn't I give you one a long time ago?' Elvis asked.

'Yeah, but I was showing it to a friend, and she licked off all the gloss,' I said, licking my lips. He rolled over on his stomach, laughing.

'Rub my back for me, baby. She licked off all the gloss, huh?' he said, laughing again.

He turned out all the lights before removing everything but his briefs, and crawled in the bed next to me. Within a matter of minutes, in our usual spoon position, we were both sound asleep in my twin bed.

Shortly after sunrise, I felt him kiss me on the forehead, and opened my eyes to see him fully dressed, sneaking out the door.

The Colonel had lived in the State of Florida for many years, and never seeing him around the hotel, I assumed he was staying with friends. This arrangement worked out great for Elvis and me. When he wasn't doing a show, we could spend more worry-free time together; what little free time there was.

Tampa was our home base for three days. From there, Elvis was driving to the neighboring cities of St Petersburg, to do three shows, and then to Lakeland, the following day, to do three more.

Attending the shows was fun, but also very tiring. I can only imagine what it must have been doing to Elvis. The dark circles under his eyes were not mascara smudges; he had them even after a shower. The fast pace was beginning to take its toll.

Pat and I decided to skip St Petersburg, stay in Tampa, and take it easy for the day. I couldn't do anything for Elvis but be there when he returned and help him unwind. Emotionally drained, and physically exhausted, he would come straight to my room to get away from everyone, including the boys. He wasn't planning to stay all night, but usually fell asleep in the twin bed with me.

While Elvis was in St Petersburg for the day, Pat and I decided to go to the hotel beauty salon and have a blonde streak put in our hair. At that time it was the in thing to do. I had discussed it with Elvis, but he thought it was a bad idea.

'Leave your hair alone, June, it looks good like it is.' Feeling like I needed a change, I decided we should do it anyway.

The salon operator knew we were with Elvis and had dollar

signs in her eyes; she saw us coming, as they say. I had paid my hairdresser in Biloxi less than ten dollars for a blonde streak, so when the hairdresser said the bill was $48.50, Pat and I almost shit. Then we really did shit when she said $48.50 *each*. The total bill was $97.00 for a streak that wasn't a streak at all; it was just a blondish yellow patch covering almost the entire left side of my head. Pat's wasn't too bad; her hair was light, but the big patch of yellow on my dark hair was awful. And to pay that much for it made it even harder to take. However, the worst was yet to come. Pat started digging in her purse, and me in mine. Because of our shopping spree in Miami, together we could only come up with thirty-eight dollars.

'That's no problem, girls,' the hairdresser said, 'you can charge it to your boyfriend's room. With all his money, he won't even notice it.'

Pat and I put our heads together and decided to charge it to Buddy's room instead. We could pay Buddy back later, and Elvis wouldn't have to know anything about it.

Pat and I were in the lobby, watching the only television in the hotel, when Arthur and Buddy walked in. They had left the theater while Elvis was still on stage. Buddy took one look at me and started to laugh.

'Did you do that to yourself, or did you have to pay someone to make you look like a skunk?'

'I didn't have enough money to pay for it, so I charged it to your room. I'll pay you back when we get home.'

'How much money are we talking about?' Buddy asked.

'Almost fifty dollars,' I answered meekly.

'Almost fifty dollars for me, too,' Pat said, patting her streak.

'Boy, is E.P. gonna be mad! He told ya'll not to do it in the first place,' Buddy said, not even concerned about the cost.

Pat and I left the lobby and were up in our room when Elvis finally returned. When Elvis knocked on our door, Pat ran and locked herself in the bathroom. He took one look at me and shook his head from side to side.

'Baby, what in the hell did you do that for?' I was crushed!

I hated it too, but it was already done. Before my tears had a chance to reach my cheeks, he held me tight and kissed each eye.

'I'm sorry. I didn't know it was gonna be this big.'

'It's okay baby, it's not too bad, really it's not,' he soothed, petting me like a hurt little puppy. Looking around the room for Pat, he went to the bathroom door and started banging.

'Get out here, Pat, let me see your fifty-dollar mistake.' She came out of the bathroom with a towel wrapped around her head, turban-style. He removed the towel and made a tsk, tsk sound, then he laughed.

'I suppose if June wants to jump off a cliff, you'll jump too. What am I gonna do with you two?'

No matter how I tried to comb my hair, I still couldn't hide the big yellow patch.

'C'mon June, quit messin' with your hair and let's go get something to eat. Tomorrow you can buy a hat,' he teased.

'Does it really look that bad?' I asked, not wanting to hear the truth.

'No, baby, it just looks like a bird – no, I take that back – it looks like an *eagle* flew over and took a dump right on your head. C'mon, the boys are waiting for us,' he said, putting his arm around me, letting me know he was just kidding. As we walked into the hotel lobby, I felt like all eyes were on my yellow patch.

'Not one word,' he said to the boys. 'She's had enough ribbing from me.'

They all covered their mouths with their hands, like little children do when they know they're not supposed to laugh. The joke was on me, but they were so funny, I had to laugh too.

Sitting in the little late-night diner, waiting for our cheeseburgers, the conversation turned to the events during the final show in St Petersburg. Elvis had forgotten what verse he was singing, but with all the screaming, nobody had noticed. He couldn't hear the band, and the band couldn't hear him. Tickets to all three shows were sold out and people had been turned away at the door. A dozen or more girls, determined to get in, had to be pulled one by one from the fire escape. There was as much commotion outside the theater as there was inside.

It was well after midnight when we finished eating. The short-order cook turned off most of the lights and put the CLOSED sign on the door, letting us know it was time to leave. Elvis was having so much fun, though, that he insisted the party be continued in his hotel room. Meanwhile, a large group of fans had somehow discovered which room Elvis was in, and were knocking on his door and shoving pieces of paper and his black-and-white photos under it to be autographed. Pat was gathering everything that came under the door and bringing it to Elvis. After signing his autograph for fifteen minutes, he asked Red to see how many were still out in the hall. Red opened the door just a crack, and you could hear the roar.

'Man, there must be fifty kids out there,' Red said, slamming the door real fast. 'You want me to call for hotel security?'

'Naw, just let 'em be. They'll go home after while,' Elvis answered, not wanting to get them in trouble.

Thirty minutes later, the pictures and pieces of paper were still coming under the door.

'Pat, do you know how to sign my name?' Elvis asked, tired of the interruptions.

'Sure El, I can do it,' Pat said proudly, signing his name and showing it to him for his approval.

'Damn, that's good, Pat. You're hired.'

Now ready for some alone time, he took my hand and led me to his bedroom. We lay across the bed, hugging and kissing, and talking about the days when things wouldn't be so hectic. It wasn't long before he fell sound asleep, with me in his arms. I was trying to sneak out without waking him, but when I moved his arm he held me even tighter.

'Don't leave me, baby,' he moaned, half asleep.

'I'll be back; I'm just going to the bathroom,' I whispered. I stood in the doorway and watched him go right back to sleep.

Pat was sitting on the floor, still signing autographs, and Gene was half asleep on the couch. I asked Gene to undress Elvis and put him under the covers. When Pat and I opened the door, we found two young girls tearing pages from a tablet.

'Elvis has gone to bed, we're going to bed, and you two need to be in bed, too,' I said. They smiled, gathered up their autographed sheets of paper, and ran down the hall.

'Goodnight! Tell Elvis we love him,' they yelled, before getting in the elevator.

23
*U*NCHAINED MELODY

*E*LVIS CALLED MY room earlier than usual the next morning, to have us meet him in the dining room for breakfast. I tried to wake Pat before going in for a shower, but she wanted to stay in bed a little longer. In a rush to find something to wear, I grabbed the new black pants I'd bought in Miami. Besides being a tad bit short, they were so tight I could hardly get them zipped. Seeing myself in a full-length mirror as I stepped out of the elevator, I decided to skip the big breakfast and just have coffee.

'Damn, baby, do you ever fill out those pants!' Elvis said, giving me a wolf-whistle.

'I know! I've got to stop trying to keep up with you and the boys. My little body can't hold all that food,' I said, holding my breath. Every morning it was always the same thing. Cantaloupe with a scoop of vanilla ice-cream, plus bacon and eggs with all the trimmings. Trying to eat a man-sized breakfast every morning, the pounds were beginning to show.

Half-way through the meal, Pat walked in wearing her new black pants too, only hers were a little on the baggy side, and much too long.

'Pat, did you try on those pants before you bought them?'

'Yes June, I tried them on, but not this pair. I tried on the

ones you're wearing,' she laughed. Evidently, during the mad
rush to get out of Miami, I'd packed the wrong pair of pants.
We went to the ladies' room and swapped. I was so relieved I
buttered a big biscuit when I got back to the table.

Elvis had three shows to do in Lakeland, and rather than sit
around the theater dressing room all day and into the night,
Buddy, Pat and I decided to drive around and see the city of
Tampa. We had been in Tampa two days, and other than
catching a few of Elvis's shows, the only place we'd been was
the diner.

Driving around the city I was surprised to learn that
Tampa, like my home town of Biloxi, is also a peninsula, surrounded on three sides by the beautiful Tampa Bay.

We stopped to have dinner at a wonderful Italian restaurant
before driving to Lakeland to catch Elvis's last show. When we
got to the theater, Elvis picked me up and hugged me like he
hadn't seen me in months. Knowing he'd been stuck in a little
room at the theater all day, I felt a little guilty for having such
a good time without him.

I passed the Colonel backstage, but he didn't recognize me.
I guess the yellow patch of hair was good for something.

Elvis had played to a full house for all three shows, and in
spite of his fatigue, he was in a great mood again that night.
Over five thousand people had attended the shows, and he
was still amazed by the crowds he was attracting. Watching
from the wings, and seeing how the fans behaved, his popu-
larity didn't come as a surprise to me. Elvis, virtually
unknown in 1955, had become the hottest singing sensation
in the USA before the summer of 1956 came to an end.

It was during this rocket ride to stardom that I started asking myself questions. Why me? He could have his choice of
any girl in the country. Why had he chosen me? Would he
someday see someone he liked better? Questions like these
were driving me crazy, so I tried to put them out of my mind
completely.

After the show, Pat went along with Buddy and Arthur to
have another greasy but delicious cheeseburger, leaving Elvis
and me alone in my room. Beginning to feel the stress of his

rigid schedule, he was talking and trying to rub his neck and back at the same time.

'If only they'd leave me alone after the show. I give them everything I can, when I'm on stage, but somehow they feel the need to have bits and pieces of me. It scares me sometimes. If they would just touch, it would be okay,' he said, showing me the fresh scratches on his right arm and hand.

Collapsing face-down on the bed, be moaned and groaned with pleasure when I straddled his thighs and began rubbing his back.

'What's it like to be loved by so many girls?' I asked, feeling a little insecure.

'They don't love me, June, they love the *idea* of me. It's fun for them to scream and jump around to the music. They can't cut up that way at home, and they certainly can't behave like that in school. It's just their way of letting it all out, I guess. Everybody needs to cut loose once in a while. I know I do,' he said.

'And you love it too, don't you? I've seen you before you get on stage and you're a totally different person after you get out there. Am I right?'

'You're right, baby. It's hard to explain. You'd have to be inside my body, to feel what I feel. It's like your whole body gets goose-bumps, but it's not goose-bumps, and it's not a chill either. It's more like a surge of electricity that goes all through you. It's almost like making love, but it's even stronger than that. It's hard to explain, baby.'

The more he talked the more insecure I became. Not only did he have his choice of girls, he was making love to all of them at the same time.

'Does the same thing happen to all entertainers?' I asked, trying not to sound jealous.

'I don't know, baby. The few I've talked to have experienced excitement and nerves, but they can't feel the way I do. If they did, they'd say more about it, wouldn't you think? They all get nervous when they first go on, but after they sing a few lines, they calm down. Hell, I don't calm down until two or three hours after I leave the stage.'

'I know that's true, believe me,' I said, rubbing his back even harder.

'Sometimes I think my heart is gonna explode, it beats so fast. Oh, baby, that feels so good. How did you learn to do that?' he said, between moans. I was massaging his back and shoulders so hard, my fingers were beginning to cramp.

'I don't know. I've never rubbed anyone's back before. I'm learning how on you.'

He jumped up from the bed and ran to the door to make sure it was locked. 'Okay, continue on, please,' he said, returning to the same position.

'I don't know which I like the most; the back rub, or the way you sit on me while you're doing it,' he said, laughing and turning over to face me.

'Well, whaddya know. I'm sitting on Elvis's famous pelvis,' I said, with a sheepish grin. He unbuttoned my blouse and pulled me down to him. Our kissing was so passionate we were almost to the point of no return. Where most couples would have thrown all caution to the wind, and gone all the way, Elvis came to a dead stop, leaving me so sexually aroused I was tingling all over.

'We can't do this, baby. The time is not right,' he said, rolling me over on my side and holding me tighter than ever. Fifteen minutes later, his hold on me relaxed, and I knew he was sound asleep. Frustrated, I laid by his side, staring at the ceiling. Except for his shoes, he was still fully dressed, so I got up, put on my baby-doll PJs and took off the rest of his clothes. He was so dead to the world he didn't even know what was going on. Just as I got us both tucked in, I heard Pat fumbling with her key at the door. Remembering it was locked I crawled out of bed and let her in.

The Colonel had left town after the last show, and Elvis slept like a baby, knowing there would be no surprise visits to worry about.

Early the next morning we checked out of the hotel and headed for Orlando. Elvis was scheduled for two shows there; one in the afternoon and one in the evening. For me it was the longest, most tiring day of the tour. We arrived at the auditorium and planted ourselves backstage, waiting for the show to begin. The cars were parked safely out of sight, so Arthur had to take a taxi to pick up lunch for everyone. Elvis started getting dressed thirty minutes before showtime. Knowing a little of how he felt on stage, I too started getting butterflies in my stomach. Watching him slip into his green sports jacket, my favorite, it was easy to see why the girls went wild. He was truly the most beautiful creature I had ever seen. I too felt the urge not only to touch him, but to grab bits and pieces of him.

Giving me a wink, he slung his guitar over his shoulder, and, hearing the drum roll, made his entrance on stage. Learning from past experience, the band didn't start up until the screams died down. Covering every inch of the stage, Elvis, with eyes like a fox, never missed a pretty face. The amount of energy between Elvis and his audience was so powerful I could almost feel the surge of electricity he had spoken of earlier.

After every performance the routine was exactly the same. Off with the jacket, off with the shirt, and straight to the nearest lavatory. With a towel around his neck, he would splash his face with water and run his wet fingers through his hair until it was thoroughly soaked. After pacing around the room for at least fifteen minutes, he would then sit down with his legs spread apart and rest his elbows on his knees, letting his hands dangle, shaking them out – as if he was releasing the tension through his fingertips.

This particular afternoon, after his cooling-down ritual, instead of resting his head in my lap he took me by the hand and led me backstage, behind the back curtain, to an upright piano he had discovered earlier.

'I've been working on something new, just for you, baby,' he said, with a proud grin on his face.

'Unchained Melody', recorded by Al Hibler in the early fifties, was my very favorite love song, and I couldn't have been more surprised or delighted when he started to sing it.

'*Oh, my love, my darling, I hunger for your touch, a long lonely time . . .*' He sang beautifully, looking at me after every unsure chord change.

Never having had a music lesson, Elvis's natural feel for the piano was much better than his self-taught guitar strumming.

That special afternoon, with just two of us at the piano, was one of the treasured times in our relationship that would stay in my mind for ever. In the years to come, every time Elvis released a new album, I would scan the list of songs, hoping to someday find the beautiful 'Unchained Melody'. It finally appeared on the *Moody Blue* album, recorded live in April 1977 at a show in Saginaw, Michigan. Making the song even more special, Elvis had accompanied himself on the piano. No one could possibly imagine the pain in my heart when I heard Elvis's recording of the song for the very first time, on the radio, on the night of 16 August 1977.

After the final show in Orlando, where the estimated attendance had been over seven thousand, we drove to Daytona Beach. As usual, I rode in the car with Buddy for the first few miles. When we stopped to change places, Elvis couldn't get Junior out of his car fast enough. He had been drinking again, and was getting on Elvis's nerves.

When we arrived at Elvis's hotel in Daytona, there were no rooms available. The hotel – as well as most of the motels – was filled with teenagers in town to see the Elvis Presley show. We drove for miles down the beach, seeing the 'no vacancy' signs flashing the word NO. We finally found a little motel on the beach side which had some rooms. I immediately called Elvis to let him know where we were staying.

'Everything happens for the best, baby: the Colonel has the room next to mine. Get a good night's sleep and I'll call you in the morning.'

Elvis was scheduled for two shows in Daytona; one in the afternoon and one in the evening. He would be leaving after the last show, going to Jacksonville, where he was scheduled to do three shows a day for two days.

It was a beautiful day in Daytona, and Pat and I were talking about skipping the shows and spending the day on the beach. When Elvis called that morning, much to my surprise, he thought it was a good idea.

'The Colonel's been on my ass about you again, so I'll see you in Jacksonville. I'll have a couple of rooms reserved for ya'll in Arthur's name. I hope you don't mind, baby.'

Pat and I, wearing our new two-piece swimsuits, were more than ready for some Florida sunshine. One look in the mirror, however, confirmed my suspicions: I had definitely gained a few pounds. Oh well – it wasn't all that noticeable; not yet, anyway.

Much to my disappointment, the sand on Daytona beach was nothing like the soft white sand in Biloxi. Heavy traffic on the beach had packed the sand down as hard as asphalt. We finally found a soft spot, off the beaten path, and spread out the sheet we'd borrowed from the motel. Being in the sunshine and smelling the salt air seemed to make the whole world disappear. It wasn't long before Pat disappeared too; her light, slightly freckled complexion was beginning to burn. Overall, I was a few shades darker, but my virgin midriff got a tender shade of red.

By the time we arrived in Jacksonville, the following afternoon, Elvis was in the middle of his first show. A few hours in the sun, away from all the madness, had done wonders for me. I wished Elvis could have been relaxing in the sun with me, but thanks to Colonel Parker his heavy schedule wouldn't allow him a day off. I was exhausted just thinking about three shows a day for the next two days.

Pat and I were in our hotel room, washing out our underwear, when Buddy came by with a local newspaper.

'It looks like we're gonna have trouble in Jacksonville,' Buddy said, reading the paper out loud.

'It says here that a Judge Gooding, a Juvenile Court judge, said that he felt Elvis's bumps and grinds were objectionable for the teenage audience, and he ordered Elvis to quieten his act. Warrants were made out in advance for Elvis's arrest. The police were there to watch for any little wiggle, and vowed to arrest him if he made one wrong move. They were even filming the show for proof.'

I was outraged by the absurdity of the article, especially coming from someone who'd never even seen Elvis perform.

Apparently the honorable judge didn't know a bump from a grind. Sure, Elvis did a few knee-jerks from side to side, but never a forward movement of the pelvic area; at least not on stage. If Tom Jones, Elvis's only competition during his reign, had put on a show in Jacksonville, Florida, in 1956, Judge Gooding would have had a stroke or shit his pants. You have to wonder why the television networks felt they had to film Elvis from the waist up. I guess it was all part of growing up in the 1950s.

After reading the article I just knew what kind of mood Elvis would be in after the show, but I was wrong. He came bursting in the room, grinning from ear to ear, feeling like he'd won the battle of his career.

'Baby, you should've been there this afternoon. Every time DJ did his thing on the drums, I wiggled my finger, and the girls went wild,' he said, demonstrating the rapid movement of his right index finger.

'Personally, I find your finger movement far more stimulating than a knee-jerk,' I said, laughing. My remark confused him at first, but then he laughed.

'I've never heard screams like that in my life, June, no kidding. If you think Miami was loud, you should've heard them today. I guess I showed them sons of bitches – calling me vulgar. You don't think I'm vulgar, do you, baby?' he said, pulling me down on the bed.

'If you want to show them vulgar, we'll have to work on your bumps and grinds. A real grind is done like this,' I said, rotating my hips.

'I'll show you a real grind, June,' he said, putting both hands under my hips and pulling me close. Pat, knowing Elvis wanted some alone time, tactfully left the room.

24
THE LUCKIEST GIRL IN AMERICA

A RADIO STATION FROM Atlanta, Georgia, along with a movie magazine, were sponsoring a 'Win A Date With Elvis' contest. Colonel Parker had approved the contest some six weeks earlier, but failed to inform his protégé. Needless to say, Elvis wasn't at all pleased when he found out about the contest the morning before the date was to take place.

'What if she's ugly, June?'

'I hope she is!' I laughed.

The winner was being flown in from Atlanta, and would be watching the show from the wings. A romantic dinner for two was scheduled to take place immediately after the show.

The press were involved with his date from Atlanta, and the police were involved with his wiggles. A movie camera set up on a tripod, covering the entire stage, was clearly visible in the aisle.

I had been trying to figure a way to skip the show and all the confusion that goes with it without making Elvis angry, but after hearing about the date contest I quickly changed my mind. I not only wanted to check out this date-winner, I wanted to check out Elvis's reaction when he saw her.

Elvis was on stage singing when the press finally stepped aside to let his date see the show. She was on one side, watching from the wings, and I was on the other side, watching her watch Elvis. Even from a distance I could see her hour-glass figure as well as a pretty face. I wanted to get a closer look, but she was surrounded by the press, with the Colonel in the middle of them all. I decided to keep a low profile, stay out of sight, and keep the Colonel off Elvis's back, fighting off the desire to introduce myself and let her know he was taken. Giving the situation more thought, I realized it would be a mistake. Convincing myself she was no threat, I made myself scarce, letting him have his date all to himself.

Under the scrutiny of the camera and the fuddy-duddy judge, Elvis was on his best behavior. He would do a few slight moves with his left leg, stop, and let his finger follow the rhythm of the drums. The crowd, most of them now well aware of the controversy with the judge, went wild with every movement. They didn't care what Elvis was moving, just as long as he was moving *something*.

Close to the end of his performance I thought I heard him say 'Fuck you very much,' instead of his usual 'Thank you very much,' while looking in the judge's direction. His mouth was close to the mike and somewhat muffled, but I was pretty sure of his word substitution. Buddy and Pat thought they heard it too, and were both laughing. Elvis then confirmed our suspicions by giving us a wink and doing it again.

'Fuck you!' he said, bowing from the waist. 'Fuck you very much!' he said again, curling his upper lip. It turned out to be a private joke, thankfully, shared only by the inner circle.

Before the end of the show, I had talked Buddy and Pat into leaving early to avoid the stampede of fans and the heavy traffic of over twenty-two hundred in attendance. I really didn't give a damn about the heavy traffic, I just didn't want Elvis to think I was cramping his style, even though he was doing his date thing for 'publicity purposes', as he called it.

Her name was Andrea June Stephens, but all her friends called her June. She was to join Elvis in his hotel suite before having dinner. The last show was at nine, but by the time all the hoop-la and lengthy photo sessions were over it was after midnight before they could eat. Aggravated by all the delays, and hungry as a bear, Elvis and his date headed for the hotel dining room only to find it had been closed for more than two hours. Canned chicken soup with crumbled crackers floating on top followed by coffee was his usual snack between shows, and hardly enough fuel to feed his fire.

The gang, consisting of Elvis's cronies, his date, his date's chaperone, and photographers and news reporters, decided to walk a short distance to a 24-hour diner. Leaving the hotel lobby, the group was again delayed by a young female fan coming face to face with her idol and fainting dead to the floor. Being the perfect gentleman, Elvis carried the young girl to a nearby sofa and stayed by her side, holding her hand, until he was sure she was okay. Finally arriving at the tiny, typical, hole-in-the-wall diner, Elvis's date sat patiently, with cameras flashing, watching a starving Elvis devour two bacon, lettuce and tomato sandwiches while reading a newspaper left on the counter by a customer.

Andrea June Stephens's dream of a romantic dinner for two – as well as her appetite – had been shot to hell.

Elvis, feeling bad about the ill-planned dinner, and trying to make amends to his date, invited everyone to the hotel lounge for a party. As soon as they arrived at the lounge, Elvis called the room, letting Pat, Buddy and me know about the party and making sure we'd be there.

I had already accepted the fact that I was going to be excluded from this night. It was my own decision. However, in the back of my mind, I was hoping Elvis would at least call or come up to my room, because he didn't want to be anywhere without me. I hung up the phone feeling very special, but, thinking the press was going to be there, I insisted Buddy and Pat go without me.

The lounge was so crowded Buddy and Pat had to push and shove to get through the door. Elvis was seated at the piano with his date by his side. He saw Buddy and Pat soon after they walked in, and motioned for them to come by him.

'Where's June?' he asked, looking around.

'June thought it best if she stayed in the room,' Pat

answered. Angrily, he got up, went to the phone, and called my room.

'Get yourself down here, right now!' he demanded.

'I don't think I should, Elvis, I don't want to impose.'

'C'mon baby, my date wants to meet you. Her name is June too. She knows all about you, so get yourself down here. The Colonel's in bed by now and all the reporters are gone. It's okay, I promise! I miss you! Get your ass down here!'

Thrilled by his insistence, I put my clothes back on, freshened my make-up, and went down to join the party.

Waiting for me by the lounge door, he took my hand and led me through the crowd to his date, still seated at the piano.

'June Stephens, this is my June,' he said, introducing me with pride.

'It's nice to meet you, June. I hope I'm not intruding,' I said, extending my hand.

'Not at all, June, I'm glad you came. Elvis has been talking about you all night. I was beginning to think he was making you up,' she laughed.

Later that evening, Elvis left the two of us to visit and sign autographs for the other fans in the lounge, giving June Stephens and me a chance to get better acquainted.

'You're the luckiest, most envied girl in the United States, June Juanico. Elvis Presley is in love with you,' she said, raising her thick brows and shaking her head.

'Elvis and I are just close friends,' I insisted.

'You can tell that to the press, June, but I know better. You should have heard him when I asked him if you were pretty. He said pretty was just a small part of you. You were not only pretty to look at, but you were pretty on the inside too. That kind of statement comes from a man in love. Now, you tell me you're just close friends? I know better!'

'It's nice to know he has good things to say about me when I'm not around,' I said, wanting her to tell me more.

'I told him if he didn't stop talking about you, I was going home!' she laughed, giving me a friendly slap on the arm.

After talking about Elvis and me, she gave me a blow-by-blow description of the 'romantic dinner' for two, and had me laughing my head off. We were both laughing when Elvis came back and sat down between us.

'Now, June Juanico, aren't you glad you met June Stephens? I told you she was great!' he said, putting his arms around us.

In order to win the date, June Stephens had written an essay in which she stated she recognized in Elvis the same spark of genius that people saw in James Dean. To her, Elvis was the 'brightest star in the entertainment heavens'.

After the party, and still too keyed up to sleep, Elvis came to the room with me and Pat. His first show of the day wasn't until 3:30 that afternoon, so we could all sleep late. He was wound up about the 'Win A Date' contest, and vowed he would never again go along with such a crazy thing no matter whose idea it was.

'I was lucky this time, baby. I felt really bad for June Stephens. She took an unpleasant, fucked-up situation and turned it into a pleasant one. I guarantee they'll never do this to me again!' he said, punctuating the end of his sentence with a sharp downward nod of his head. 'And,' he said, getting cranked up again, 'if I ever come back to this fuckin' town, I hope they take me out back and shoot me!'

Winding down, he rested his head on my shoulder, and by his breathing I could tell he was only minutes from falling asleep. I shook him and with a few sweet words convinced him to go to his room so he could get a good night's sleep. I didn't want him sneaking down the hall in a few hours to keep from being seen. He didn't object when I walked him to his room; he was so exhausted he was bumping into the walls of the hallway. Fishing his keys from his pocket, he opened the door to his room, kissed me, and pushed me into the room, saying, 'Sleep tight, baby,' thinking he was walking *me* to *my* room. In a way it was funny, but yet at the same time it wasn't. I got him inside the door and yelled for Gene to help him find his bed.

The unbelievable breakneck pace of his back-to-back performances of the past eight days was beginning to show, not only on Elvis, but on everyone around him.

After all was said and done, I was glad Elvis had insisted on my being at the party. Not only did I have a good time, I also had made a good friend in June Stephens. We exchanged addresses and stayed in touch for many years.

We all met for lunch the next day in the hotel dining room. After a good rest Elvis was all bright-eyed and back to his clowning self.

'If I have to look at another egg, I'm gonna puke!' he said, looking over the luncheon menu. We both ordered a club sandwich, and Elvis ordered a large scoop of every flavor ice-cream they had.

'We have twenty-eight flavors,' the waitress said, smiling. 'Did you want one of every flavor?'

'Yes ma'am, every flavor,' he smiled back.

After we'd finished our sandwiches, the waitress came out with the ice-cream arranged on a platter in layers, like a pyramid. It was a beautiful sight, at least ten inches high, with every shade of the rainbow and more represented. We both grabbed a spoon and dug in. We were feeding each other different bites, with our eyes closed, to see if we could guess the flavor. I was feeding him big spoonfuls so fast he accused me of trying to 'freeze his brain'. It was a great, memorable time. Pat and I skipped the afternoon show but made it for the last two. Elvis didn't cut loose until the very last one, but then he was in rare form.

'The hell with it! What are they gonna do, throw me in jail?' he said, just before making his entrance.

He ended his performance with another muffled 'Fuck you very much' and left the stage knowing he'd had the final word. He was so happy to be leaving Jacksonville he didn't care about the consequences. Thankfully, there were none.

25
HECTIC PACE

WITH THE FLORIDA leg of the tour now over, we packed up the cars and headed for New Orleans, the last city on the tour. We didn't stop driving until we reached Mobile, Alabama, in the early hours of the morning. Stopping for breakfast at a Howard Johnson's motel and 24-hour restaurant, Elvis and I both laughed at the big bold letters on the marquee: FEATURING 28 FLAVORS. My first thought was, 'Oh no, not again', but we didn't; we all had breakfast instead.

Buddy ordered eggs over easy, knowing Elvis couldn't stand the sight of them, and promised he wouldn't have to look at any runny yolks. He carefully cut all the white from around the yolk, and, without breaking it, popped the whole thing in his mouth. Elvis gagged, while everyone else laughed.

Two hours later Elvis pulled up in front of my house. I couldn't think of anything but getting into my own bed. I didn't know what I'd missed the most: my bed or my pillow.

The plan was for us to meet Elvis the following day, an hour before showtime at the Municipal Auditorium in New Orleans. My mother and Eddie, along with half the city of Biloxi, drove to New Orleans to catch Elvis's final show of the tour. The drive to New Orleans was fun in itself; almost every

car we passed belonged to someone we knew, on their way to
see the show.

The advance ticket sales were sold out. They hadn't
planned on such a large turn-out, and had to open both sides
of the giant auditorium to accommodate the thousands lined
up outside. Elvis had two audiences, front and back. He was
all over the stage, playing equally to the estimated thirteen
thousand in attendance.

I don't know how it happened, but after the show, Pat
and I found ourselves stranded at the auditorium. We were so
busy socializing with friends, new and old, we didn't hear
Elvis's last song or realize he had left the building. Caught in
the middle of the crowd, we couldn't find my mother and
Eddie or Buddy either. Elvis left the auditorium thinking we
were with Buddy, and Buddy left thinking we were with
Elvis.

Trying to find a taxi in all the traffic was impossible. We
could see the top of the Roosevelt Hotel, so we decided to
walk. It was the middle of August, and it was hot as hell! And,
to top it off, we were both wearing high-heel shoes. We were
moving a lot faster than the bumper-to-bumper traffic,
though, so for the first twenty minutes we didn't mind at all.
An hour later, with four blistered feet, we finally got to Elvis's
hotel. We went to the front desk, removed our shoes, and
asked for the room number of Arthur Hooton, praying he was
still using Arthur's name.

Pat and I collapsed on the sofa in the living room of Elvis's
suite. Elvis was laying on the bed next door, still wearing the
clothes he'd worn on stage. I closed his door and began telling
the boys about our long walk. About fifteen minutes later,
Elvis was calling my name over and over. I went in his room
to find him soaked with perspiration, even though the room
was as cold as ice. He was having a bad dream, and couldn't
seem to shake it off. His breathing was fast and shallow, and
I could see his heart pounding in his throat. I ran to the bathroom, wet a face cloth, and put it on his brow. I kept telling
him to take a deep breath and let it out real slow. I didn't
know anything about hyperventilation at that time, but I had

seen the same thing happen to a school-mate, and my PE
teacher had made her slow down her breathing. As soon as he
felt better, he picked up the phone and called his mother.

'Hi, it's me. I just called to let you know I'm okay, and I'll
see you sometime tomorrow. Yes, she's right here. I'm fine. I
love you too. She wants to talk to you,' he said, handing me
the phone.

His mother could tell by his voice that he wasn't feeling
well, and wanted reassurance from me that he was going to be
all right. I told her it was fatigue, and that he'd be just fine
after a good night's sleep. While I was on the phone, Elvis
removed his wet clothes and got under the covers.

'I'm so glad you're here, baby. What took you so long?' He
got real upset when I told him about Pat and I walking.

'Damn it, June, why didn't you stay put and call the room?
I would've sent someone after you. It's not safe to walk on the
street at night.'

We were all tired, but Elvis was more than just tired, he was
mentally and physically exhausted. It's a good thing the tour
was over – he couldn't possibly have done another show.

One of the boys went out for coffee and sandwiches, and he
started feeling better after having something to eat. Pat and I
hadn't planned on staying, but we didn't have much choice.
She slept on the couch, and I slept in the twin bed with Elvis.
Before we went to sleep, he told me about the dream he had
had earlier. He said he saw himself in a coffin, with his mother
standing over him, crying.

'I don't wanna talk about it, baby, it was too bad. I don't
even wanna think about it any more.'

He took a deep breath, sighed as if finally giving in, and
closed his eyes. With his long lashes resting on his cheeks, he
looked like a little boy, crashing after a long hard day at play.
My mothering instinct was now fully aroused, so I held him
close to my breast, running my fingers through his hair until
he was fast asleep.

Watching him sleeping peacefully in the safety of my arms,
I couldn't help recall an incident that had happened earlier
that evening, shortly before Elvis went on stage. Pat and I had

made our way through the crowd, trying to locate the ladies'
room. As soon as we were inside, a group of girls from Biloxi
recognized me. 'There she is, that's her,' one of the girls yelled.
'That's June Juanico!' Before I had a chance to go into one of
the stalls, I was surrounded by teenage girls wanting to touch
me. 'She's Elvis Presley's girlfriend!' I heard them telling others coming into the ladies' room. They were screaming with
excitement and slowly backing me into a corner. Smiling, I
quickly excused myself, saying I was about to wet my pants,
and locked myself in a stall. 'Elvis will be on stage in five minutes; you girls had better get back to your seats,' I yelled from
the safety of the stall. All of a sudden there was a shuffling of
feet and a mad dash for the exit. When I leaned down and
looked under the door, I was relieved to see Pat's tiny size 4½
shoes were the only ones left in the room.

'Good job, June!' Pat yelled.

Up until that point, I hadn't given the fans' attention much
thought, one way or another, but what I had experienced was
only a drop in the ocean compared to what Elvis had to go
through every time he stepped out in public. It's no wonder he
slept like a baby.

It was next to impossible for me to take my eyes from his
perfect chiseled features. Trance-like, I stared at his beautiful
face until the arm I was propped up on finally gave out. When
I changed positions he grabbed for me, mumbling a few barely
audible words, followed by a loud and clear '*Don't leave me!*'

I had an awful time trying to fall asleep that night. Tired
and homesick, I was ready to get back to some sort of nor-
mality. I wanted more than anything to be with Elvis, but at
the same time I wanted Elvis's life to be different. I found
myself wanting to get away from it all, wishing I was home in
my own bed.

First thing the next morning he made arrangements for
Arthur and Junior to ride back to Memphis with the band,
making room for Pat and me. I apologized for making him
drive so far out of his way but he insisted he was pleased
about the mix-up, saying he was planning to go home via
Biloxi anyway.

With some of the pressures of the tour now lifted, he wasn't driving at his usual breakneck speed, but taking his sweet time, all the while trying to convince me to go with him to Memphis. He kept me so close to his side, there would easily have been room for a fourth passenger in the front seat alone. I loved the attention, but tiptoed around the subject of going to Memphis by blaming my mother.

'I've been away from home not only for the past eleven days, but for most of the entire summer. There'll be no convincing my mother; I daren't even bring up the subject of leaving.'

Maybe I could have tried talking to Mama, but, believe it or not, I was ready for some time to myself. Sure, I was over eighteen, and could have gone with or without her permission, but, out of respect, I would do whatever made my mother happy. All that aside, considering that Elvis would only be in Memphis for five days before going to Hollywood, I knew the pace would get hectic again with all the preparations for his new adventure: filming what would become *Love Me Tender*.

As soon as we pulled in front of my house, I felt as though a weight had been lifted from me. I pushed the thought of being on the road again completely out of my mind. The long tour had taken its toll on me, too.

He walked me to my door as usual, but held me, looking into my eyes before kissing me goodbye. Bone-tired, I fell across the bed and slept through the remainder of the day. I hadn't been awake but a few hours when Elvis called to tell me he was home. Feeling well rested after catching up on some lost sleep, a part of me wanted to be there with him.

Elvis phoned me every one of those five days. His first day home he called to see if I wanted him to drive back down to Biloxi and pick me up.

'I have four days with nothing to do, baby, and I miss you. Talk some sense into her, Mama,' he said, pretending to be broken-hearted, handing his mother the phone. We talked for a few minutes but she didn't pressure me about coming to Memphis. Unlike Elvis, she understood completely my feelings about all the commotion constantly surrounding Elvis, and said it was even starting to get to her. Like me, she too wondered if his life would ever be any different. Would he ever be able to settle down? Give her the house full of blue-eyed grand-babies she so desired?

Even then, I think we both had our doubts.

26
WESTERN UNION

BUSY WORKING ON the movie, Elvis had very little free time on his hands. His phone calls were coming every three to four days instead of every day, always apologizing for his busy schedule and not having enough hours in the day.

On the afternoon of 21 August 1956 I got the most romantic surprise of my life. A young man from Western Union knocked on my door.

'I have a telegram for Miss June Juanico,' he said, smiling.

'That's me!' I announced, smiling back.

'Sign here, please,' he said, handing me a clipboard; the smile on his face even bigger. My entire face lit up when I saw the word 'Hollywood'; I knew immediately it had to be from Elvis. My hands were trembling as I ripped open the sealed envelope. I had trouble making out the first two words, then I realized it was 'Little Bitty', in Elvis's baby-talk. It read WIOOLE BITTY, instead of WIDDLE BITTY. The Western Union typist had apparently misread Elvis's capital Ds.

After reading the telegram, I looked up to find the young man from Western Union still standing there. I had no idea why; I wasn't thinking about anything but the piece of paper in my trembling hands.

'Will there be a return message?' he asked, his smile now a sheepish grin.

'No, thank you very much,' I answered, somewhat confused by his question. Maybe he was waiting for a tip. Was I suppose to tip a delivery man? I didn't know; I'd never received a telegram before. He walked down the steps of my front porch until, half-way to the street, he turned around, grinning from ear to ear.

'Oh! By the way – have a nice day, Widdle Bitty!' he yelled. Realizing that he knew the contents of my telegram, I grinned too, embarrassed at first but then proud to have him know I was loved by Elvis Presley. Biloxi, at that time, was such a small town it was a cinch to say everyone working for Western Union knew I had a telegram from Elvis, long before it was ever delivered.

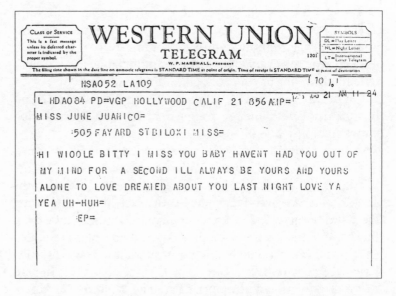

I loved every phone call but now I had something tangible; something that wouldn't end with a dial tone. Clutching the telegram to my heart when I wasn't reading it over and over, memorizing every word, I happened to have it in my hand when the phone rang that same night.

'Did you get my telegram, baby?' he asked, instead of his usual hello.

'Yes! I got it just a little while ago. I've read it at least a hundred times. I'll always be yours and yours alone too,' I cooed, quoting from the telegram.

'I meant every word, June. I miss you, baby.'

'How's the movie coming along? Are they treating you okay?' I asked.

'The movie's going good, baby. It took a while but we finally got down to serious filming. The only problem is my schedule; it's turned upside-down. I have to get out of bed before the sun comes up, and that's usually when I'm going to bed. Other than that everything else is okay, except I miss you like crazy.'

'I miss you like crazy too, Elvis,' I said.

'I had a great dream about you last night. We were in the swimming pool, but this time we didn't have anything on,' he said suggestively.

'I'm glad you didn't put that in the telegram. As it is everyone working for Western Union knows you dreamed about me last night. They don't have to know we were naked,' I giggled.

'I love you, June. Guess what? I finally got to really meet Debra Paget.'

'And just what do you mean, "really"?' I snapped. Debra Paget was his beautiful co-star on the movie.

'Well, uh, I'd met her earlier on the *Milton Berle Show*, but it was only to say hello. This time I got to say more than just hello. She's a beautiful lady, June,' he said, sounding like a typical star-struck fan meeting a celebrity for the first time.

'I'll have to hang up now, Elvis; I'll talk to you later!' I said, pretending to be jealous.

'Don't you dare hang up, June! She's pretty but she don't hold a candle to you, baby. She don't have your big beautiful eyes, and she don't have your smile, either,' he answered softly, trying to reassure me.

'Keep talking like that and maybe I won't hang up after all,' I cooed. I let him off the hook by asking who else, besides

Debra Paget, did he get to meet. I was interested in everything
and everyone he was involved with. After a few seconds of
silence, I said, 'Never mind, I think I'd like to hear just what
else, besides hello, did you get to say to Debra?' Then there
was an even longer pause. Maybe he was trying to think of
what he'd said to the beautiful young starlet, or maybe he was
trying to figure out a way to make me believe he hadn't been
flirting with her. That was a lost cause: knowing Elvis as well
as I did, if he hadn't turned on his boyish charm with her then
there wasn't a cow in Texas.

'I don't exactly remember . . . but I met Richard Egan,
too,' he snickered. The handsome Egan was Elvis's other co-
star.

'Oh! I *l-o-v-e* Richard Egan!' I sighed.

'Oh really? And just how much do you love Richard Egan?'

'Probably as much as you love Debra Paget. Okay, now we
have Richard and Debra, who else did you get to meet?'

'Have you ever heard of an actor named William
Campbell?' He paused, waiting for a yes or no, then continued. 'A nice-looking guy with wavy black hair; he plays in lots
of Westerns.'

'I think so, but I'm not sure,' I answered, knowing good
and well the only Campbell I was familiar with was the
chicken-noodle soup variety.

'Well, he plays my brother in the movie. Anyway, they
wanted him to wear a hat in one scene and he refused. He was
afraid it would mess up his hair. This guy can't pass a mirror
without stopping to inspect himself. He combs his hair more
than I do.'

'Now, Elvis, I don't see how that could be possible.
Nobody, but nobody, combs their hair as much as you do!'

'June, I'll get you for that, you little shit!'

'Mama and Eddie said hello,' I quickly interrupted.

'Don't change the subject, June. I'm really not that bad
about my hair, am I?'

'No, my baby boy, I was only kidding. If my hair was as
pretty as yours, I'd be combing it all the time too. Just kidding! Just kidding!' I assured with a giggle.

'You'd better be kidding, June Juanico; I'd hate to have to come down there and spank my PP britches' little ass.'

'If I didn't love you, Elvis Presley, I wouldn't be teasing you.'

'You'd better keep on loving me, June. I need you, baby! I need you now more than ever! I can't explain how I'm feeling but I need to know that you love me.'

'You don't have to worry about me, Elvis, I'll love you till the day I die.'

'You promise?'

'I promise!'

'No matter what?'

'No matter what!' I answered.

'Listen baby, I've got to run. I need to shower and get some shut-eye. I'll talk to you later. Sweet dreams, baby. I love you.'

'Sweet dreams to you, my love,' I said, holding the phone to my ear until I heard the dial tone.

After hanging up I started thinking about the last part of our conversation. Was he still under too much pressure? What did he mean when he said 'no matter what'? Was he asking for my help? Surely he would have said something. Was I going to pick up a newspaper and read something about Elvis that would break my heart? I was probably reading too much into it; anyway, I either had to put it out of my mind or have a sleepless night worrying about it. I picked up the telegram and read it over and over again. Clutching it to my breast brought a smile to my lips and eased my worried mind.

27
*D*REAMING

*E*LVIS PHONED ME a few days later to tell me about the changes being made in his movie. Instead of the excitement of his last call, I immediately detected a note of disappointment in his voice. Already well established as a singer with gold records, he was pleased to know his first movie was going to be a straight acting part. Now he seemed less sure.

I remember how happy he had been just a few weeks earlier in Miami, as we thumbed through the pages of *The Reno Brothers* script.* Becoming a good character actor was the one thing he wanted for himself, and now he was going to have the opportunity to do what he had only dreamed of doing. 'I sorta got lucky, and backed up into the singing business just at the right time' were his words to me when he explained his success. Now he'd been given a chance to prove himself as a serious talent.

'I'm gonna sing a song in the movie, June,' he said, with some trepidation.

'Why? There was no singing in the script; what made them change it?'

* *The Reno Brothers* was the original title of *Love Me Tender*.

'I don't know, baby, I don't know! It's okay though, it's a pretty good song.'

'Whose idea was this?' I asked.

'I don't know, baby, it just sorta happened. It's a love song. Its original title was "Ora Lee" but they changed it to "Love Me Tender".' Wanting my approval, he sang the song, a cappella, down the phone.

'Oh wow!' I sighed. 'That's not a pretty good song; it's a beautiful song.'

'You really think so, baby?'

'Yes, Elvis, I really think so. It's a beautiful song.'

'They're planning to make it the theme song for the movie. I had no objections at first; I was supposed to record the song and have it playing in the beginning; then they were going to have the instrumental version play throughout the movie. All this was okay with me, but now they've changed my character from a farm boy to a singing farm boy. Oh, and they've also changed the name of the movie. It's no longer *The Reno Brothers*; it's now called *Love Me Tender*, like the song.'

'Do one thing for me, Elvis. Let them change anything they want, but please don't let them change you. Okay?'

'Don't worry, baby, like the song says: *for my darling, I love you and I always will*. I miss you so much, baby. As soon as I finish up here, I'm going home and I want you to come home with me, okay?'

'As soon as you finish, just let me know and I'll be there. I miss you too, Elvis. Don't worry about the movie, I'm sure everything will work out. Just get it finished so we can be together.'

'I've got to run, baby. Someone's at the door, and I've got a feeling it's the management asking me to get the boys under control. I've rented the entire floor of the hotel and flew the gang out here to keep me company. Sometimes they get a little rambunctious. I don't have to tell you, June, you know how they cut up whenever they're bored. Let me run, baby, I'll talk to you soon.'

I said a quick goodbye, I love you, and listened for the dial tone.

*

In the early days of shooting Elvis's movie, producers, direc-
tors and most definitely Colonel Tom Parker would at any
given time call a meeting to discuss changes to be made in the
script. It was my guess that because Elvis's role was not a
starring role the Colonel wanted his Golden Boy to have more
screen exposure, through the introduction of 'silly songs' as
Elvis called them.

It was during these meetings that Elvis had extra time on
his hands. He would go to the nearest telephone and call me.
These quickie conversations lasted anywhere from five to fifteen minutes. Elvis always opened these daytime calls with:
'It's me, baby, the Colonel called another meeting.'

If Elvis was checking up on me with his random phone
calls, timing was on my side. I was now working at home,
making costumes for different friends for the upcoming Mardi
Gras season, and could be found any time, night or day, close
to the telephone.

Not that I had that many requests for dates anyway. I was
now well known as Elvis Presley's girlfriend, and all my former dates were involved elsewhere. I did receive a few date
invitations while Elvis was in Hollywood, however. The director of entertainment at Keesler AFB called and asked if I
would accompany singer Mel Tormé to a formal dinner at the
Officers' Club. At that time Mel Tormé had a few hit songs
being played on my favorite radio station (for the life of me,
I can't remember any of them), and had also made several
television appearances. I politely declined, saying I was busy.
I didn't give it much thought until a few weeks later, when the
same entertainment director called again. This time he wanted
to fix me up with someone he considered to be a close friend,
who was also an entertainer and a juggling comedian, as well
as being taller and better looking than Mel Tormé. I laughed
my head off at first, thinking it was some kind of joke, but
after hanging up the phone I realized it was no joke at all. This
guy was dead serious. Then I became outraged; so much so
that for the next few weeks the mere ringing of the phone put
me on the defensive.

'What's with this guy, calling me to accompany entertainers?

Does he think I'm some sort of call girl or something? The nerve of this bastard!' I thought, every time the phone rang. The guy never did call back; I guess my laughter was insult enough.

The quickie daytime phone calls from Elvis stopped coming after a week. I guess the Colonel had finally had his say and ironed out all their differences. I enjoyed hearing from Elvis at any hour, but it was the night-time calls I looked forward to the most. His voice, like his mood, was softer, more romantic, when he was alone in his room and ready for bed.

I hadn't been out of the house in over a week, so it didn't take much for Pat to convince me one night to take time out from my sewing and go to a movie. Returning home from an early show, I heard the phone as I was unlocking the door. By the time I reached the phone it had stopped ringing. Twenty minutes later it rang again, and I answered on the second ring.

'Where have you been, baby? I was getting worried,' Elvis said, sounding relieved to hear my voice.

'Nowhere; I've been in this house so long I feel like a piece of furniture,' I answered, without thinking it was a lie. Going to a movie two or three times a month wasn't my idea of doing the town.

'You should get out and do things, baby, staying home all the time is not healthy. If I'm cooped up too long I go crazy.' He laughed his silly laugh, letting me know he wasn't letting any grass grow under his feet, but I knew that anyway. I didn't care how many oats he sowed, as long as he didn't become *involved* with anyone else. I knew in my heart he was mine and mine alone.

'I can't wait to see you, June. Sometimes at night when I have trouble falling asleep, I close my eyes and I can see your face, but then your face changes and it's not your face any more. I get so aggravated I open my eyes and close them again, trying to start over. Sometimes it works, but then you quickly fade away again. Dreaming about you is better; at least you stay with me longer. The only trouble is, I don't dream about you enough. If I could only push a button and select my dreams, they'd all be about you.'

'I've had a few dreams about you too, Elvis, but they're always crazy and in slow motion. The last time I dreamed of you, there was this man with a cigar holding me back. It was so real, I could smell the stench of cigar on his breath.'

'You're kidding!' he laughed.

'No, I'm not kidding, Elvis, it was awful!'

'That was probably Colonel Parker, June.'

'Oh shit! I'd forgotten all about him. Don't tell me the old coot is going to plague me even in my dreams. When you see him again, tell him not to breathe in my face, okay?'

He burst out laughing, making me laugh with him.

'That's the one thing about you I miss the most. I don't get a chance to laugh out here. It's all make-believe, nobody is real. I can't wait to finish this movie so I can get the hell out of here. I wanna go home, baby, I wanna be with you.'

'How much longer before you're finished?'

'I don't know, baby. We're just getting started good. Hey, I've got a great idea! Why don't you come out here?'

'I wish I could!' I answered, not really wanting to.

'Why can't you, June? Give me one good reason.'

'I wouldn't fit in with all those people, Elvis.'

'Yes you would, June, you'd fit in anywhere. You could even take a screen test, baby. You could be a movie star. You're prettier than any girl out here, I swear!'

'Oh yes, I'm sure! You're only saying that 'cause it's true.'

'No, it *is* true, June. Everybody would love you, especially these big shots out here. They'd take one look at you and sign you up. I'm serious, baby!'

'Thanks, my love, but I have no desire to become a movie star.'

A few years back, the thought of becoming a costume designer had crossed my mind, but that was the extent of it. I'd never mentioned this to Elvis, and then would not have been a good time. I'm sure he would have insisted I came out and gave it a try.

'Well, you could come out here and be my movie star, June.'

'Did you forget about the Colonel? I'm sure he'd love me to show up in Hollywood.'

'He wouldn't have to know, baby, we could keep it a secret.'

'Be serious, Elvis. Besides, I hate all that secret shit. Anyway, the whole world would know as soon as I stepped off the plane. How do you think I know so much about what's going on with you?'

''Cause I tell you everything, that's how.'

'That's a crock and you know it. Every day I read something different about you. You can't even blow your nose without it being in the news.'

'Is it all good stuff?'

'Well, so far so good. I haven't read anything about any other girls – yet!'

'What do you mean, yet? There are no other girls, June. You're the only girl in my life. Besides, I wouldn't have time for a girl even if there was one.'

'Then how would you have time for me?'

'I'd *make* time for you, baby. I'm not happy being this far from you. Do you realize there's three thousand miles between us? That's a lot of miles, baby. Makes me tired just thinking about it. I'm so tired right now, I could sleep for a week,' he yawned.

'Why don't you tell me goodnight, hang up the phone, and get a good night's sleep.'

'I can't! I haven't had anything to eat yet. I'm waiting on room service, and if they don't c'mon soon, it's gonna be too late.'

'Did you order one of everything?'

'Not this time. I save silly things like that just for you. I ordered a club sandwich, but they must be baking the bread or something. Yeah! Someone's at the door. It's room service, finally! I'll talk to you later, baby, I love you!'

'I love you too, Elvis. Sleep tight, my love.'

I dreamed of Elvis that same night, but I couldn't get to him. I was riding a bicycle, of all things, all the way to California. I would stop and ask how far it was and the answer was always the same: '*Three thousand miles*!'

When he called a few days later I told him about my dream.

He laughed, saying he had had a crazy dream too, only he was running and jumping over tall buildings. 'I must have thought I was Superman or something. I never did get to Biloxi.'

His early-evening calls were coming every other day, usually beginning with an apology for not calling the day before.

'I didn't get to call last night, baby. We had a late day on the set and by the time I got back to Beverly [the Beverly Wilshire Hotel] I was so beat I fell asleep before I even had a chance to eat. I can't get used to the hours I'm keeping. My day starts at 5:00 A.M. Ain't that a pisser? They've got me in a complete reverse and my brain refuses to co-operate.'

One night he fell asleep with me on the other end of the phone. I could hear music in the background, and his slow, steady breathing. I called his name and even whistled, but nothing worked. I didn't want to hang up and leave the line open, because in those days the caller had to hang up in order to break the connection. Finally I heard a little groan.

'Hello! Hello! Can you hear me, Elvis? Are you awake? Don't go back to sleep! Talk to me!' I yelled.

'Is that you, June? Why are you yelling at me?'

'You fell asleep, my love. Say goodnight and hang up the phone. I'll talk to you tomorrow.'

'June, I thought I was dreaming! I could hear your voice but I couldn't find you. Where are you, baby?' he asked, still in a sleeping stupor.

'I'm right here, Elvis, talking to you on the phone. Now hang up the phone like a good boy, and go to sleep.'

I could hear him trying to put the phone back in the cradle, and then I heard the dial tone. It was 11:00 P.M. my time; only 9 P.M. in California, and already he was dead to the world.

28

THE PRESSURES OF HOLLYWOOD

ONCE A QUIET little resort town, Biloxi was fast becoming 'the' place to live. Wealthy families from nearby Mobile, Alabama, to the east, and New Orleans, Louisiana, to the west, were building summer homes on the beautiful Mississippi coast. Another influx of families came strictly from the military. Yankees living north of the Mason–Dixon line, stationed at Keesler, were all smitten with a taste of real southern hospitality, and fell in love with the coast and its people. While some found it the perfect place to retire, others found it the perfect place to settle down and raise a family. Elvis too had expressed a desire to build or buy a home for his parents here on the coast.

We were growing so fast that even the telephone company had to add a prefix – or exchange, as it was explained to me – to our four-digit number. We used to be Idlewood 6. The Idlewood was soon dropped and 436 used in its place. When Elvis called in the middle of the change-over, he gave the operator the four digits he was familiar with. She was giving him a hard time because he didn't know the prefix. By the time the call was put through, he was aggravated to the point of being really pissed off.

'When did you get the prefix, June?' His words were so

sharp and deliberate I wasn't sure it was Elvis on the phone.
It sounded like Elvis, but his question didn't make any sense
to me. I was not yet acquainted with the word 'prefix', and his
tone of voice confused me even more.

'Is that you, Elvis? What's going on, and did I get what
fixed?'

'A prefix, baby, a prefix on your phone number,' he said
loudly, anger still in his voice.

'Oh, that! We just got it a few days ago. I didn't know it
was called a prefix. I thought it was called an exchange.'

'Hell, I've been on the damn phone with a Biloxi operator
for at least twenty minutes. She'd ask me a dumb question
and then make me hold the line. I felt like telling her to kiss
my ass, but I figured if I wanted to talk to you any time soon,
I'd better play her little game.'

'She probably knew it was you, Elvis,' I laughed.

'I didn't tell the bitch my name, June.'

'You didn't have to. She knew you were calling me and she
knew you were calling from Hollywood. And she probably
recognized your sexy voice. Did you write the new number
down?'

'Yeah, I got it safely tucked away in my little black book. I
wouldn't want to go through that shit again,' he said with a
little chuckle, sounding like my Elvis again. 'Guess what,
baby? The end is finally in sight. We're headin' for a wrap. It
won't be long now! Oh, that reminds me – what did the monkey say when the train cut off his tail?'

'I give up, Elvis, what did he say?'

'It won't be long now!' he laughed. 'Ain't that a cute joke,
baby? I heard it today on the set. This guy was running
around saying, "It won't be long now! It won't be long now!"
and Richard Egan said he sounded like that damn monkey. I
said, "What monkey is that, Mr Egan?" and he said, "The
monkey that was sitting on the railroad track." We were
shooting a serious scene, and every time I thought about that
silly joke I got tickled. They were yelling, "Cut! Cut! Let's take
it again" all afternoon. It was funny, baby. Today was a good
day.'

'It's good to hear you laugh, Elvis.'

'I can't help it, baby, I'm excited about going home.'

'I'm excited too, Elvis. I miss you!'

'I miss you too, baby, and just think – it won't be long now!'

He asked me to call the airport and check the price of tickets to Memphis, and suggested I bring along my friend Pat. We laughed and talked for over an hour. He was so tired he had a real case of the sillies. I wasn't even tired, but I had them too; Elvis was contagious. Every time he called, his mood became my mood. If he was down about something, I would be down for days after. I didn't realize his phone calls were affecting me until my mother brought it to my attention.

'June, your bottom lip is dragging along the floor. If Elvis knew he had this kind of effect on you, he wouldn't call you at all. The next time he calls, I want to have a talk with him.'

'I'll be okay, Mama. It's just that I hate it when he's upset and I can't do anything to help.'

'Elvis is a grown man, June. He can take care of himself.'

'I won't let it bother me any more, I promise.' I did keep my promise – by not letting my mother see me unless I had a smile on my face. To me, Elvis wasn't a grown man, he was a little boy who needed me. Except for Colonel Parker setting up his performance dates, he was more or less his own boss, calling his own shots. I knew Elvis, the perfectionist, was trying to absorb as much as possible and as soon as possible, in a new profession. I also knew he'd be fine as soon as he got away from the pressures of Hollywood.

After he'd invited me and Pat to visit, I dialed 411 for information. Several calls later I had the price of a round-trip ticket to Memphis, Tennessee. I called Pat and invited her to join me for an all-expense-paid vacation with Elvis.

'When do we leave? When do we leave?' she screamed.

'As soon as he's finished with his movie. Probably a week or so; I'm not sure.' While she was screaming to everyone in her house, I multiplied the ticket price by two and had all the information I needed, including the flight schedule, written on a scratch pad next to the phone.

Back then, air travel was not the most popular mode of transport, especially from the tiny airport in Gulfport, Mississippi, our neighboring town. Flights to Memphis were available four days a week, one flight per day.

Pat and I spent the next few days shopping for some odds and ends needed for our trip. We both bought new outfits, down to the shoes, for our plane trip. Unlike the casualwear of airline passengers today, back then people used to get all dressed up for a flight. It was considered a special occasion.

I was expecting Elvis to call from Hollywood any day now, telling me he was on his way home, so I was completely taken by surprise when the voice on the other end of the phone said, 'Little Satnin, this is your Lovie. I have a sleepy little boy here wanting to speak to you.' It was Elvis's mother, and, without waiting for a reply, she handed the phone to Elvis. His sleepy voice told me he was recuperating from his long train ride, had slept twelve hours straight, and was well rested and happy to be home. He didn't waste any time on the phone, saying he was grabbing a bite to eat then heading out to the Western Union office to wire the money for our airline tickets.

'As soon as the money arrives, call and make your flight reservations. Maybe you can come tomorrow? Can you get packed and ready that fast?'

'Are you kidding? I've been packed and ready for three days now.'

'Good! I can't wait to see you, baby. Mama said to bring a sweater; it's a little cooler up here than in Biloxi. I love you, baby. I'll see you in a little bit.'

Pat just happened to be at my house when the call came in, and we decided that, rather than wait for Western Union to call, we'd go to their office and be there when the money arrived. When we got to the office I noticed the same young man that had delivered my love telegram standing behind the counter.

'What brings you here, Widdle Bitty?' he asked, remembering the nickname Elvis had given me. I told him we were having money wired to us and thought we would wait there instead of hanging around the house.

'Elvis is sending us money! We're flying to Memphis!' Pat shouted with excitement.

We took a seat on the long wooden bench across from the counter and waited, and waited, and waited, and waited.

'Are you sure he was sending it today?' Pat asked, after two hours had passed.

'That's what he said.'

Our rear-ends were numb from sitting on the hard bench, so we informed the attendant that we could be found next door at Klein's Bakery, sitting in a cushioned booth, having crème puffs and coffee. Three cups of coffee and two crème puffs later, we returned to find the money still hadn't come. We waited thirty minutes more and then called it quits.

We had bounced into the office three hours ago, filled with excitement, like a couple of balloons, and now we felt like all our air had been let out. We went back to my house wondering what had gone wrong. We were there just a few minutes when the phone rang. It was Elvis.

'Baby, I ran into a little trouble on my way to Western Union. I didn't get to send the money. I'll send it as soon as I can,' he said, sounding out of breath.

'Are you okay, Elvis?'

'Yeah, I'm fine, baby, nothing to worry about. I'll talk to you later. I love you.'

Before I had a chance to say anything, he hung up the phone. Now I was really confused. First it was excitement, then it was disappointment, and now the caffeine had kicked in. It was Colonel Parker, I thought to myself, trying to place the blame. The Colonel must have stopped Elvis from sending the money. I was pacing through the house, so fidgety I couldn't sit still. That's what it was, I was sure of it. The Colonel was to blame.

The disappointment was suddenly replaced by anger. My imagination was running wild. It was not just the Colonel, it was Elvis, too. If he was going to let his cigar-smoking bastard of a manager run his life, then he could count me out! Ranting and raving and pacing like a wild animal, everything was 'bastard' this and 'bastard' that. Finally Pat started laughing so hard she couldn't stop. Soon I joined in and started laughing too. Why not? I'd already been through every emotion I could possibly experience that afternoon; I may as well end it with laughter.

'Now, I want you to tell me exactly what Elvis had to say to you on the phone just now,' Pat said when she stopped laughing.

'He said, "Baby, I ran into a little trouble on the way to the Western Union, and I didn't get to send the money. I'll send it as soon as I can." Then he said he was fine and would talk to me later.'

'Well, the way I figure – let me see – Elvis was probably alone at the time and when he got there, he didn't have any money in his pockets. You know how he is about paying for things; somebody else always took care of the money 'cause Elvis couldn't be bothered. That's probably all it is, so stop worrying.' I collapsed on the couch and started crying. Now that I had run the emotional gamut, I was totally exhausted.

When the phone rang again I made a mad dash for it, thinking it was Elvis again, but this time it was Buddy. He had called Pat's house and heard about our trip to Memphis.

'Are ya'll gonna be home? I'm coming over,' he drawled.

'Sure, come on over; we're not going anywhere,' I answered. Twenty minutes later Buddy showed up with three bottles of champagne.

'*Well, I heard the news*,' he sang – the first line of 'Good Rockin' Tonight'. 'This calls for a celebration.'

The three of us proceeded to drink the champagne, one bottle at a time, clicking our jelly glasses with a toast after each refill.

Other than a slight numbness in my lips and a 'who cares' attitude, I felt relatively normal. It wasn't until I got up from the kitchen table and staggered to the bathroom that I realized I was completely plastered. Checking my reflection in the mirror, I noticed my left eye appeared to be floating to the left.

No matter how hard I tried to focus, I couldn't get my left eye to return my gaze.

'Oh no!' I laughed to myself, 'I look like Junior Smith.' Elvis's cousin, Junior, had one eye that always appeared to be looking elsewhere. Maybe it was a birth defect, or maybe it was because Junior was always a little tipsy. Whatever the cause, it was no laughing matter; up until then, that is.

'Look at my eyes; I look like Junior Smith!' I exclaimed, returning to the table. Buddy, slamming his hand down over and over on the table, was laughing hysterically, while Pat, holding her stomach, pounded her feet on the floor. The screams of uncontrollable laughter lasted until we were all out of breath. When the laughter subsided, I panicked, realizing my mother was due home in fifteen minutes. I didn't dare let her see me in my drunken condition, and suggested we go for a ride. We cleared the table, put the empty bottles in a bag and placed them in Buddy's trunk. With no particular destination in mind, we piled in the front seat of Buddy's mint-green Continental. Feeling a little tipsy himself, Buddy drove us to north Biloxi, away from all traffic. We were on a deserted country road when I felt a wave of nausea.

'Stop the car! I'm gonna be sick!' I moaned. Buddy pulled the car as far as possible to the side of the road. I opened the door, leaned out and began to barf. The coffee and crème puffs no longer churning in my stomach, I immediately felt better – but then I reached out to close the car door and tumbled head over heels straight into a drainage ditch. Thank God we hadn't had much rain. Pat screamed 'Oh my God!' and stepped out to help me. As soon as her foot hit the downward slope of the ground, she came tumbling down too. Too drunk to think about the dangers lurking in the snake-infested ditch, we laughed at ourselves while Buddy struggled to get us back in the car.

Buddy drove us to our favorite drive-in restaurant, fed us cheeseburgers and milk, and we were back to normal by 10 P.M. that night. Happy, for a change, to come home to an empty house – Mama was out with Eddie – I took a quick bath and went to bed.

I woke up at 3 A.M. feeling like my head was splitting in half, swallowed three aspirin and prayed for relief, promising it would never happen again.

The constant ringing of the phone kept my mind busy the next day. People who'd heard about my upcoming trip were calling to see if they could help out in any way. They all wanted to take part, however small, in anything to do with Elvis. The owner of Rosie's Dress Shop wanted to give me the outfit of my choice to take with me; she wanted Elvis's girl to look beautiful. Alma, my beautician, wanted to make sure my hair was perfect; what little I had left. Now less than two inches in length, I was sporting a new pixie hairdo after cutting off the awful blonde streak.

Early the following afternoon a friend called asking if I had seen the *Times Picayune*, one of the largest newspapers in the South. In it was an article about Elvis. I ran to the corner drugstore and bought a copy. The article *was* about Elvis, but the picture was of a man named Ed Hopper. Ed had the biggest black eye I'd ever seen. The story read:

'ELVIS PRESLEY was engaged in a short fist-fight with Ed Hopper and another service-station attendant in Memphis. Elvis stopped by Hopper's gas station in his $10,000 Lincoln Continental Mark 2 when a crowd began to gather, blocking the pumps . . .' I stopped reading the paper to answer the phone. It was Western Union; the money was here at last. Pat and I drove to the office, taking along a copy of the paper. Somehow I thought I had to show the guys at Western Union why we hadn't received the money on the day we were supposed to. I plopped the heavy paper on the counter at the same time the clerk was handing me the receipt. Remembering me from the long wait, he didn't even ask to see my identification.

'Sign here please, Miss Juanico,' he said with a grin. Glancing over the document, I had to laugh. I signed it and pointed out a few interesting things to Pat. The recipient was June Juanico, but the sender wasn't Elvis; it was his father, Vernon Presley.

'Lovie must have punished my widdle baby for fighting,' I said to Pat, laughing.

We made our reservations for the following day and I phoned Elvis to let him know everything was set. Pat was jumping up and down, excited about her first flight. My excitement was in counting down the minutes until I would see Elvis's face. I was already a veteran of the sky, having had my first flight earlier that year with Elvis, and with the amount of adrenalin I had flowing through my body, I felt as though I could fly *without* a plane.

When we finally touched down at Memphis airport I was weak at the knees. Holding on to the handrail of the portable stairway, I scanned the faces of the small gathering below, searching for Elvis, but he was nowhere in sight. Following along with the rest of the passengers, we were almost to the terminal when I heard Mrs Presley's voice.

'June, Patsy, over here!' I looked around to see Mr and Mrs Presley both waving to get our attention. 'We thought it best if Elvis stay out of the public for a while. There's too many men out there wanting to start trouble, and you know how Elvis can be sometimes. He's not one to back down,' Lovie said, noticing my disappointment at seeing the empty pink Cadillac.

Pat and I climbed in the back and Mrs Presley sat quietly on the passenger's side, waiting for Mr Presley to make room in the trunk for all our luggage. Mrs Presley had a worried look on her face, so I leaned up and put my hand on her shoulder.

'Try not to worry, Lovie, Elvis can take care of himself,' I said, sounding like my mother. She squeezed my hand and turned to look at me. I could tell she was about to cry.

'I know he can, June, but what happens if some crazy man decides to pull a gun or a knife on him?' She choked out the words, tears now running down her face.

'Everything's gonna be all right, Lovie, I promise! Everything's gonna be okay!'

When Mr Presley got in the car, he saw his wife trying to dry her eyes. 'It's okay, Mama, he's gonna be just fine,' he

said, leaning over and patting her leg. 'I guess ya'll heard
what happened.'

'Yes sir! We saw the black eye in the paper. That was the
biggest black eye I've ever seen,' Pat chuckled, trying to
lighten up the conversation.

'Yeah, it was pretty big at that, wasn't it?' Mr Presley
chuckled back. Mrs Presley shook her head back and forth,
giving me a look. She didn't think it was funny at all. Not
knowing what to say next, we rode in silence for quite a
while.

'Well, did ya'll have a good flight?' Lovie asked, after
regaining her composure. Pat, usually the one to sit back and
listen, started talking, giving no one a chance to say a word.

'It was wonderful! We had special treatment all the way. The
stewardess asked our destination, and we told her we were
going to Memphis. I couldn't resist; I told her we were going to
see Elvis. She said she hoped we had better luck than she did.
She had tried to see him several times when she had a lay-over,
and never even got a glimpse of him. I said, but we're going to
stay at his house. She said, so did I, for hours and hours. I
started to tell her that El was picking us up at the airport, and
almost had the words out, when June hit me in the side with
her elbow, and told me to be quiet. Anyway, I told her that
June was Elvis's girlfriend, and we were staying at his house.
After that, she couldn't do enough for us. Every time she
passed our seats, she stopped to talk. We had a stop in
Greenville, Mississippi, and she said we could get off the plane
and stretch our legs if we wanted to. We were supposed to be
on the ground for fifteen minutes, so we got off and went
looking around the little airport. After about five minutes, she
came yelling for us. The plane was ready to take off. June and
I were a nervous wreck, thinking what if we had missed the
plane. She told us not to worry, she wouldn't let the plane
leave without us. She wouldn't want Elvis to be disappointed.
About ten minutes before we landed in Memphis, she asked if
we would like to see the cockpit and meet the pilot; he was a
fan of Elvis's too. I had a great time. I think that's what I'd like
to do; be a stewardess,' Pat ended, finally taking a deep breath.

'Would you really? You wouldn't be afraid?' Lovie asked.

'Oh, no ma'am! I wouldn't be afraid. I think it would be a fun job.' (That's exactly what Pat did, from 1959 onwards. Her thirty-one-year career ended when Eastern Airlines folded its wings and called it quits in 1990.)

When we arrived at the house on Audubon Drive, the first thing I noticed was the new iron fence, and Elvis running down the driveway to open the gates. Pulling me from the car, he gave me a quick kiss, put his arm around my waist and walked me up to the house. He had been standing in the drive, waiting for our arrival, talking to George Klein, a friend of Elvis's, and Cliff Gleaves, a DJ from Jackson. After a quick introduction he said he'd see them later; he had some very important business to take care of. He then grabbed my hand and we ran through the house straight to his bedroom. *I* was the important business he wanted to take care of. He closed the bedroom door, looked me over, then pulled me down on his bed. Realizing I was uncomfortable with the door closed, he gave me a big kiss, jumped up and opened the door.

'Okay, okay, I forgot how you feel about closed doors,' he said, returning to the bed. We talked, between hugs and kisses, for over an hour.

'Baby, it's so good to have you here. You have no idea how bad I've been missing you. You're just gonna have to move to Memphis with me. That's all there is to it. I can't stand being away from you. I'm not letting you go back to Biloxi.' At that time, going back to Biloxi was the farthest thing from my mind. I was exactly where I wanted to be.

'I've missed you too, Elvis. I'm always wondering where you are, and what you're doing, and if you're okay.'

'I'm okay, baby, and now that you're here, I'm great! I love you, June, I love you!' he said, kissing me all over my face.

'I love you too, Elvis, but I'm worried about you. Your mother is worried about you too.'

'You know how Mama is, June, she worries about every-thing. I promised her I would stay out of crowds; that's why I didn't come to the airport.'

'I figured as much. I told her I was glad she punished you

and made you stay home. She was crying, Elvis, she's afraid something bad is going to happen to you.'

'I can't stay home forever, June, and no matter where I go, there's always a crowd.'

'That's for sure! I can't believe all the people standing around out in front of the house.'

'It's like that most of the time. They come and go in droves. It's like they have visiting hours or something. On weekends it's even worse; I feel like the main attraction at the zoo. I guess we'll just have to get used to it, baby. The way things are going, we might have to live in the jungle like Tarzan and Jane,' he laughed, pounding his chest, emulating the Tarzan yell.

'That's a great idea! Instead of a house full of kids, we could raise a tree-house full of monkeys.'

'Seriously though, June, I don't have a choice in the matter. The public is my career. Crowds are a way of life for me. I can't afford to hibernate.'

'I understand all that, but promise me one thing; promise me you'll be careful.'

'I will, baby, I promise. Nothing's gonna happen to me, June, I've got too much to live for. You're the reason I'm gonna live forever.'

I was feeling very secure, snuggled up tightly next to Elvis, in the middle of his oversized bed. With my head resting on his chest, I was suddenly moved to tears, causing my nose to run. Hearing my sniffling, he put his hand under my chin, lifting my face to meet his.

'What's the matter, baby? Why are you crying?'

'I'm not crying, I'm just happy to see you, that's all.'

'C'mon now June, I know you better than that. What's bothering my little Satnin?'

I had promised myself I wasn't going to mention anything to Elvis about other girls, but it was gnawing at me.

'Sometimes I believe you really do love me, and other times I get this unsure, empty feeling inside.'

'What can I do to make you believe me, baby?'

'I do believe you, sometimes.'

'Sometimes? Why only sometimes?'

'Just the other day I heard on the radio you were having some kind of secret romance with Jayne Mansfield,' I said, spitting out the truth.

'You can't believe all that shit, June! I don't even like Jayne Mansfield; she's not my type! She wants me to be on a TV show with her, but I'm not interested. It's all a bunch of shit! You, of all people, should know me better than that. You know how the press is, baby, you're the only girl for me. I love you more than all the world.' He began singing 'Is It So Strange?' to me, letting me know he had learned all the words to the song I loved.

'Yes, I know, June. One day I'll record it, just for you, I promise,' he said, stroking my face. His soothing voice, singing my song, was the panacea for all my insecurities.

'You know something, baby? You're not the only one with doubts; my whole life is full of 'em. Tell me something, June, would you still love me if I wasn't Elvis Presley? Would you love me if I was still driving a truck?'

'Be serious, Elvis Presley! You know the only reason I love you is because you're famous and have lots of money!' With that remark, he pulled back the covers, threw me a pillow and grabbed one for himself.

'Defend yourself!' he said, giving me a whack upside the head. Kneeling in the middle of the bed we began swapping licks with the pillows. Elvis, being a lot stronger, was taking it easy on me, but I was giving it all I had. Accidentally knocking him to the floor, I decided I'd better run for my life. We looked like the Keystone Cops, running through the house with our pillows in our hands. Lovie joined in the chase, brandishing a broom.

'That's enough! Ya'll stop now, before somebody gets hurt,' she said, stepping in between us. Elvis collapsed on the sofa next to his dad, practically sitting on his lap. Mr Presley wrapped his arms around Elvis and pretended to hold him down.

'Now's your chance, June, get him while you can!' Mr Presley said, joining in our horse-play. It was the first time I ever recall seeing Elvis's handsome dad laughing.

'Let 'em be, June. Come help me straighten up Elvis's bed,' Lovie said, taking me by the arm. 'I'm so glad you're here, little Satnin. It's good to hear my boy laughing again.'

'I'm glad I'm here too, Lovie. I haven't been laughing much either.'

'Promise me you'll look after him, June. He'll listen to you; he thinks you're very wise for your young years.'

'I'll do my best. Elvis is very lucky to have a loving mother like you.'

'I try real hard, June; as hard as I know how.'

29
*H*OME-TOWN MOB

*P*AT, ELVIS AND I went to a movie that night, or at least we tried to. A neighborhood theater was showing a short film of Elvis performing at the Mississippi–Alabama State Fair, which had been held in Tupelo, Mississippi, the previous month. Mrs Presley suggested we use the black limo belonging to the band, because she thought it less recognizable. Elvis gave me money for tickets, while he and Pat went upstairs to a private viewing room. We had been in the theater approximately twenty minutes when two policemen came to get Elvis's car keys. A mob had formed outside the theater, and was tearing the car apart. The police moved the limo to a safe place, but the damage had already been done. The fenders were dented, windows were broken, and the upholstery was shredded. So-called fans were taking pieces of upholstery as souvenirs. After moving the car, the same two policemen came back to the private viewing room. Realizing the crowd was out of control, they thought it would be wise to move Elvis himself to a safer place.

All the excitement had given Pat a nervous bladder. They wanted to escort us safely out, but Pat was in the ladies' room. I couldn't just go off and leave her, so the police took Elvis, saying they would wait outside for us. A theater usher joined me in the search for Pat. By the time we found her, the stairway was blocked with fans and police were everywhere. The usher led us away from the crowd and down the fire escape. We ran to the front of the theater, where several hundred fans had surrounded the police car containing Elvis and the two policemen. Pat began to panic, wanting to run the other way, but I grabbed her by the hand and we pushed and shoved our way to the car.

Elvis, seated between the two policemen in the front seat, spotted us and unlocked the door. I opened the door, dropping Pat's hand, and scrambled into the back of the car. Someone had grabbed Pat by the collar of her blouse and was holding her back. Her buttons popped and she managed to wiggle out, leaving her blouse behind – a little trick she'd seen Elvis use on his Florida tour.

Safely locked in the car, siren blasting and lights flashing, we moved slowly through the crowd. Crouched in the corner as far as she could, Pat was wearing nothing but her little bra. When Elvis turned to make sure we were okay, he saw Pat with her arms folded across her chest and began laughing his head off. One of the policemen gallantly removed his jacket and threw it to her. Shivering, she put the jacket on and started laughing with the rest of us.

Luckily, Elvis had escaped unscathed. Pat, other than being almost nude, was none the worse for wear, but I had a good size scratch on my neck that was beginning to burn. Considering the size of the crowd, the police thought we were lucky to be in the shape we were in.

They drove us to the police station to pick up the limo. The two front windows had been broken and it looked like someone had taken a knife to the front seat. Pat was happy to find her coat on the back seat, exactly as she had left it. She returned the jacket to the policeman, thanking him for his quick response.

When he turned on Audubon Drive, my first thought was Lovie. This would really frighten her. Elvis drove the limo past the house, and we rode around trying to get our stories straight. We unanimously agreed that Elvis's mother shouldn't find out what had happened. Elvis decided to take the limo to his friend, Dewey Phillips. Dewey would take care of the repairs, and Mama would never know. If she asked about the car, we were to say it broke down. On the way to Dewey's house, I asked Elvis to tell me about the service-station incident.

'It all happened real fast, June. After a few punches were thrown, we were all taken to jail. They charged us with disorderly conduct and assault and battery. We each had to post a bond of fifty-two dollars. You know me, June, I hardly ever carry any money. I had your ticket money in my pocket, so that's what I used. The next day we had to go to court. Hopper, you saw his picture in the paper, and a guy who worked with Hopper named Brown, were both fined twenty-five dollars for assault, and I was acquitted. It wasn't my fault. I stopped for gas and a few fans drove in and were blocking the gas pumps. I got out of the car to get some money out of my pocket, to pay for the gas, and this big son of a bitch starts pushing me around. I decked him, and then the other one starts some shit. It was all unnecessary, June, it really was.'

'It's all this "unnecessary shit" that has your mother so worried. Me too, for that matter. Look at this car! Can you honestly tell me that your fans would do something like this? I don't think so. I've been around lots of your fans, and they don't behave this way. Sure, maybe most of the crowd were fans, but I think the damage was done by someone trying to hurt you. Those men from the service station have friends too. Maybe they were trying to get their fifty dollars' worth.'

'I hadn't thought about that. One thing's for sure, they got a hell of a lot more than fifty dollars' worth! Well, it's too late to worry about it now. Dewey will take care of the car, and Mama doesn't have to know.'

Dewey brought us back to Elvis's house. As soon as we walked in the door, Lovie wanted to know why we were home so early.

'It's all June's fault, Mama. There was a big crowd at the show and she wouldn't let me get out of the car. Mmmm,

something smells good! What's cookin'?' Elvis said, kissing his
mother on the cheek, then turning to give us a wink.

'I'm baking some peanut-butter cookies,' Lovie said.
'Would you like some hot chocolate to go with 'em?'

The cookies and chocolate were so delicious I asked Lovie
for the recipes. She said she would give me the cookie recipe,
but the hot chocolate was a family secret. Then she laughed,
showing me the empty chocolate milk carton. The more I was
around Elvis's mom, the more I realized what a special person
she was. I loved everything about this lady.

The theater mob incident made the paper in an article the next
morning; some of which was accurate. Mr Presley, getting to
the paper first, showed the article to Elvis, warning him not to
let his mother see it. The paper stated that Elvis, his date,
Barbara Hearn (Elvis's 'Memphis girlfriend') and a girl known
only as Jane, went to a local theater last night and that fans
had mobbed his Cadillac, jumping on the hood, ripping the
upholstery and denting the fenders. It took police ninety minutes to restore order.

Elvis teased Pat about having her blouse torn off, and the
paper not getting her name right.

'One good thing about it, June, they don't know you're
here. They assumed you were Barbara. That means the
Colonel won't be on my ass about that girl from Biloxi. At
least not for a while.' He removed the entire page, crumpled
it up and threw it in the trash.

Lovie called us in to a big country breakfast and appointed
me to say the blessing. Bacon, sausage, eggs, biscuits and milk
gravy covered the kitchen table.

'June, have you seen Elvis's little monkey yet?' Lovie asked,
passing me the biscuits.

I grabbed my napkin, covered my mouth, filled with coffee,
and began choking, coughing and laughing at the same time.
Lovie's question had reminded me of last summer, on one of our
deep-sea fishing trips, when Elvis had had to use the bathroom.

'Who's in there?' Elvis had asked, finding the door locked.

'I'll be out in a minute, Chief,' cousin Gene answered.

'C'mon man, I gotta go! Quit spankin' your monkey and get out here!' Elvis yelled.

Any phrase linked to masturbation I had always found very offensive, but 'spankin' your monkey', somehow struck me as funny. I didn't know if it was because I was older and more broad-minded, or because Elvis himself had said it.

'No ma'am, I haven't seen Elvis's little monkey,' I managed to choke out.

'It's a cute little thing, but it sure is nasty,' Lovie said, patting me on the back. Now everybody was screaming with laughter.

'You did see it, didn't you?' Lovie asked.

'No ma'am, I haven't seen it. Not yet,' I answered.

'Will somebody tell me what's so funny?' she said, looking from me to Elvis and back to me again. I was so tickled I couldn't say a word. Elvis told her I was laughing at something that happened earlier. After the laughter died down, I managed to regain my composure.

'So when do I get to see your little monkey?' I asked, in a serious tone, looking straight into Elvis's eyes. Holding a glass of milk to his lips, he snorted, and milk came gushing out through his nose. Laughing hysterically, we both had to leave the table. Everyone was laughing except Lovie; she couldn't figure out what was so funny. Elvis and I decided that the only way we could finish our breakfast was not to look at each other and not to talk to each other.

'No look me, no talk me,' I said, returning to the kitchen. It was hard, but we did manage to get through breakfast without any further outburst.

After the meal Mrs Presley suggested we all go to the back porch. Actually it wasn't a porch at all, but a glassed-in room across the back of the house. Elvis had recently purchased a little spider monkey, and had him in a custom-built cage half the size of the room. The little monkey's big black eyes followed my every step. He was so adorable I started talking to him in baby-talk, when all of a sudden he grabbed his long skinny pecker with both hands and began masturbating. Trying not to show our embarrassment Pat and I both screamed and laughed. I covered my blushing face with my hands, and turned my back to the monkey. Lovie held me in her arms and fussed at Elvis for embarrassing us.

'I told you it was a cute little thing, but it sure is nasty,' Lovie said, taking me from the room.

Elvis fell in love with the creature, and had purchased him mainly because he thought he deserved more than the tiny cage he'd been confined in. His new cage was furnished with every kind of trapeze and monkey toy available.

'If Mama had known he was gonna do that, she wouldn't have let you in the room. He don't always do that, June. Evidently he found you attractive. Mama was embarrassed at first, but now she's used to it. She keeps telling me to get him a girlfriend,' Elvis said, catching up to me, laughing it off.

Elvis invited Red West to come and have supper with us that night. Lovie always prepared extra, knowing Red could put away more groceries than Elvis. Red also wanted to know if I had seen Elvis's little monkey.

'Yes, I've seen Elvis's little monkey, Red. I don't think we should talk about it at the dinner table. Do you?'

'Yep! You've seen it all right,' Red laughed.

Later that night, Pat, Red, Elvis and I went to the amusement park. Still feeling stuffed from the big supper, we got on the Ferris Wheel for a nice relaxing ride.

'Hey June!' Pat yelled from the seat above our heads.

'How would you like some mashed potatoes and gravy?' she said, making me believe she was going to throw up. Remembering our last Ferris Wheel incident, I was ready for the ride to be over. And so was Elvis, after hearing a brief but descriptive re-cap of what had happened.

Elvis had a great arm and enjoyed showing off his pitching skills. In no time at all, a small crowd gathered to watch Red and Elvis throwing baseballs in one of the booths. We could hear a voice, somewhere in the background, heckling Elvis about not being big enough to give him a black eye. At this point in Elvis's life, he used initials instead of foul language, in an attempt to protect his public image.

'Just ignore the A.H. [asshole],' he said to Red. Taking their frustrations out on the pyramid of milk bottles, they kept on pitching. Elvis was in complete control, but Red had had just about all he could stand. His face was blood-red when he took off his rings and handed them to Pat. The heckler saw Red coming and started walking up the midway. Elvis turned to find Red, threw his last ball and missed, hitting the padded backdrop with a thud. Pat opened her hand and showed the rings to Elvis.

'Oh shit! Not again!' Elvis said, running after Red. Red and the heckler were having a heated discussion when Elvis intervened.

'Look man, we don't want any trouble, we're just trying to have a good time,' Elvis said, taking Red by the arm. 'C'mon man, let's go throw some more balls,' he went on, softly, trying to soothe Red's anger.

I was never prouder of Elvis than I was at that very moment. He was keeping his promise to me and to his mother. I sighed with relief, thinking it was over, although I admit I wasn't real happy with my self-appointed role as guardian.

Hand in hand, the four of us were walking back to the baseball throw, when the same guy yelled out, 'Hey, pretty boy! It'll take more than you and your big fuckin' bodyguard to make me shut up!'

Hearing that remark, Elvis dropped my hand, turned and went back. He punched the guy once, in the face, knocking him to the pavement. Two park guards came out of nowhere and stood between Elvis and the heckler, sprawled on the ground. Taking the guards' advice, we left the park in a hurry. Checking his knuckles and cussing under his breath, Elvis became concerned about his mother finding out, so we went back to the park to talk to the guards. Elvis was a regular at the park and they didn't want any bad publicity either, so the incident was kept quiet.

Pat and I had been in Memphis less than two days, and we were both feeling the stress. We all stayed home for the next few nights, and I was much happier: I'd already had enough action to last me a lifetime.

We passed the time shooting pool, throwing darts and listening to music. After a while, Elvis started pacing like a wild animal.

'I can't take this shit anymore. I might as well move in with the goddamn monkey!' he screamed, gathering at least a dozen darts in his hands and hurling them into the ceiling. Anyone walking through the den the following day had to beware of falling darts. Lovie finally removed the darts with a broom, promising Elvis the broom would be used on him if he ever pulled a stunt like that again.

The Elvis that I loved was changing, and I was powerless to do anything about it. He would grab my hand and retreat to his room, wanting to slam the door and shut out the world, but always remembering to leave the door ajar, out of respect for my wishes.

Watching Elvis go through this trying period in his life, it was easy to understand how he began relying on prescription drugs to ease his torment. I can only guess, from what I've read, that his abuse of prescription drugs started when he was in the Army, shortly after the death of his mother. His pills – some to make him sleep and others to wake him up – became a vicious cycle.

John Lennon once said, 'Elvis Presley died the day he went in the Army.' Another unnecessary move on the part of Colonel Tom Parker.

30

*R*EBEL WITHOUT A CAUSE

*E*LVIS'S MOOD QUICKLY changed the minute the Jordanaires arrived at his Audubon Drive home to rehearse for the upcoming *Ed Sullivan Show*. He greeted each one with a handshake and a pat on the back before making all the introductions. Within minutes of meeting the talented quartet, I felt as if I had known them for ever. After a brief discussion of business, they went to the den and sat in a tight circle in the middle of the floor. Elvis moved over, making room for me by his side. They practiced the songs they were singing for the Sullivan show until they thought them good enough, then, after a short break, they began singing just for fun. The unmistakable richness of Elvis's voice, blending in harmony with the magnificent voices of the Jordanaires, was, for me, the thrill of a lifetime. Even my goose-bumps had goose-bumps.

Starting out with a few traditional barber-shop quartet selections, to loosen up the vocal chords, the tempo changed to finger-snapping gospel songs. Mrs Presley was sitting on the sofa across the room, facing me and Elvis. This was one time she didn't stay in the kitchen. Feeling overcome with the Holy Spirit, she raised both arms in the air, shouting, '*Hallelujah*!' The rest of us followed in unison with a big 'Amen'.

I loved watching Mrs Presley watching her son; you could almost feel the love coming across the room. Elvis would look at his mother and give her a wink. She would smile and wink back. She knew I was watching and would give me a wink too.

'I love you, June, and Mama loves you too,' he said, giving me a little kiss on the cheek.

When the group paused for a moment, trying to think of what to sing next, Mrs Presley requested 'Amazing Grace'.

'Now you're in for a real treat, baby,' Elvis said, knowing how much I loved close harmony.

They sang every hymn I had ever heard, and some I had never heard before. 'How Great Thou Art', 'The Old Rugged Cross', and 'In The Garden' were among my favorites.

My graduating class had selected the hymn 'In The Garden' for our baccalaureat sermon, and I had sung in the alto section. When they began singing 'In The Garden', feeling confident of every note, I joined in with the group. The Jordanaire who sang alto stopped singing, gave me a nod and a big smile of approval, and allowed me to take his part alone. I wasn't shy at all singing with Elvis, but if someone had told me I had to sing with the Jordanaires, I'm sure my throat would have closed with fright. It was all so spontaneous I didn't have time to get nervous until the song was over. They all applauded me, each one shaking my hand. Elvis, a smile as big as the sun on his face, put his arm around me, pulling me even closer to his side. Feeling the blood rush to my face, I managed a meek smile.

After a singing session lasting close to three hours, my three-hour piece of heaven, the Jordanaires finally said goodnight. They would have liked to have stayed longer, but the tenor and baritone voices were beginning to get a little hoarse. Elvis and I walked the guys out to their car and watched them drive away. His hands started dangling and his fingers twitching as soon as we were back inside the house – a sure sign he was becoming restless again.

Lovie was back in the kitchen making a batch of chocolate chip cookies. Nothing was too much trouble for her boy.

Although Lovie considered me wise beyond my years, I didn't have an inkling of what was going on in Elvis's head. I presumed he needed time alone, and busied myself cleaning what little mess Lovie had made in the kitchen.

'Go tell Elvis the cookies are ready; he likes 'em hot,' she said, taking the first batch of cookies from the oven. She wasn't as concerned with the cookies as much as she was with Elvis being alone. 'An idle mind is the Devil's workshop,' I remembered her saying, earlier that same day.

I went into Elvis's room and found him propped up in the middle of his bed, reading *The Prophet*.

'Remember this?' he smiled, holding up the book. 'I love this book, June, I read it whenever I'm feeling uptight. It helps me relax and forget everything.'

I climbed up on the bed, kissed his forehead, and told him the cookies were ready. He jumped up, raced me to the kitchen, grabbed a few dozen cookies, still warm, and put them in a paper bag. He kissed his mother and told her we were going for a little ride.

'It's almost midnight, Elvis,' she said, not wanting him to leave the house.

'I know, Mama. The rest of the world is sleeping; it'll be okay.'

Because of the late hour, we took the highly recognizable white Eldorado convertible, and drove around for an hour or so, finally ending up on a deserted Mudd Island. As soon as we stopped, Elvis put the convertible top down and took a deep breath of fresh air.

'Looks like something right out of the movies,' he said, looking up at the star-studded sky.

Neither of us feeling the need for conversation, we sat in silence for a long time, enjoying the picture perfect October night.

'It's nights like this that remind me of our good times together,' he said, breaking the silence. 'The times when my life wasn't so damned complicated.'

Instead of Elvis's life settling down, it was becoming more and more hectic. He wasn't happy in Hollywood, having absolutely no control of what was going on around him. His band had been cut from the movie and replaced by local musicians. And to top it off, his close friends the Jordanaires had been replaced by the Ken Darby Trio singing back-up on all the songs in the movie. Elvis referred to this as 'political bullshit' because Darby had written the goddamned silly songs he was forced to sing.

Without warning, his mood changed from serious to silly, expressing a desire for a magic potion that would turn him into the Invisible Man.

'If I were invisible, I could go anywhere and never have to worry about anything,' he said, laughing happily at such a notion.

'I wish you could be invisible for a while, just to see how people behave when you're not around. Not so much the boys, but the girls. Something about you seems to drive girls crazy.'

We were again enjoying the stars in complete silence when a passing tug-boat blasted its horn.

'Was that you, baby? Are you sitting on a frog?' he laughed, holding his nose. I laughed too, trying to hide my embarrassment, until the horn sounded again and I blamed it on him.

'Boy, you should hear my cousin Gene. For a little guy, he sure cuts a loud one,' he said.

'Speaking of the guys; where are they and how are they?' I asked. They were usually as close as his shadow, but so far, I had only seen Red.

'Huh, the CBs? They're probably out somewhere chasing cherries.' I remembered a classmate nicknamed CB because he was always on the make, so my immediate interpretation of CB was 'cherry buster', and I asked Elvis if I was right.

'You're sharp, June, really sharp,' he answered.

(When Elvis adopted the 'TCB' logo, in later years, I had to laugh. Knowing how he loved an inside joke, I knew it couldn't stand for 'Takin' Care Of Business'; if so, he would have included the 'O'. Recently, I was an invited guest at a Fan Club Convention in Orlando, Florida, and was introduced to a monster of a man who, at one time, had been Elvis's hairdresser. When I asked him about the TCB logo, he neither confirmed nor denied my suspicions. 'The only thing I can say, June, is – you knew him very well, very well indeed!')

We had been parked on Mudd Island for at least three hours. Not used to keeping such late hours, I was falling asleep on Elvis's shoulder when he began telling me about his new friend, the actor Nick Adams. Nick, the only member of the 'Rebel' group that Elvis considered his true friend, was coming to Memphis for a visit.

'You'll like him, June, he's a real funny little guy. He had a bit part in *Rebel Without a Cause*, and was good friends with James Dean. He's even writing a book on Dean's life.' Elvis said, bragging on his new-found friend.

We didn't know it at the time, but Nick had been singled out by Colonel Parker as the weakest link in the chain of Rebels, and assigned to spy on Elvis and report back to him. A struggling actor, with no money, Nick's expenses were paid by the Colonel.

A big fan of James Dean, Elvis thought the late actor was the greatest, after Marlon Brando, to ever hit Hollywood. Elvis's common bond with Nick Adams was their admiration for Dean. Elvis knew the meaning of hard times, and because of the vast differences in their backgrounds, had difficulty relating to the rest of the 'Rebel' group. He wasn't nearly as shy as people thought him to be. His slight stutter was due in part to his lack of confidence as a conversationalist. With me, his stuttering stopped. I was as down to earth as down to earth could be, and definitely not one for throwing around ten-dollar words; probably because I only had a hundred dollars' worth to throw around.

It was close to 4 A.M. when we left Mudd Island. While we were putting the top up on the car, I discovered the bag of cookies, now cold and crispy, on the back seat. Munching on the cookies, we drove past a milk truck making home deliveries. Elvis made a U-turn and parked behind the delivery truck. When the delivery man returned, Elvis asked if he could buy a quart of milk. When he reached in his pocket he discovered, as usual, that he had no money. The milkman

recognized Elvis and asked him to autograph an IOU, which
he gladly did. On the way home we drank the cold milk from
the bottle, sharing a milk mustache. Elvis wiped the milk from
his upper lip with the back of his hand; the same way James
Dean had done in *Rebel Without a Cause*. I had to do the
same; we didn't have napkins.

'When I was a little boy, I used to go to the store for a quart
of milk, and before I got home all the cream was gone from
the top. Did you ever do that?' he asked.

'Boy, that brings back memories. I remember peeling back
that little cardboard stopper and sucking all the cream too. I'd
probably do it today, if I could find some pasteurized milk.
Wouldn't you?' I asked, licking my lips.

'I don't know who came up with the idea of homogenized
milk, but they sure took all the fun out of it,' he laughed.
Raising the bottle to his lips, he drank his fill, handing the rest
to me. With only a tiny bit left, I had to tilt my head back and
hold the bottle vertical, causing milk to splash from my nose
to my chin. Elvis placed his hand under my chin to catch the
dripping milk, then kissed away the rest, laughing between
licks.

Daylight was just beginning to break when we pulled into
the driveway. Trying not to disturb anyone, we tiptoed in the
house and down the hallway, only to find Lovie with her head
sticking out of her partially opened bedroom door.

'Is that you, Elvis? It's about time you love-birds were getting home. I've been worried,' she whispered.

'We're okay, Mama, go back to sleep,' he said softly, walking to the end of the hall and kissing her cheek.

31
*B*IG BOYS' TOYS

*A*FTER ONLY A few hours' sleep, I woke to the aroma of freshly brewed coffee. I helped myself to a cup and joined Lovie at the kitchen table. She wasn't real pleased about us staying out so late, but after telling her about the milkman she was back to her good-natured, easy-going self. I thought Mr Presley was still sleeping until he came through the door, his arms filled with three large bags of groceries. He immediately began putting the groceries away, and Lovie jumped up from the table to help.

'Go read your paper, Vernon, I'll take care of this,' she said, shooing him out of the kitchen. 'I don't know why I let him go to the store, June. He knows whole chickens cost less, but look what he gets,' she said, showing me the two trays of cut-up fryers.

'Are we having fried chicken tonight?' I asked, thinking at any moment I'd start clucking, we'd had so much of it.

'It depends on what Elvis is in the mood for,' she answered. I volunteered to clean the chicken and was standing at the sink when Elvis walked up behind me and put his arms around my waist.

'Get away! June is washing chicken!' Lovie screamed. Elvis backed off, let out a disgusted '*Yuk*!' and left the room.

'What was that all about?' I asked.

'Elvis is funny like that, June. He won't eat chicken if he sees it before it's cooked,' Lovie said, shrugging her shoulders. I finished cleaning the chicken and put it in a covered bowl in the refrigerator. I found Elvis in the den, reading the morning paper, and started teasing him about the raw chicken and having a weak stomach.

'It's not a matter of a weak stomach, June. It's a matter of bad memories. Did you ever have to kill and pluck a chicken?'

'I never did kill one, but I helped my mother pluck one.'

'How could you stand that smell, June? When you stick that dead chicken down in boiling hot water, and the steam hits you in the face. Yuk! That's the most disgusting smell in the whole world. I didn't mind chasing them around the back yard, throwing them over the clothes line, even wackin' off their heads and waiting for 'em to stop flapping blood all over the place; that part was easy. It was that God-awful smell I couldn't stand. Did you wash your hands good, with soap?' he asked, taking both of my hands and putting them to his nose. Now *my* stomach was getting queasy, thinking about the raw chicken; I too could remember that nasty smell.

'Are we having fried chicken again? We had fried chicken a few nights ago. I like fried chicken, but not every other day,' Elvis said, screwing up his nose.

'How about I'll fix the chicken tonight?' I suggested. He took me by the hand and led me to the kitchen.

'Mama, June's gonna fix the chicken tonight,' he announced.

'Good!' she answered. 'How you gonna fix it?'

'Smothered with brown gravy, if that's okay.'

'Sounds good to me. We all like chicken, any way it's fixed. Anything special you need?'

'You probably have everything I need. Do you have any bouillon cubes? Maybe some green onions, celery and parsley,' I added, giving it a little more thought.

'What the hell is a bouillon cube, June?' Elvis asked.

'It's a little cube you mix with water. It tastes like chicken broth, and gives the gravy a good flavor. Normally you'd use a hen for stewing, but we have fryers so I'll use bouillon cubes. Does that answer your question?' I asked, seeing the confused look on Elvis's face.

'Your answer was so long, June, I forgot the question. Sounds like a bunch of bull-ony to me.'

Everyone enjoyed dinner that evening, and Lovie commented on what a nice change it was to have rice and gravy instead of the mashed potatoes Elvis always requested.

'You can do the cooking any time you want, June,' she said, grateful for a break from the stove.

The next day, after another enormous breakfast, Elvis pulled out a large box filled with a collection of gasoline-powered toys: cars, trucks, airplanes, and race cars; a little boy's dream come true. When Elvis thought the neighborhood was awake, we went outside and raced the noisy little vehicles up the driveway, always starting at the front gate so they would slow down when they hit the grass. Elvis used a pull rope, similar to those used on lawnmowers, to start the little engines. Pat and I were no help starting the engines; we were afraid the propellers might cut off our fingers.

Elvis had us running our legs off. He did the racing, we did the chasing. After several trips into the house for iced water, Lovie made us a pitcher of lemonade to keep outside. We played with the little vehicles until a crowd began gathering at the front gate. Elvis was pacing to and from the front door, keeping an eye on the crowd outside. When it finally thinned out, he jumped in the car, announcing 'I'll be right back.' An hour later, he returned driving a pick-up truck with a male passenger in the front, and a Hammond organ strapped in the back.

'Where do we put this, Mama?' he asked, grinning like a little boy. They shifted the furniture in the den around, making room for Elvis's new toy. He sat at the organ, experimenting with every sound, for the next few hours.

Elvis's organ-playing was briefly interrupted by a phone call from Nick Adams. Nick was at Memphis airport, expecting Elvis to pick him up.

'Okay, good man. We're kind of tied up here, right now, so

jump in a taxi and I'll have someone looking out for you at the front gate,' he said to Nick, then went to the side door to inform his security guard, Bitsy Mott.

I had recognized Bitsy the moment we arrived at Audubon Drive, but it took me a while to remember where I'd seen this familiar face before. Then I remembered – it was on the Florida Tour. Bitsy, like Colonel Parker, also hung out in the theater lobbies, peddling Elvis pictures and programs.

It wasn't until doing research for this book that I learned Bitsy Mott was the Colonel's brother-in-law, and, like Nick Adams, was also a paid informer. On one of the colder October nights during my stay with Elvis, I volunteered to take a hot cup of coffee out to Bitsy, only because Lovie had her hands full in the kitchen.

'Thanks, June. It is June, isn't it? From Biloxi, right?' Bitsy said when I handed him the coffee. I thought he was just being friendly, but really he was getting his facts straight before reporting back to the Colonel.

Nick Adams arrived, wearing sunglasses – even though the sun was on its way down – looking like Mr Hollywood with his California suntan. When Elvis had referred to Nick as a 'nice little guy', I thought it was because Nick was young, but it wasn't that at all. Nick was indeed a little guy. Even in his stacked shoes, Nick and I stood eye to eye when I was in my bare feet, and I'm only five feet six inches tall.

Nick appeared to be much older than Elvis, probably because of his receding hairline. But he didn't act older: he was as silly as we were, even more so at times. Nick was constantly cracking jokes in the voices of Mr Magoo, Walter Brennan, and even Sylvester the Cat. His more serious impressions were John Wayne and Marlon Brando. Keeping us laughing most of the time, Nick had no problem fitting right in with the rest of us.

Whenever Elvis was home for a reasonable amount of time, he would make arrangements to visit the local children's hospital. Signing autographs and visiting with the seriously ill children, even though it was depressing, gave Elvis a lot of gratification.

On this particular day, Elvis invited Nick to join him for a hospital visit. As they drove through the gate, the crowd of fans followed behind. While everyone was gone, Pat and I decided to race the little cars. It took a while, but I finally got the little red racer started. Nervous about holding the loud little machine in my hand, I quickly placed it on the driveway, about ten feet from the iron gate, and let it go. In my excitement, I had it facing in the wrong direction. Like a bolt of lightning it roared off and crashed, wedging itself half-way under the iron gate. Little pieces of red plastic were scattered all over the driveway. In a panic, we took all the vehicles out of the box and put what was left of the little red racer, pieces and all, in the bottom of the box. I didn't know what I was going to tell Elvis about the red racer, if he discovered it, but I knew he would. It was not only the fastest, but also his favorite.

When he and Nick returned from the hospital, he immediately got out the box of toys and took them to the front gate. He pulled them out, one by one, showing them to Nick. When he saw the little red racer, or what was left of it, in the bottom of the box, he looked at Pat and then at me. I was trying to keep a straight face, pretending not to know anything about it.

'Okay, June, you wanna tell me how it happened?' he asked, seeing the guilt on my face like a neon sign. Still trying to keep a straight face, I burst out laughing.

'I couldn't tell the front from the back, and when I let it go I expected it to go up the driveway, but it didn't; it went the other way. It almost fit under the gate; almost! I'm sorry, I really am. I didn't mean to hurt it; and I don't know why I laughed,' I said, still trying to control my nervous laughter.

'It's okay, baby, it was only my favorite,' he said, picking up the smashed little racer, hugging it to his chest and pretending to cry.

32

$\mathscr{S}$KIN FLICKS

ELVIS RECEIVED A phone call from Dewey Phillips later that evening, and the four of us – Nick, Pat, Elvis and I – piled in the car and headed for Dewey's house. Elvis was so anxious to get there I figured the black limo must have been repaired and was ready to be picked up. As soon as we walked in the house, I could see a projector and screen set up in the den. Elvis introduced everyone and instructed me and Pat to stay in the living room with Mrs Phillips and the children, while he and Nick joined Dewey and several other men in the den.

Pat and I sat watching the children play on the floor, while making small talk with Mrs Phillips. We waited for what seemed like for ever, and finally one of the men came out of the room. I was facing the den and could see nude bodies on the screen when the door was opened. I felt the blood rush to my face; not from embarrassment, but from anger. I sat quietly, hoping it would be over soon; not really knowing what to do. My neck was aching from gritting my teeth and I had fingernail marks on the palms of both hands from clenching my fists. Finally I'd had enough. I went to the door, knocked a few times, then opened it wide. All heads immediately turned in my direction. Assuming my 'Elvis position', I stared blankly at the screen. Elvis jumped out of his folding chair, stumbling over other chairs, and stood in front of me.

'What the hell are you doing, June? I don't want you watching this shit!' he said, taking me by the arm and closing the door behind us.

'You can watch that shit as long as you want, Elvis, but first you can take me and Pat home,' I demanded.

'Okay, baby. I was ready to leave anyway. Let me go get Nick.'

'Don't be long!'

He knew I was mad as hell, and started apologizing as soon as we got in the car.

'I'm sorry, baby. Dewey said he had something he wanted me to see. I didn't know it was skin flicks,' he said, softly, not wanting Nick, in the back seat, to hear.

'You can go back if you want to; I just don't want to be in the same house,' I answered, not caring who could hear.

'You tell him, June! Shame on you, Elvis, embarrassing all of us like that,' Nick said, laughing like it was all a big joke. Pat, not having seen the screen, joined in laughing with Nick.

'If ya'll are trying to make me out to be a stick-in-the-mud, then ya'll can kiss my ass,' I said, now laughing too. Elvis cooed and gooed, pulling me next to him, changing the subject, and the incident was never mentioned again.

When we got back to the house, Elvis and Nick visited and signed autographs for the ever-present fans lined up along the fence. Pat and I also visited with some of the girls. They were at the gate every afternoon after school, and by this time their faces had become familiar to us. Elvis knew all the regulars and called them by name.

The three of us went inside and watched a horror movie on television, but Nick stayed at the fence, talking to the girls; probably trying to gather a few fans of his own. Elvis left the side door open for Nick and instructed Bitsy to remind Nick to lock up. Leaving the guest room light on for him, Elvis slept in the bed with me and Pat.

We were in the middle of breakfast the next morning when Nick came in, still half asleep, but hungry enough to get out of bed. Elvis teased him about flirting with the girls all night long, and not getting enough sleep. When Lovie got up from the table to fix Nick some scrambled eggs, Elvis really got upset.

'Sit down, Mama, and finish your breakfast. If Nick wants eggs, he can fix his own. If you went to bed at night and left the girls alone, you'd be here in time to eat,' he said, this time addressing Nick. 'Do you ever think of anything but girls?'

'I've got other things on my mind too, Elvis. Will you please pass the pusscuits?' Nick said, calmly.

Lovie was the first to laugh. You had to admire the way Nick's charm and wit had gotten him out of an uncomfortable situation.

Alberta was running the vacuum cleaner through the house, so we all went into Elvis's bedroom to get out of her way. Lovie came in to find Nick and ask him to unpack his things and put them away. Nick had two large suitcases and an overnight bag, wide open and laying in the middle of the floor. It looked like he was planning to stay a while.

'Alberta wants to clean the guest room, Nick. Would you mind unpacking all your things and putting them away. I'd do it for you, but I don't like meddling in other people's things. There's plenty of room in the closet, and lots of drawer space,' she said sweetly, thanking him and leaving the room.

'That boy sure is messy,' she said to me, the next time we were alone.

Nick didn't seem to mind the mess at all. Reluctantly, he got up from his sprawled position in the middle of Elvis's bed and went in to unpack. He returned about ten minutes later, holding a dress.

'I almost forgot, Natalie sent you a souvenir, Elvis,' Nick said, prancing around the room, holding the dress up to his shoulders.

I recognized the dress from a recent photograph of Natalie Wood in a movie magazine. It was a tight-fitting white, black and red floral print, with a split up one side, slightly Oriental. Just my style – but definitely not my size. Nick announced the

dress had been made by Natalie's personal dress-maker; the
same one who made the blue velvet shirt Elvis wore at the
Mississippi–Alabama State Fair. Being a seamstress myself, I
turned the dress inside out, inspecting the workmanship. It
was definitely well made. But then again, it should be; this
lady was a professional. The dress didn't have a label. I
guessed it to be maybe a size one, no larger than a three. On
the silver screen, Natalie appeared to be my size, but in reality she must have been even more petite than Pat.

'You should see her in this dress, June. Boy oh boy, does she
fill it out,' Nick said, taking the dress from me.

'I know, Nick. I saw a picture of her in that same dress and
it fitted her like a glove. She looked great!' I answered.
Pushing Elvis's clothes to either side, Nick found a hanger
and placed the dress in the center of Elvis's closet.

Nick was trying to make me jealous, and I couldn't understand why. I refused to let him get to me and went along with
everything he said – I could play his little game better than he
could. I was secure enough in my relationship with Elvis, and
didn't consider Natalie to be a threat. She was cute enough,
but definitely not his type. Elvis winked at me for being a
good sport.

Later, when Elvis and I were alone, I asked him what Nick
was trying to prove.

'I don't think Nick likes me,' I said. 'I wish you would've
invited him to come visit some other time when I wasn't here.'

'I didn't invite him, June; he more or less invited himself.
He's okay, baby. He's just a lonesome little guy struggling to
make it in Hollywood. Keep being nice to him, June, he needs
friends,' Elvis said, showing his tender side. He always felt
sorry for the underdog.

Nick was hard to figure out. Around Elvis, he was light-
hearted and funny. But when Elvis wasn't around, he was
very serious, constantly asking me personal questions to the
point of being downright nosey. He knew things about me he
could only have heard from Elvis, and Elvis wasn't much of a
talker when it came to his personal life, so I figured he must
have been pumping Elvis for information as well.

'Just how serious is it between you and Elvis, June? Do you two plan to get married any time soon, or what?' he asked.

'Nick, I know you're supposed to be writing a book about James Dean. Are you thinking of writing one about me too?' I answered politely, evading his questions. 'If you want to know anything about Elvis and me, I suggest you ask Elvis. If I didn't know better, I'd swear you were a reporter,' I said, laughing him off. Nick would laugh too, but then he keep on talking.

'I'm just a curious guy, June. I like people and I like to know everything there is to know about them. I'd just like to get to know you better, that's all,' he said softly, trying to make his remarks seem complimentary.

Nick even asked Pat if Elvis and I were sleeping together. She told him it was none of her business and none of his business either, stopping him dead in his tracks.

When I complained to Elvis about Nick's constant badgering, he told me not to pay him any attention.

'He don't mean anything by it, June. That's just the way he is. He's always asking me questions too. Sometimes I answer, and sometimes I tell him to shut his mouth before he drives me crazy enough to shut it for him.'

Nick was like Elvis's shadow. If we wanted to spend some time alone, Elvis had to tell Nick to go find something to do; usually suggesting he do a little PR at the front gate. Nick loved being the big shot, signing autographs, even though they were all Elvis fans.

Having heard all about Lovie's delicious fried chicken, Nick requested fried chicken for dinner one day. That night, in the dining room, Elvis pulled out a chair for his mother, flapped his arms, and whispered 'cluck, cluck' in her ear. Everyone was in a good mood, and half-way through the meal, Nick started telling a joke. When he accidentally used the word 'fuck', in front of Mr and Mrs Presley, Elvis leaned across the table and slapped him across the top of his head.

'Nick, you'd better shove some of those mashed potatoes in your mouth before I do!' Elvis warned. Even with the California suntan, we could see Nick's face turning red. He lowered his head, eating all the mashed potatoes without coming up for air. He then apologized to everyone for the slip of the tongue.

'May I have some more potatoes, Mrs Presley?'

'Why, Nick? Are you getting ready to say it again?' Lovie responded, putting Nick at ease and making everyone laugh.

33

$\mathcal{H}$OLLYWOOD SMILES

ELVIS HAD GIVEN me and Pat his master bedroom, so naturally we were also using the master bath. Our personal things were neatly grouped on the long ceramic-tiled vanity. One morning, while brushing my teeth, I noticed a glass of water with something strange soaking in it. Looking through the side of the glass, it looked like false teeth, but looking down into it the teeth seemed to disappear. I learned later that the curved, thin strip of teeth belonged to Nick. It was his Hollywood smile.

Nick gave us a demonstration by slipping the strip over his natural teeth and smiling like a Cheshire cat. The teeth made a definite improvement over Nick's not-so-bright smile. Elvis then announced that he too had some Hollywood teeth. I didn't believe him until he pulled two tiny teeth from his mouth. The cosmetic caps were used whenever he was in front of the camera. Smiling with and without the teeth, he showed me the difference, which I thought was negligible: Elvis had a pretty smile without them. His two natural teeth next to his front teeth were a tiny bit smaller than they should've been; at least that's what the Hollywood experts thought. But the caps did help even out his perfect smile.

However, he had one major problem with his two tiny

teeth; he couldn't eat with them, and Elvis was always snacking on something. He had several sets made, but they were always getting either lost or broken. He would remove the teeth, put them in his shirt pocket, and forget about them. Every time Alberta did the laundry, the teeth were either broken or went down the drain. He was losing, on average, a pair a day.

One afternoon, clowning around, we both put on a pair of boxing gloves and used the empty swimming pool as our ring – his suggestion, because I was hitting him and running away. In the pool, however, I couldn't run very far. Showing a little mercy, he put himself at a disadvantage by using only his left hand. I connected with a good left hook, right to his mouth, and he immediately called for a time out. He removed his cosmetic caps and carefully placed them on the top rung of the pool ladder. Pat came out to watch the boxing match, and decided a safe place to sit was between the hand-rails of the ladder. She stepped on one of the caps, crushing it like an egg shell, and knocked the other one in the pool. Like Humpty Dumpty, it didn't survive the long fall. Our day had just begun and already he'd lost four teeth. His average was improving.

Growing up with a brother who had been a Golden Glove boxing champion, it wasn't my first time engaging in the sport of pugilism, and I was pretty adept defensively as well as offensively. My brother had a speed bag, a small punching bag, mounted in our back yard, and I could literally make it sing.

Elvis had to start using both hands to protect himself from my straight left jab. Countering with his right (which was supposed to be behind his back), he hit me a few times in the face, forcing me to run up the slope to the shallow end of the pool. Lovie saved the day by telling us all to come in and get dressed in our Sunday best.

We were invited to have dinner with some friends of Mr and Mrs Presley, and she insisted we wear our Sunday-go-to-meeting clothes. Elvis was truly beautiful in his charcoal suit.

'You two have got to be the most beautiful couple in the

whole world,' Lovie said, seeing me and Elvis standing side by side.

'Ain't that the truth!' the normally taciturn Mr Presley exclaimed. Pat made a similar comment, while Nick, silent for a change, flashed us his Hollywood smile.

I had deliberately chosen a royal blue dress, my own creation, because of its similarity to the dress Nick had brought to Elvis as a souvenir. The dress had three-quarter sleeves, and the split up the side wasn't as high, but otherwise they were very similar in design.

So far Nick had only seen me in casual, loose-fitting clothes. Not that I valued his opinion, but suddenly I wanted him to know I could fill out a dress too. Feeling confident about my appearance, I returned Nick's Hollywood smile with a vindictive little wink.

I can't remember the names of the people who had invited us to dinner, but I do remember referring to them as Mr and Mrs Nutriment. The Presleys' friends were excited about their corporation being involved in a new product, Nutriment, a food supplement that provided a completely balanced, nutritional meal in a can. You could drink it in place of a meal to lose weight, or with a meal to gain weight. This turned out to be the main topic of conversation at the dinner table.

Mrs Presley, knowing how silly we could be at times, made us promise to be on our best behavior. We arrived just in time to be seated at a long dining-room table covered with a beautiful lace table-cloth. 'Make sure your food stays on your plate, June,' I thought to myself. A centerpiece of freshly cut flowers and silver candlesticks complemented the beautifully set table. It was another first for me. I had never before dined on fine china, eaten with silver cutlery or drank from crystal glasses. Mrs Presley had nice dishes, but hadn't as yet gotten into the finer things. A gorgeous crystal chandelier hung directly over the table, and an array of desserts were arranged on the buffet, with candelabra on each end. Simply put, it was awe-inspiring elegance.

The Presleys and the Nutriments did most of the talking; mostly the Nutriments, about business. Elvis said an occasional 'yes ma'am', 'no sir', and 'thank you'. I just smiled a lot.

Before starting with a fruit cup, Elvis inconspicuously removed his two little teeth and handed them to me.

'Hold these, baby, I can't afford to lose another pair,' he whispered. I didn't have a pocket, and the housekeeper had taken my purse and coat, so I placed the teeth in my lap under my lace-edged napkin.

After the main meal, Mrs Nutriment asked us to select the dessert of our choice from the buffet. Remembering the teeth Elvis had entrusted to me, I held them in my hand before standing up. Elvis wanted a piece of chocolate cake and asked if I would slice it for him. I needed two hands to slice the cake and place it on a plate, so I put the two teeth in my mouth for safe-keeping. As soon as I returned to the table with our cake I sat down, wondering what to do with the teeth. When I was sure no one was looking, I placed one tooth on each side of my mouth. Holding them in place with my lips, I looked just like a vampire. Pat and Nick, sitting across from me and Elvis, just happened to be looking in my direction, but Elvis was so busy enjoying his cake I had to nudge him to get his attention. He took one look, gulped the bite of cake, and screamed with laughter.

The Presleys and the Nutriments were standing at the buffet, trying to decide which dessert to select, and had no idea what the outburst of laughter was all about. Knowing we were supposed to be on our best behavior made matters worse. I excused myself and went in the adjoining room, with Pat, Nick and Elvis following right behind. The harder we tried to get ourselves under control, the harder we laughed. We returned to the dining room, each of us refusing to look at the others, and took our seats.

Up to that point, everyone being too prim and proper, the dinner party had been as stiff as an over-starched collar. My silly stunt turned out to be a great ice-breaker after Elvis insisted I do it again.

'It's about time you kids relaxed and had some fun,' Mr Nutriment said, laughing as hard as the rest of us.

After midnight that same night, the six of us went to a private
rough-cut screening of *Love Me Tender*. The film, lasting about
thirty minutes, was the first time Elvis had seen himself on the
big screen. He wasn't overly excited about the way he looked,
and complained of things no one else had even noticed. Lovie
and I both tried to assure him the movie was good, and he was
good too, but good wasn't what he wanted; he wanted great.

'If I could just get them to cut some of those damn silly
songs, I'd like it a whole lot better,' he complained.

Leaving the theater, on the way back to the car, Elvis got
between me and his mother and put his arms around us both.

'I've got my two favorite girls, what more could I ask for?
Everything's gonna be okay, right, Mama? Right, June?' he
said, trying to convince us all. Mr Presley, Pat and Nick were
walking right behind us. 'Everything will be okay,' Mr Presley
and Pat agreed, but Nick took a different line.

'Quit being so damn hard on yourself, man, and give it
some time. I'd give anything to have a leading role. I've been
working my ass off, trying to prove myself, and getting nothing but bit parts that end up on the cutting-room floor. After
this, you can call your own shots about what you like and
what you don't like. You've proved yourself as an actor, man.
Don't worry about it!' he raged theatrically.

I immediately detected a note of jealousy in Nick's voice,
but Elvis, hanging on his every word, took it as a compliment.
Whatever it was, Nick's approval made him feel better about
himself. I had the urge to look Nick in the face and tell him to
shut the hell up, but remembering my promise to be nice to
the lonesome little guy – 'he needs friends' – I clenched my
teeth and kept on walking.

The next morning I phoned the airlines and made reservations for me and Pat to fly home, the same day Elvis was
scheduled to leave for New York to do the *Ed Sullivan Show*.
Insisting I go with him to New York, Elvis phoned the airlines
and cancelled my reservations.

'You have plenty of time to decide, June. You don't need to
make reservations now,' he said, pleased with himself for taking charge.

'But the airlines told me to make my reservations at least two days in advance. I'm just doing as I was told.'

'Relax, baby, you can get a reservation thirty minutes before you leave. Don't pay any attention to them. I know!'

I didn't know about this New York thing. It was all news to me. The thought of being so far away from home frightened me, and I kept thinking of all the reasons why I shouldn't go.

For one thing, my mother had agreed to let me spend ten days in Memphis with Elvis and his family. I couldn't go to the biggest city in the world; I was a small-town girl. And besides that, I didn't have enough warm clothes to be going way up north. Elvis didn't take the word 'no' very well, and considered my excuses to be lame.

'June's just like me, Elvis. I don't like going to big cities either, so leave her alone,' Lovie said in my defense.

'Okay, okay. If you won't go with me, at least stay here until I get back. You'll get to meet Natalie; she's coming to visit for a few days,' Elvis said, thinking I would be thrilled about meeting a big movie star like Natalie Wood.

Nick butted in so fast I didn't have time to answer.

'Wait a minute, Elvis, if June's going to stay, I'd better call Natalie so she can make arrangements to come at a later time. You don't have room enough for all of us.'

'Don't worry, Nick! I'm not staying!' I said, leaving the kitchen and going to Elvis's room. I felt like my blood was boiling when I picked up the phone and made my reservations again. Elvis and Nick, following behind, came into the room, just as I was hanging up the phone. Elvis, not in a very polite tone, told Nick to leave us alone for a while.

'Please stay, baby. I want you to be here when I get back.'

'I've already made up my mind, Elvis. When you leave, I'm going home. You heard Nick; there's not enough room for me and Natalie.'

'Baby, I didn't invite Natalie, Nick invited her. He can call and tell her not to come. It's all for publicity purposes anyway; nothing more, I promise.'

'To be perfectly honest, Elvis, I'd like to meet Natalie, but there's not enough room here for me and Nick Adams. When he leaves I'll come back,' I answered angrily.

'Okay, June, if that's the way you want it,' he said, sharply.

'That's the way it's going to be,' I answered, even more sharply. When Elvis left the room I threw myself across the bed and buried my face in the pillow, too angry to cry. We were polite but cool to each other for the rest of the day. It didn't take long for Lovie to notice something was definitely wrong between Elvis and me.

'Come have a cup of coffee, little Satnin. Let's talk about what's bothering you two,' Lovie said, stroking my face.

I asked if she had seen the dress in Elvis's closet, and told her about Nick inviting Natalie, and his comment about not having enough room for all of us. After getting that off my chest, I began getting a bad case of self-pity and had a hard time talking through a quivering lower lip.

'Nick insisted there wasn't room for Natalie if I was going to be here. He said he'd call Natalie and tell her to come later, after I was gone. He keeps telling me that in order for Elvis to get ahead in this business, he has to be seen with other girls, and not just me all the time. He thinks I'm not good for Elvis's career. He's trying to come between us, Lovie, I can tell,' I said, between sobs.

'Now, now, little Satnin, dry your pretty eyes and don't worry about a thing. I'll take care of Elvis. I just wish he'd be a little more careful about choosing his friends,' she said, handing me a Kleenex.

'I don't think Elvis chose Nick, Lovie, I think Nick chose Elvis.'

'I think you're right. He's such a pushy little feller. I wish someone would let me know something once in a while. I never know what's going on around here any more. Don't worry, little Satnin, Lovie's gonna fix everything. I promise!'

By this time I was emotionally drained, so Lovie suggested I go in Elvis's room and take a little nap. To avoid seeing Elvis, sitting in the den, I went through the living room and down the hallway to his room. I didn't have to worry about Nick seeing me in tears; he was out at the front gate, as usual.

Instead of laying across the bed, I stripped down to my undies and snuggled under the covers in a foetal position, falling sound asleep. I had been sleeping a good while when Elvis came in the room and woke me with a kiss.

'I love you more than anything in the world, baby. Let's not fight.'

'I love you too, Elvis, and I hate fighting.'

He lay next to me, on top of the covers, and kissed my slightly swollen, bloodshot eyes, commenting how much bluer my eyes were with a touch of red. We settled our differences and walked out of the room an hour later, holding hands.

Lovie was so happy to see we'd patched things up that she stood up from her usual spot at the kitchen table and came over between us, hugging and kissing us both.

Everything had been going great between Elvis and me until Nick barged in to our lives. I was determined to get things back the way they were – by pretending he didn't exist. However, he did serve one good purpose; he was good company for Pat. Not having much else to do, Pat would join Nick at the front gate and visit with the fans too. She was even signing autographs along with Nick.

Tired of being cooped up all day, Elvis was looking for an excuse to get out of the house, and called Nick and Pat to come inside.

'Lets go see what the competition is doing,' Elvis suggested. The four of us jumped in the pink car and drove to a downtown record shop. Pat and I stopped in the front of the store to look at some merchandise in the display case. Nick, on Elvis's heels, worse than a bloodhound, followed him to the record section in the rear of the store.

Feeling the need to treat myself to something nice, I asked the clerk to show me a tiny transistor radio that caught my eye. No larger than the palm of my hand, the tiny radio was a pale lavender, almost completely covered with rhinestones. I said 'thank you' and handed it right back. The price tag was lots more than the fifty-one dollars I had in my purse. We joined Elvis in the record section and helped pick out some new releases. We left the store with at least twenty new singles, none of which were Elvis's, and three new albums, including a new Platters album to replace the one we'd worn out.

Listening to the records in Elvis's room, he waited until my favorite song, 'Unchained Melody', dropped on the turntable, and, singing along with the record, handed me a small package wrapped in white paper and tied with a pink satin ribbon.

'Happy birthday, baby. I know your birthday isn't until next month, but I probably won't get to spend it with you.'

'Thank you, my love,' I said with a kiss, clutching the package to my breast.

I was going to wait and open it on my birthday, but he insisted I open it right then. Much to my surprise, it was the little rhinestone radio I had admired in the store.

'I saw you looking at it when we were in the record shop. I hope you like it,' he said, with a big smile on his face.

'Like it? I don't like it. I love it!' I shouted. I tore myself from his arms and ran to the kitchen to show Lovie.

'I saw it already, June. I'm the one who wrapped it. It's the cutest little thing I've ever seen,' she said, her smile beaming.

I turned it on and just happened upon a station playing 'Hound Dog', of all things. I ran back to the bedroom, yelling for Elvis to listen. Nick, the asshole, got up from the floor and turned up the volume on the hi-fi. I felt like telling him to go back outside and sign some more autographs; that the fans weren't choosy, they were even glad to get Pat's autograph. I didn't. Instead, I held my tongue and pretended he didn't exist. Elvis had to go with me in the hallway to hear what the little radio was playing.

Nick pulled a few more underhanded stunts, always behind Elvis's back, over the next few days; all of which I tried to ignore. Try as I might, I could never figure out what Nick had against me. Determined to be a bigger person than he, I was nice to the little guy, but only because Elvis had asked me to be.

Due to the pre-Sullivan photo session and news interviews, arranged by Colonel Parker, our final two days in Memphis were maddening. Reporters and photographers were arriving by the car-load; each one clamoring for Elvis's undivided attention. Even a representative from RCA was on-hand, presenting Elvis with a gold record of 'Love Me Tender'. It was a real circus! But then, of course, that's what the Colonel was famous for. Elvis took it all in his stride. He had to; he had no other choice.

On the morning of our last day, I woke at the crack of dawn and couldn't go back to sleep. I sneaked quietly to the kitchen, thinking I was the first one up, to put on a pot of coffee, but Lovie had already beat me to it. Knowing Elvis was leaving for New York that afternoon, she too had trouble sleeping.

'This will probably be our last meal together for a while, so I want it to be especially nice,' she said, planning a big breakfast.

She did a quick inventory of the refrigerator and pulled a new sack of flour and a box of grits from the kitchen pantry. We had grits for breakfast more often than we had fried chicken for supper.

Like a true grit-eater from the South, Elvis would make a hole in the mound of grits with the back of his spoon, and fill the hole with margarine. Having been raised on the cheaper spread, Elvis hadn't as yet acquired a taste for the real thing, complaining that real butter always tasted stale.

Lovie happily agreed when I suggested hash brown potatoes instead of grits, and I volunteered to make them. She had plans for every burner on the stove, so I made the hash browns in advance, planning to reheat them in the oven while the biscuits were baking. While I was doing the potatoes she decided to do the biscuits in advance too.

'I'm gonna miss you, June. As soon as Nick leaves, I want you to come back. Okay? When you're here, I don't worry about Elvis as much.'

'Don't worry, Lovie, I'll be back. If for no other reason than to visit you,' I answered, giving her a kiss on the cheek.

By the time we finished our second cup of coffee, everyone was awake and had gathered in the kitchen. Elvis warned his mother that the media circus would be starting at 10 A.M., and if we wanted to have breakfast without any interruptions we should eat early.

I went in to shower and make myself presentable for the onslaught. I packed all my things and put on the outfit I had saved for my plane trip home. When I returned to the kitchen, Elvis gave me a wolf-whistle, and, much to my surprise, even Nick complimented me on the way I looked. Whether or not he was sincere I couldn't tell, and really I didn't care. I knew he was glad to be getting away from me, and the feeling was mutual.

Elvis was right about the circus: by 11 A.M. the house was a zoo; almost as maddening as the day before. We did however manage to steal fifteen minutes of alone time, locked in Elvis's bathroom, before heading in opposite directions.

When I fastened my seat belt for the flight home, I breathed a sigh of relief. I was already missing Elvis, but I was more than ready for some peace and quiet. With my heart aching, I was wishing Elvis could have some peace and quiet too, but I knew, for him, that there was no escape.

34

A PICTURE IS WORTH A THOUSAND WORDS

*E*LVIS HAD BEEN after me to have a studio picture taken, so several days after I returned home from Memphis I phoned the studio for an appointment.

'This picture has got to be special; I'm sending it to my boyfriend,' I informed the photographer as he switched on light after light.

'I just so happen to know who that is, June,' he said, studying my face from every angle.

Having received a considerable amount of press, it seemed that everyone in Biloxi knew who my boyfriend was unless they were either dead or illiterate.

'What kind of picture did you have in mind, June? Serious or smiling?' he asked.

'Nude!' I answered quickly, then laughed. 'Just kidding, just kidding. What other choices do I have?'

'Well, I've never taken a picture of someone crying,' he teased back.

'Why not?' I asked. 'That might be interesting.'

After snapping a few serious pictures, he left the room, returning with two large squares of black fabric. He placed one around my shoulders, securing it with a safety pin, and draped the other on my head like a scarf. Except for the pixie bangs on my forehead, I looked like a nun.

'Almost perfect!' he exclaimed, leaving the room again, returning this time with a jar of Vaseline.

'We need a little shine,' he said, dipping his finger in the jar and applying it to my cheekbones, nose and chin.

'Okay, June, do you think you can give me some tears?' I looked directly into the bright lights, trying not to blink, and sure enough, the tears began to flow.

'Great! Great! Keep it up! I'd like to catch a tear on your cheek,' he said, clicking the shutter as fast as he could.

We had one minor problem: along with the tears came a runny nose. I'm sniffing between clicks, while he's dabbing a Kleenex under my nose. Needless to say, when I left the studio, I looked like I was suffering from a broken heart.

I returned home just in time to receive a phone call from Elvis. Still sniffing when I answered the phone, he was concerned I might be coming down with a cold. I didn't say anything about the photo session, but I did tell him my mother had surprised us by coming home with our first television set. She had been planning to buy it for Christmas, but after learning Elvis was appearing on the *Ed Sullivan Show*, she had it delivered early. It was a small set, black and white, but it was all ours.

'Great news, baby. That means you got to watch the Sullivan show? Did I do okay?' he asked, not waiting for a yes or no.

'You were wonderful! You just weren't on long enough,' I complained.

'Could you tell I was nervous? If you'd been there, you could've held my hand.'

'I was wishing I was there the whole time I was watching the show,' I confessed.

'Yeah, well, wishing don't make it so, baby. I wish you hadn't been so quick to say no. Cool it, Nick! I'm trying to talk on the phone, if you don't mind,' Elvis yelled at Nick.

I could clearly hear Nick Adams in the background, speaking loudly in his Mr Magoo voice.

'You had your chance, baby, you blew it, you blew it!' Mr

Magoo was saying, making sure he said it loud enough for me to hear.

'Are you back in Memphis, Elvis? Is Nick Adams still with you? If so, will you tell him to kiss my ass, please?'

'Dammit, Nick, shut the fuck up! You could've been there with me, June,' he said, anger still in his voice.

'What else can I say? I'm sorry I wasn't.'

'Well, it's probably for the best. The Colonel's been giving me a hard time; he found out you were in Memphis, so we're gonna have to cool it for a while, baby. I'm sorry.'

Every time I heard the Colonel's name, I could feel the blood rush to my face. I held the receiver to my ear in silence.

'I've got to do what I've go to do, baby. I'm sorry. I do wish you'd stayed, Natalie will be here this evening.'

'Well, like you said, Elvis; it's probably for the best.'

'I'll be talking to you, June. Remember, I love you, baby.'

'I love you too, Elvis. Say hello to Natalie for me.' I hung up the phone, not waiting to hear the dial tone. I felt as though I had been talking to two separate personalities. Again, I was too angry to cry.

Keeping up with Elvis and his two house-guests during the week, via the *Memphis Commercial Appeal*, I read where Elvis had purchased motorcycles for his guests so they could go riding around the city. '*Big fucking deal!*' I thought to myself angrily.

Elvis called to say he loved me the same day his companions left, making me feel secure again. We talked for several hours about nothing in particular; mostly he was trying to convince me he had no choice other than to do what the Colonel ordered him to do. His sincerity was enough to pacify me. For the time being, anyway.

Meanwhile, the photographer called to say my proofs were ready. When I walked through the studio door, I gasped! Hanging on the wall behind the counter was an 18 by 24 inch matted and framed photograph of me in tears.

'I only wanted an 8 by 10. I can't afford this!' I said, in a panic, thinking there had been some misunderstanding between us.

'This one's for me, June. I took the liberty of having it made up to surprise you. What do you think of it?' he asked, proudly admiring his work.

'It's nice, very nice,' I answered, still in shock over the size of it.

He wanted to use the photo in an upcoming photography contest, and planned to make copies for me free of charge. My photograph didn't earn him the blue ribbon he expected, but a red one for second place. In the judges' opinion, my neck needed more exposure in order to balance out the overall picture.

'Picky, very picky,' I said, when he called to give me his disappointing news.

I walked the two short miles to the post office to mail my photo to Elvis, singing a tune, in rhythm with my every step. In such a happy mood, I phoned Elvis as soon as I got home, but he wasn't there; he was in Las Vegas, and Lovie didn't know when he was coming home. We had a nice long chat anyway.

'I wish you were with him, June. I've been worried about him lately. He's still keeping company with that pushy little Nick Adams.'

'Elvis is a big boy, Lovie, I'm sure he's okay, and will be home soon,' I said, trying to soothe her.

'I'll tell him to call you as soon as he walks through the door, little Satnin. I love you, you take care now.'

Two weeks went by, then another week. Surely he would call for my birthday, I thought – but he didn't. The first week in December, I picked up a copy of the *Commercial Appeal*, and learned that Elvis had a Las Vegas showgirl as his house-guest in Memphis.

'Is this supposed to be for publicity purposes, you two timing bastard!?' I thought to myself. '*Ha!*'

I phoned Pat to ask if she had seen the latest news on Elvis.

'Yes I have, June, I'm sorry. I wasn't going to say anything. You know my feelings: anything you don't know can't hurt you. It's probably all for publicity purposes anyway. The girl

isn't even pretty,' Pat said, being supportive of me and standing up for Elvis at the same time.

'I didn't find her pretty either, but being a showgirl, she
probably has legs running all the way up to her straddle. And
you know how he loves legs,' I answered, in my pissed-off
tone.

'Yeah, but June, he probably asked her out while she was in
her stage make-up. Can you imagine how he felt when he
saw her without all that make-up? Ha!'

Elvis was such a huge star, no matter what he did, it always
made front page news. Especially in his home town newspaper. The *Memphis Commercial Appeal* had a wide circulation, and was available at every news-stand. It was as if
Colonel Parker himself was sending me personal reports on
Elvis's love life.

For Christmas I went out partying with all my friends.
Anything was better than staying home waiting for a call that
might not come. A few days after Christmas, I saw a picture
of Elvis and another showgirl, a different one, who spent
Christmas with Elvis and his family at his Audubon Drive
home. At least the second one was prettier than the first; but
not by much.

I crushed the newspaper and threw it in the nearest trash-
can, along with a mental message to Elvis.

'You can't blame this on Colonel Parker, Elvis Presley! You
can go straight to hell!'

I was home the following day when the phone rang. I
answered it and was surprised to hear Elvis on the other end
of the line.

'Merry Christmas, baby. I tried to call you Christmas day,
but I couldn't get through. All the circuits were busy.'

'That's okay, Elvis, I wasn't home anyway,' I answered
sharply.

'Did you have a good Christmas, baby?' he asked, sweetly.

'Yeah, Elvis. I had a great Christmas, really *great*! How
about you?'

'You don't sound like yourself, June, is anything wrong?'

'Wrong? No! Everything is just fine, Elvis. Just fine!'

'You're mad with me for not calling, aren't you.'

'Heavens no! Why on earth should I be mad with you? You're only doing what you've got to do. Besides, Colonel Parker probably has your phone tapped.'

'I wouldn't put it past him, June. The old fart knows every move I make,' he said, trying to sound cheerful.

'The whole world knows every move you make, Elvis, not just the Colonel. I know every time you take a shit!' My voice sounded like I'd been on a diet of razor blades. He was very quiet on the other end of the line, and so was I.

'Are you still there, baby? June, are you still there?'

Sitting on the edge of my bed, facing the mirror on my dresser, I could see the tears streaming down my face. Real tears; not like the tears I forced myself to make for the picture. I thought about hanging up the phone, but I couldn't bring myself to do it. I wanted him to mention the showgirls, and convince me he was forced into the situation. Some excuse. Anything. But not one word of regret came from the other end of the line. I had to clear my throat before I could answer.

'Yes, Elvis, I'm still here.'

'Listen, baby, I've got to run. In case I don't get to call you, have a happy new year. I love you, June. I've got to run.'

'Happy new year to you, Elvis Presley!' I said, slamming down the phone.

Seeing my reflection in the mirror, I thought about the photograph: I forgot to ask if he'd received it. I'd given great thought as to how I would sign the picture, and decided to make it simple yet meaningful: 'To my Beloved, Always and Forever, June.' With all the bags of mail arriving daily, I wondered if he even received the damned thing, but just then I really didn't care. Another strange thought popped into my head. Was the picture of me crying a premonition, or just an ironic coincidence?

I didn't mind sharing Elvis with his fans; that part was easy. I just couldn't share him with other loves. I couldn't spend my life waiting in the wings; and I wouldn't! I had to be not just his number one, but his one and only.

My new year's resolution was to forget I'd ever heard of

Elvis Presley, but it wasn't easy – how can you forget a person whose name is a household word? I put on a happy face and struggled to keep it there. I convinced myself that I wasn't cut out for Elvis's kind of life. Sure it was exciting, but the excitement never stopped; Elvis would never have a life of his own. He belonged to the public.

PART TWO

NSA010 SSM030   1957 (189/NMT 29

NS LLC153 (D SAA934) PD (ATTEMPT DLR UNSUCCESSFUL FM
NEWORLEANS DAFI)=SANDERSON TEX 17 1054P=

JUNE JUANICO=

:307 FAYARD ST BILOXI MISS=

MEET ME UNION STATION NEW ORLEANS 445 ARRIVING

SUNSET LIMITED=

ELVIS PRESELY.=

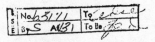

TELEGRAM SENT BY ELVIS TO JUNE, 18 MARCH 1957

35
WRONG DIRECTION

*T*HE FIRST TIME Fabian Taranto asked me out on a date, I accepted. I hadn't been out on a real date in such a long time, I'd almost forgotten how to act. We went to an early movie, then out to dinner, and after dinner we went dancing – something Elvis would never be able to do. I was having so much fun I didn't want the date to end, and neither did Fabian. He came into my life at a time when I needed him most. He was a godsend.

It was a real whirlwind romance; within a few short weeks, we were both in love. I had completely convinced myself that nothing and no one else mattered. We were the only two people in the world.

When I received Elvis's telegram, dated 18 March 1957, I was already engaged to be married. I made the trip to New Orleans to see Elvis one last time, and to tell him of my engagement. Unashamed at the time, I thought, 'vengeance is mine'.

My mind was so jumbled with questions I couldn't think straight. Where would I begin? Would I be able to choose the right words? How was I going to feel when I looked into his eyes? Maybe I wouldn't tell him anything. No, I couldn't do that; I had to tell him the truth, and have no regrets.

We parked near the front entrance of Union Station, and all of a sudden I began feeling queasy, thinking I was going to throw up in the parking lot. I looked at my watch; I didn't have time to be sick.

We got inside the huge train station, crowded with people, and didn't know which way to turn. Red West and Gene Smith suddenly appeared out of nowhere. Red took me by the hand and Gene took hold of Pat. We pushed and shoved our way through the train terminal and back to the railroad yard, where rows and rows of trains were lined up side by side. Stepping over track after track, we finally turned between two trains. About ten cars down, I saw Elvis, leaning out, looking for us. My heart skipped a beat when he jumped down from the train and ran to meet us. My heart wanted to run, but my feet kept walking calmly in his direction. He scooped me up, gave me a quick kiss and put me back down. Grabbing my hand, we ran to a different train, one that had been waiting for his late arrival. He climbed aboard and pulled me up the high steps right into his arms. He carried me to his private car and began kissing me all over my face.

'Oh, June, I've missed you so much, baby. I'm so glad you're here. I was afraid you wouldn't come. Let me look at you,' he said, holding me at arm's length and then turning me around.

'You look wonderful, June. I'm not letting you out of my sight. You're coming home with me, baby. Wait till you see the surprise I have for you, June. You're gonna shit when you see what I bought for you, baby, you're really gonna shit.'

I'd never seen him this excited before – or this handsome, either. I fought my feelings, remembering Fabian, and the reason for making the trip.

'I can't go home with you, Elvis. I don't have any clothes,' I blurted out, avoiding the truth.

'You don't need anything, baby. We'll buy you a whole new wardrobe when we get home.'

'But I didn't make plans to go home with you, Elvis.'

'You don't need plans! The only plans you need are to spend your life with me. We'll call your mother when we get to Memphis. I told Mama you were coming home with me, baby, she can't wait to see you.'

'We have Pat's daddy's car. She can't drive back to Biloxi by herself,' I said, still avoiding the issue.

'That's no problem, June. One of the boys will drive her home. Wait till you see the surprise I have for you, baby, you're gonna love it.'

He was holding me in his arms, in the center of his private car, and kissing me after every word. I kept thinking about Fabian. I couldn't go home with Elvis. Elvis didn't need me; he had many, many girls to turn to. I was in love with Fabian and I knew Fabian was in love with me. Fabian needed me. I wouldn't break his heart. I had trusted him with my heart as well, something else I'd never be able to do with Elvis. I had to quit stalling; I had to tell him the truth. Finally I just blurted out the words.

'I can't go with you, Elvis. I'm engaged to be married.'

'What did you say?'

'I said, I'm engaged to be married.'

His face was expressionless as he released me and slumped down on the couch. He put his head in his hands for a few seconds, then raised his head and looked up at me.

'You're kidding, June. You can't be serious. You're trying to get even with me, right?'

'No, Elvis, I'm not kidding,' I said, looking into his eyes, trying desperately not to cry.

He put his head in his hands again. The conductor was yelling 'all aboard' and the train gave a slight jerk. Elvis looked up at me with a blank stare. I leaned down and kissed his forehead.

'I love you, Elvis Presley. I always will. Take care of yourself,' I said, running from the car, grabbing Pat by the hand, and jumping from the train.

My eyes were so filled with tears I could barely see. Pat and I walked slowly toward the terminal between the trains. As I turned to look back at the moving train, I saw Elvis leaning out of the door, waving. I returned his wave and blew him a kiss. I stood, unable to move, watching the train, as Elvis became smaller and smaller in the distance. And then he was gone.

The two-hour ride back to Biloxi was silent. Even the car radio was turned off. I was despondent enough without taking the chance of hearing 'I Want You, I Need You, I Love You' or 'Love Me Tender'. In fact, any song by Elvis – even 'Milkcow Blues Boogie' – would have made me suicidal.

The very next day a news story came out in the paper. The headlines read: ELVIS BUYS GRACELAND! Was this to have been my big surprise?

36

OUT OF CONTROL

I FELT A BIT guilty not telling Fabian about my trip to New Orleans to see Elvis one last time, but I thought the less said about my former love the better. Trying desperately to get him out of my system, I found that talking about him only stirred up painful memories; painful because it was a time in my life filled with sunshine: a wonderful, carefree time when I had experienced my first love. And painful because it was all my own fault.

The mere mention of Elvis's name made my heart ache more than just a little. I knew Elvis wouldn't have just broken by heart; he would have shredded it to pieces. I justified my actions by believing I was saving myself from the pain and heartache I had helped my mother live through.

I began spending every available moment with Fabian. It seemed as though every time Pat called, I was busy doing something or had plans to be with my new love. One night when she called, I noticed a definite tone of resentment in her voice.

'So, you're home? Are you going to be there for a while? I'd like to come over and show you the new me, if that's okay.'

'Sure, come on over; I haven't seen you in a while. Fabian's on his way over too; I'll put on a pot of coffee.'

I don't know what it was about friends coming over for a visit, but Mama always put on a pot of coffee and I guess I was following in her footsteps.

Fabian and I were sitting in the living room, having a freshly brewed cup, when Pat finally arrived. She looked better than she had ever looked in her life. Her hair had been bleached a soft ash blonde and my beautician, Alma, had given her a complete make-over. After complimenting her on her new look, I offered her a cup of coffee.

'No, thanks! I'll have a glass of wine, if you have any. I was Alma's last customer and we shared a bottle of wine to celebrate the new me. I hate to change drinks mid-stream,' she said, adding a sarcastic little laugh. I was hoping she wouldn't mention Elvis's name, but it was the next thing out of her mouth.

'Did you tell Fabian about your little trip to New Orleans to see Elvis?' she snapped.

'No, Pat, I didn't tell him. Would you like to tell him?' I snapped in return.

'Well, I think you should be the one to do it; that is, if you're serious about all this marriage *shit*?'

Fabian, holding his mug of coffee in both hands, was glancing back and forth, waiting for one of us to say something. Pat was glaring at me, ignoring Fabian's presence altogether. I was shocked by her behavior.

'Pat, you've had too much to drink. I think you'd better come back some other time,' I suggested, nicely.

'I haven't had too much to drink; I've only had a few glasses of wine. At least I can think straight, which is more than I can say for you. You don't have time for Fabian, you didn't have time for Elvis, and now you don't have time for me,' she yelled, standing up and placing her hands on her hips, as if daring me to say something. Unfortunately, my choice of words was like a slap in the face.

'What's the matter with you, girl, are you queer for me?'

It turned out I was right; Pat *had* been in love with me. But now she just seemed full of hate. In a flash, she ran toward me, hitting me in the face and knocking me to the floor. I got up, put my arms around her and tried to pin her arms to her side. I was much taller, heavier, and stronger than Pat, and didn't want to hurt her. Fabian took her from me and led her to the door, telling her to 'go home and sober up'. He locked the screen and closed the door, but within seconds she was banging on the door and shouting obscenities at the top of her voice. We tried to ignore her, thinking she would go away, but she didn't.

Meanwhile, my nosey next-door neighbor phoned me to tell me I'd better put a stop to all the commotion because he'd already phoned the police. Fabian went outside to quieten Pat down as the patrol car rounded the corner. Holding Pat by the arm, he told them everything was under control. As soon as the police drove away, Pat told Fabian she wasn't leaving until she had talked to me. Sounding much calmer now, Fabian brought her back in the house, but she started screaming and tried to attack me again. Fabian took us both down the street, away from all the houses, and out of hearing range.

'Now, if you want to settle this argument like an adult, you'd better do it now. I'm tired of listening to this kind of behavior, and I know June's had enough of it too,' he said, speaking directly to Pat, in his soft spoken, easy-going way.

Pat just stood silent, glaring at me with both fists clenched.

'Listen, Pat, I don't want to hurt you; I want you to leave me alone, go home, and we'll talk this out tomorrow, when you're not so angry. Is that okay with you?' I asked, trying to keep my voice soft and calm, hoping we could come to an agreement.

'That's fine with me, June. Just fine!' she said through clenched teeth.

Fabian and I turned and started walking back to my house. I had taken only a few steps when Pat jumped on my back like some kind of wild animal, knocking me to the street, cutting both my hands and knees on the loose gravel. I somehow got her pinned to the ground, and pleaded with her to stop.

'Please don't make me hurt you, Pat, please!'

She stopped struggling and went limp. I loosened my grip, got to my feet and started walking home again. I couldn't believe all this was taking place between me and my best friend. But, as unbelievable as it may sound, I'm damned if she didn't get up and do the same thing again. This time my hands and knees were dripping blood. Losing all control, I got up from the street and tore into her. The sound of my fist smashing her face made me feel sick. I stepped back, waiting for her to get up, afraid of turning my back. She charged at me again, bringing out a rage in me I had never experienced before. She kept getting up and I kept knocking her down.

The battle finally ended with Pat on her knees, holding her face in her hands. I had beaten her to a bloody pulp. Fabian tried to help her to her car, but she pushed him away, spitting in his face.

I cried every step of the way home. How could something like this have happened? I know she thought the world of me, and me of her. I had asked her to be my maid of honor, but now it seemed our friendship had ended.

A few days later, Fabian and I were having a sandwich at our favorite little café when Pat came in. She walked past our table to the ladies' room, stayed a few minutes, then walked by again, leaving the café. I don't know how she had the nerve to be seen in public. Feeling ill, I pushed my half-eaten sandwich away. If she wanted me to feel guilty for what I'd done to her face, she succeeded: both eyes were black and swollen almost shut. Her lower lip was also swollen and purple, with what appeared to be black stitches hanging out. Knowing I was responsible made it all the more horrible.

Pat told several of our mutual friends that she'd driven her car up under the back of a truck, and was lucky to be alive. I never told them any different. It was a horrifying experience and I wanted to forget it had ever happened.

37

*J*UST FOR YOU

As CATHOLICS, FABIAN and I wanted to be married in the Church, and made the necessary appointments to talk to a priest. Our first appointment was on April Fool's Day, giving the priest ample time to nullify Fabian's first marriage, a civil marriage not recognized by the Church.

The priest turned out to be a real hard nut to crack, insisting Fabian patch things up with the wife he had recently divorced, practically ignoring my presence at every visit.

If Fabian's civil marriage wasn't recognized by the Church, what was all the hullaballoo about? This part had me puzzled.

'Father, forgive me if I sound disrespectful, but Fabian and I will be married on the first of June regardless of who performs the ceremony – you or a Justice of the Peace,' I announced on our final visit, fed up with his double standards and his procrastinating.

I thought this would make him realize we were serious about our June date, but the last week in May arrived and the priest still hadn't given us consent to be married in the Church. We were married as planned, however, on the first day of June 1957. The quiet – civil – ceremony was held at the home of Fabian's Aunt and Uncle, with family and a few close friends in attendance.

Exactly twenty-four days after the wedding, Elvis phoned my house and talked to my mother. Mama called me after she was sure Fabian had left for work.

'June, Elvis called here last night,' she said in disbelief.

'Elvis Presley?' I asked with astonishment.

'What other Elvis do you know, June?' she asked, laughing at my dumb response.

'What did he say, Mama?'

'He wanted you to meet him in New Orleans, at Union Station, tomorrow at four o'clock. I told him I would give you the message. He asked how you were doing and I told him you were fine, that married life was agreeing with you. He hesitated at first, and then he said, "Oh, she did get married?" I told him you got married three weeks ago. All he said was, "Oh, I see, well, it was nice talking to you, Mrs Juanico. I hope June will be very happy." Then he hung up the phone. He acted surprised, June. I thought you told him you were getting married?'

'I did, Mama. I guess he didn't believe me.'

I wanted to call Pat, but we were no longer on speaking terms. I had to talk to someone, though, so I called anyway. Pat answered the phone and I politely gave her all the information.

'Are you going to meet him?' she asked, also being polite.

'No way! Are you kidding? I can't go traipsing all over the country to see Elvis; I'm a married lady now.'

'Well, I'm going! Thanks for calling, June.'

Pat, Gayle Higgens and a few other friends from New Orleans went to Union Station to meet Elvis – but he wasn't there. Red West informed the disappointed group that Elvis had got off the train in Lafayette, Louisiana, rented a car, and driven to Memphis alone.

'Red didn't give any information as to why Elvis had left the train, and, thinking it was none of my business, I didn't ask,' Pat said. 'It's my opinion, for what it's worth, that he was afraid you'd be there, or even more afraid you wouldn't be there. You can draw your own conclusions. However, it was a very unusual thing for him to do. I suppose he had his reasons.'

A few weeks later Pat stopped by my apartment for a visit. She was not overly friendly by any means, and was holding a record in her hand with a picture of Elvis on the cover.

'Are you ready for this?' she said, handing me the record.

The record, *Just for You*, was an extended play album, with four songs on it including 'Is It So Strange?'. It had been recorded in January 1957, but wasn't released until after I was married. Pat took the record from my hand and put it on the hi-fi. Listening to the song I was fighting back the tears, not wanting Pat to see me cry. But I couldn't help myself; I cried anyway.

'I'm not going to say I told you so, June. Your big problem was not believing Elvis really loved you. You were too damned busy being afraid he'd break your heart. What about *his* heart, June? Did you ever think of that?' she asked, appearing to get great pleasure out of my misery.

'Did you come here just to see me cry, Pat?'

'No, June. I knew you would cry, and I knew I'd see you crying, but that's not the reason I came. I thought you'd like to have your record, that's all. It was recorded just for you. Consider it a gift from a friend,' she said, on her way out the door.

Struggling to pull myself together before Fabian came home, I washed my face, blew my nose, and put ice on my swollen eyes. I dived head-first into making my marriage the perfect one. I had to; it was the only way for me to survive.

In September 1958, six weeks after the birth of my first child, a son I named Tony, Pat showed up at my front door carrying a tiny package wrapped in blue ribbon. It had been almost a year and a half since I had seen or heard from her. When I opened the door, a big lump came to my throat, and my eyes filled with tears. I was holding my precious baby in my arms. Pat looked at me, and then at the baby, and started crying too. I put my arm around her and we hugged and cried together. We both laughed when the baby started making little grunting noises between us. I invited her in, handed her the baby, and poured us both a glass of wine.

'What? No coffee?' she laughed.

'Nope! Caffeine is not good for the baby. The doctor recommends a beer or a glass of wine daily. How about that?'

We talked first about the tragic death of Elvis's mother, and hoped he was doing okay.

'I would have gone to the funeral, but Tony was born on the fifteenth of August, and I learned of her death in the delivery room. Thinking of Elvis, and the news of Lovie's death, actually helped me to bear the pain of childbirth. I did love her, you know,' I said, taking my sleeping baby from Pat and placing him in his crib.

'I know you did, June. She loved you too.'

I poured us another glass of wine and we talked for hours. Pat brought me up to date on her last visit with Elvis, shortly after he moved to Graceland.

On a whim, she and Buddy Conrad had decided to make a surprise visit to Memphis. Buddy had read where Elvis, taking a needed rest between movies, was spending time at home with his parents, before going in the Army. Buddy picked up Pat from Perkinston Jr. College, where she was just beginning her freshman year. They drove to Memphis, arriving at two in the morning, and checked into a motel down the street from Graceland. Buddy had no problem getting Elvis on the phone at around noon that same day. The guard at the gate motioned for the mint-green Continental to drive on through. Pat said Buddy's smile was as big as the grill on the car when they drove up to the front of the mansion.

'June, I wish you could have seen the smile on Elvis's face when he greeted us at the door. He hugged us both for a long time, and said, "Gee, it's so good to see you guys, it reminds me of the good old days."'

As she was describing Elvis's smiling face, I could feel myself smiling too. For me they were also the 'good old days'.

'Did he mention me, Pat?' I said, not wanting to ask but unable to resist.

'As a matter of fact he did, June. He wanted to know if you

had gotten married just to spite him,' she said, feeling herself no doubt that that was the reason.

'What did you tell him, Pat? Did you tell him he hit the nail on the head?' I asked, assuming that would have been her answer.

'No, smart-ass. I couldn't think of anything to say, I was so shocked by his question. I babbled something like, "I, uh – gee, I – she, uh," and he said, "Never mind, I don't wanna talk about it" and changed the subject. I do know he was upset. He pressed his lips together and shook his head. He still cares, June. I know he still cares,' Pat said, shaking her head too.

'I don't want to talk about it either, Pat. It gets me upset too,' I said, taking a deep breath and sipping my wine.

Pat changed the subject and began telling me about life in her college dorm. Later on, she did tell me about visiting with Mrs Presley while she was in the kitchen, doing her thing.

'She asked how you were doing, June, but by the tone of her voice I think she was angry with you for breaking her little boy's heart.'

The baby started crying about that time; it was time for his afternoon feeding. I changed his diaper, put him to my swollen breast, and we joined Pat in the living room.

'Gee, aren't you the perfect mother! I didn't know mothers did that sort of thing any more; I thought they all used bottles. I hope he don't get drunk from the wine!' she laughed, surprised to see me breast-feed my baby.

'We have a widdle glass of wine every night, don't we widdle-bitty?' I said, watching my son tug hungrily at my breast.

'Don't tell me you're going to talk baby-talk to him too,' Pat said, a slight grin on her face.

'Certainly! How else do you talk to a baby?'

As soon as the baby finished feeding, Pat handed me the tiny package that had been sitting on the coffee table for hours. I opened the package to find a tiny gold band – tiny but still too large even for his thumb. The way time was flying, I knew it wouldn't be long before he grew into it.

The fight was never mentioned. We both knew some things

are better left unsaid. We kept in touch with occasional phone calls, and she always mailed postcards from all the exotic places her flight attendant's job took her.

I knew, after that day, that our friendship would last a lifetime.

38

THE MOTHER OF TWO

P AT ARRIVED ON my doorstep for another surprise visit in early 1963. I was now the proud mother of two. My beautiful baby girl, Tori, with her big eyes the color of split-pea soup, was born in May 1962. This time Pat was carrying a package slightly larger than the last one, wrapped in pink ribbon.

She gave me a quick hug, commented on my long hair, giving it a tug, and raced past me to the center of the floor, where Tori was sitting playing with her toys. Pat sat on the floor, next to my little girl, and handed her the neatly wrapped package. Tori managed to get the package opened, with Pat's help, but her tiny hands were not yet strong enough to hold the sterling silver piggy-bank, already filled with silver dimes.

My son Tony, now four and a half, woke from an afternoon nap and came in the living room to investigate the strange voice.

'Is this the little baby I held in my arms not too long ago? God, June, he's absolutely gorgeous!' Pat said, unable to believe her eyes.

'Tony, say hello to Pat; this is the lady who gave you the gold ring you're wearing in your baby picture.' Tony flashed a shy smile in Pat's direction, and his little face turned red. The picture I had mentioned was taken when Tony was six months old, and wearing nothing but the gold ring. Even though he was lying on his stomach, the picture was still an embarrassment to him. On his insistence, I had to remove it from the living room and hang it on my bedroom wall. When I asked Pat if she'd like to see the picture, Tony ran to block the entrance to my room.

'Maybe some other time,' Pat said, seeing the 'Oh no you don't' look in Tony's big blue eyes.

Much to Pat's disappointment, I didn't have any wine in the house, so I put on the traditional pot of coffee and we talked and talked. She had recently made another trip to Graceland, and couldn't wait to give me all the details.

On one of her flights to Memphis, Pat had an overnight layover, and as soon as she got checked into her hotel she phoned Barbara Reiff. Pat and I had met Barbara in 1956, while visiting Elvis in Memphis. Spending most of her time visiting fans at the front gate, Pat and Barbara became friends and exchanged addresses, keeping in touch throughout the years. Barbara, a regular visitor to Audubon Drive, became close friends with Elvis and had an open invitation to visit Graceland any time he was in town. Barbara, now happily married, was thrilled to hear from Pat. It just so happened that Elvis was in town, and Barbara and her husband were planning to attend a small gathering that night at Graceland. Barbara, following all the rules, phoned Graceland to get permission to bring another guest. She got the message through, and Junior Smith was there waiting for them at the front door, excited about seeing Pat again.

Junior, a real pain in the ass because of his drinking, used to follow Pat around like a lost puppy. Pat was surprised to find him sober for a change. Junior found a place for the two of them to sit and visit, while Barbara and her husband mingled with some other regulars.

'How've you been? And how's old June Juanico?' Junior asked, wanting to know everything that was going on in Biloxi.

'Everyone's doing great!' Pat answered, bringing Junior up

to date with everything going on in her life, and mine too.

'Good old June. She really cooked his goose. Ain't nobody ever said no to the King before,' Junior said, laughing his evil little 'He! He! He!' like he was glad.

'Well, Junior, I'm sorry it happened the way it did; I thought they were perfect together,' Pat said, remembering there was always a slight resentment between Elvis and Junior.

'Don't get me wrong, Pat. I'm sorry it happened too. I really liked old June, mainly 'cause she was the kind that wouldn't take no shit! He's still looking for another one like her, but it ain't gonna happen.'

The mansion was filled with young girls, all dressed in their sexiest garb. They were moving around the room, apparently jockeying for position. After reading about his teenage house-guest from Germany, supposedly now living at the mansion, she had scanned the room looking for the little girl named Priscilla.

'Which one is Priscilla, Junior?' she asked.

'Oh, she ain't here; she's over at Vernon's with the rest of the kids,' Junior said, laughing his villainous 'He! He! He!' again.

The 'kids' Junior was referring to were the three children of Dee Stanley, Vernon's wife of almost three years. Junior said Elvis wasn't happy with the marriage, but he did like the kids.

Pat was happy to see Elvis finally making his entrance from the top of the stairs. She was tired of Junior's sarcasm. Drunk or sober, he was still a pain in the ass. Elvis paused at the foot of the stairs long enough to do a few karate moves with some of the regular guys before scanning the room, looking for Pat.

'Here she is, cuz,' Junior said, standing to give Elvis his seat.

Elvis came over, pulled Pat from her chair, and gave her a big hug. Pat said the room was buzzing, with all the girls looking in her direction, wondering who this new girl was, dressed casually in Bermuda shorts and monopolizing Elvis.

Pat, flying out of Miami, hadn't prepared for the unex-pected layover, and other than her flight uniform was wearing the only clean clothes she had.

'How's June? I hear she has two kids now,' Elvis said, taking a seat next to Pat.

'How did you know June had two kids? I just found out myself recently,' Pat said, surprised.

'I've got connections, Pat. Believe me, I've got connections.'

The two of them talked for a while, mostly small-talk, until Elvis excused himself, saying he had some people to see and would talk to her later.

'Junior, show Pat around the place while I'm gone.'

'Upstairs too, cuz?' Junior asked.

'Yeah, why not! Show her everything,' Elvis answered. Pat felt honored; it seemed very few people were ever allowed beyond the immediate area.

The mansion had been completely redecorated since Pat's last visit; strictly to suit Elvis's far-out taste. Pat skipped the descriptions of most of the rooms, and began telling me about Elvis's bedroom.

'He still has his bigger-than-king-size bed, and sitting on the night-table, next to the bed, was a gold telephone; knowing Elvis, it was probably the real thing, too. But that's not the best part, June. I went to get a closer look at the telephone, and, sitting on the table next to the phone, was a copy of *The Prophet*. What do you think about that?' she asked, seeing my surprised reaction.

I took a deep breath. It seemed that something or someone was always stirring up old memories, bringing back the pain.

'It couldn't have been the copy I gave him, Pat. That was a long time ago. It probably got lost.'

'That's not the point, June; it doesn't matter if it's your copy or a copy he bought for himself – it's still a copy of *The Prophet*. The fact he still has the book says something, don't you think?'

I didn't answer. I would not get into a heartbreaking debate about Elvis still loving me or not loving me. Six long years had passed, and I was doing fine. It didn't matter any more.

'Well, June? Don't you think?' she said, insisting on an answer.

'The only thing I think, Pat, is that Elvis likes the book.

Nothing more, nothing less. Would you like another cup of coffee?'

Pat followed me to the kitchen, and before I could reach for the coffee pot, she took the cups from my hand, sat them on the counter, and gave me a much-needed hug.

'I'm sorry, June. I didn't mean to stir up old memories. I won't say anything else, okay? I do have a few more things to tell you; funny things, nothing that would make you sad, I promise.'

As we were putting sugar and cream in our coffee, her mouth went into high gear again.

'Elvis now likes his coffee black, and drinks it by the gallon. I've never seen anything like it; his cup never gets empty. Let me see, where was I? Oh, Barbara and her husband had to leave, so I went to find Elvis and say goodbye. When I found him, he insisted I stay, saying he would bring me back to my hotel later. Naturally I agreed, and went to say goodbye to Barbara. Elvis introduced me to Bonnie, his date for the evening, and pulled out a chair for me at the kitchen table. You know how Elvis was always a kitchen person.

'Everyone was sitting around the table, drinking coffee. Frankly, I would have preferred a glass of wine, but I didn't dare ask. I know one thing, June – Elvis was hyped up on something, either drugs or caffeine or a combination of the two. His legs were bouncing under the table so fast you could feel the vibrations through the floor. It was making me so nervous I had to keep my hands off the table. Between that, and the four or five cups of coffee I'd had, I knew sleeping was out of the question.

'We left the mansion around 4 A.M.: Elvis, Bonnie, Junior, me, and Joe Esposito, a real nice guy. To my surprise, we dropped Bonnie off first. Elvis then picked up his car phone and called Anita Wood. You were right about one thing, June. Elvis would never be faithful to one person. He had Bonnie on his arm, Anita on the phone, and poor little Priscilla waiting patiently in the wings. Oh, well – I guess it was appropriate; his last movie was called *Girls, Girls, Girls*,' Pat said, ending her story.

Other than on the silver screen, Pat never got to see Elvis again. I didn't know it at the time, but later that same year I would make a trip to Memphis myself, and visit my former love.

39

 NEW LOVE

Memphis, 1963

The city of Memphis was host to the WIBC National Bowling Tournament. My team, despite having been ten-pin bowling for only three years, signed up to give it a try. We were all pretty fair bowlers, and excited about going to our first national tournament. Naturally, Graceland was included in our itinerary, but the chances of seeing Elvis were slim.

As soon as our plans were finalized I spent every available afternoon sun-bathing, just in case I saw Elvis again. I hadn't had a suntan in years, and if, by chance, I did get to see Elvis, I wanted to look the same as I did the first time we met.

Our team sponsor was the C. F. Gollott Seafood Company. Our shirts were white with a big oyster on the half-shell embroidered on the back. I gave the shirts a personal touch by sewing a pearl button in each oyster. I made the grey culottes to match the colors of the oyster for all five team-members. Back then, even the WIBC (Women's International Bowling Congress) frowned upon women in slacks.

We arrived early in the evening with no plans for our first night in town, so the girls decided this would be a good time to visit Graceland. By this time, Elvis was fast becoming a legend; already one of the most famous people in the world. We pulled up to the front of the Graceland gate and I stepped from the car, introducing myself to the guard. I didn't recognize him, and was surprised to find he knew who I was.

'If Elvis was in town, I know he wouldn't mind if we drove up to take a look,' I said, honey dripping from my lips.

'Elvis is in town, he's just not home at the moment. You don't have to bat those blue eyes at me, June. You and your friends can drive up to the house, but only if you promise not to stay long. I'd hate to have Elvis come home early and find a car-load of women in his front yard,' he laughed.

My heart was pounding so fast I couldn't find the door handle to get back in the car. I had no idea Elvis was in Memphis. The last I'd heard, he was in Hollywood, making movie after movie. The guard gave us the name of the theater where Elvis and his friends had gone, and opened the gate for us to ride through.

Looking up at the mansion, I was filled with mixed emotions. I was happy for Elvis, but at the same time I was heartbroken; not because of me, but because of his mother. The mansion was similar to the antebellum homes she had admired on the Gulf Coast of Mississippi, hoping to someday have one of her own but not living long enough to enjoy it. I could still picture her ooh-ing and ah-ing, trying to get Vernon to share her enthusiasm.

Our plan was to drive to the theater after leaving the mansion. I had carefully blotted the tears from my eyes, and pulled down the sun visor to check my make-up, just in case. I was a bundle of nerves, thinking if I did get to see Elvis, how would he react to me? It had been a long six years.

The glass doors to the theater were all tightly locked. I noticed a man walking in the lobby, so I knocked on the door. Seeing a group of fans gathering was not an unusual sight, but he did walk over to check us out. Much to my surprise, the man stared at me for a moment, then opened the door.

'You're June, aren't you? he said, smiling.

'Yes, I am! How did you know?' I asked.

'I've seen pictures of you at the mansion. You haven't changed a bit. Does Elvis know you're here?'

'No, we just arrived today,' I answered, now a nervous wreck.

'I know he'll be glad to see you, June. I'll go tell him you're here,' he said, turning to leave.

'No! Don't do that!' I said nervously. 'I'd rather surprise him, if that's okay.'

The girls waited in the lobby while the nice man showed me where Elvis was seated. The theater was divided into three large sections, where thirty or forty of Elvis's invited guests were sitting in the side sections. Only two people were seated in the center section; Elvis and his date.

I walked one row behind Elvis's seat and gently tapped him on the shoulder. He turned around and gave me a quick glance, as if to say, 'what's with this girl annoying me?', then did a fast double-take, stood up, turned around, and kneeled backwards in his seat.

'June! What in the world are you doing here?' he said, pulling me to him and hugging me tight. 'God, June, you look great! What are you doing here?' he asked again, holding me at arm's length and smiling.

I explained that I was with a group of girls, bowling in the national tournament, and had arrived that afternoon.

'Oh!' he exclaimed, like he was slightly disappointed that he wasn't the main reason for my trip to Memphis.

We were hugging again when Joe Esposito ran from the front of the theater to see who was bothering Elvis.

'Joe, this is June, Wally Taranto's sister-in-law,' Elvis said to Joe. It was such a strange introduction, coming from Elvis, I had to laugh. My husband's brother, Wally, had told me he was close friends with Elvis, but I thought he was bullshitting me as usual.

'It's nice to meet you, Joe. Any friend of Wally's is certainly a friend of mine,' I said, shaking Joe's hand.

'So, this is June Taranto. I've heard a lot about you, June. Nice meeting you at last,' Joe said with a grin, making me wonder what my crazy brother-in-law had said about me.

'I hate to ask what, if you've heard it from Wally.'

'Not just Wally, June, Elvis has told me lots about you too. Pardon me for interrupting; I thought someone had Elvis in a head-lock. I'll leave you two alone; I know you have lots of catching up to do. It was very nice meeting you.'

Elvis's date was sitting quietly by his side, her eyes never leaving the movie screen. She had to be aggravated by the intrusion; I know I would've been. I thought of apologizing for the interruption but Elvis started talking again.

'How are you, June? Are you happy? How many kids do you have now?' he asked, all in one breath. Misunderstanding his question, thinking he meant how many were with me in Memphis, I said, 'Six.'

'*Six*! Jesus, June, you don't waste any time, do you? The last I heard, you only had two,' he said, shaking his head in disbelief.

'You're right, I do have two children; a boy and a girl.'

'Someone told me you named your little boy Elvis,' he said, looking just a tad bit proud.

'You, of all people, should know better than that. My poor husband takes enough ribbing about you as it is.'

'I didn't think it was true. It would've been a nice compliment, though.'

At the time I thought it was probably some of Wally's bullshit, but I didn't ask. 'It may have been a compliment, Elvis, but it would also have been grounds for a divorce,' I laughed.

'Are you doing okay, June? Is there anything I can do for you, baby? You look great, June, really great, you must be happy.'

'I am, Elvis, I couldn't be happier,' I answered, picking up on him calling me 'baby' – even though it was probably a slip of the tongue.

'I'm glad, June. I'm happy for you. God, it's been a long time. Let's see; it's been six years already. Can you believe it? Funny how time slips away.'

He hadn't changed a bit; he was still using song titles in his conversation. He invited me and my friends to come to his house, the following night, any time after ten o'clock. I apologized for interrupting his movie, gave him a quick kiss on the mouth, and said goodbye. He stood up between the seats, folded his arms across his chest, and, as I figured he would, watched me walk away. Still a leg and ass man; he was always crazy about my ass. He blew me a kiss and gave me an 'okay' sign with his hand, letting me know it was still there and still looking good. And then came the final 'icing on the cake': as I stepped from between the row of seats and turned into the theater aisle, I heard him *mmmooo*-ing. It was his 'see something you really like' kind of moo. He only did two kinds of moo; the other moo was a shorter, deeper, more monotone kind, which meant 'man, what a cow'. Hearing his *mmmooo*, I turned and blew him a kiss goodbye.

The original moo had come from a scene in *Rebel Without a Cause*, when James Dean's high school class had gathered in the Planetarium. Elvis had picked it up after seeing the movie a dozen or more times. When Elvis and Nick were together, the two of them used it often, as a private joke.

My bowling team were disappointed when I returned to the lobby alone, but they cheered up knowing we had been invited to Graceland the very next night. Needless to say, I got very little sleep that night, trying to recapture our short but meaningful conversation.

By the luck of the draw, our team shared a pair of lanes with an all-black team from Detroit, Michigan. When the Detroit team learned we were from Biloxi, Mississippi, a few eyebrows were raised. The South had received the blame for all the recent racial turmoil at that time, so the raised eyebrows came as no surprise. It made us all the more determined to show the northern black team what true southern hospitality was all about.

Contrary to popular belief, all southerners are not inbred, redneck bigots. True, we did have more than our fair share, but they were fast becoming a thing of the past.

The girls from Detroit confessed to being somewhat leery about the long drive that far south, and had considered flying or taking a Greyhound bus.

'Thank God you didn't take the bus; ya'll would've been

mighty tired riding all that way in the back seat,' I laughed, breaking the ice.

They cheered as much for our team as they did their own, and we did the same, which resulted in higher scores for both teams. Our two teams finished in the top twenty, which, in a national tournament, is not too shabby.

After bowling we went back to the motel to freshen up for our visit to Graceland. Again, my stomach was in knots, but when we arrived at Graceland the guard told us Elvis was having 'personal problems', would not be able to see us and sent his regrets. My bowling companions were disappointed, but not nearly as disappointed as me. I'd spent twice as much time as usual in front of the mirror, making sure everything was perfect.

Was he really having personal problems, or was he, for some unknown reason, avoiding me? Either way, his current love affair with Ann-Margret was in every newspaper and magazine; maybe his live-in girlfriend from Germany had had enough of other girlfriends, old *and* new, and had finally put her foot down. I was hoping I was right, if only because his mother was now gone and I felt Elvis needed someone to stand up to him. I guess I'll never know.

40
$\mathscr{H}$URRICANE

Biloxi, Mississippi, and Las Vegas, Nevada, 1969

The national headlines read: 'HURRICANE CAMILLE – The most violent and destructive storm ever recorded on the North American continent devastates the entire coastline of Mississippi.' All the world was reading of our plight, while other front-page news had to take a back seat. All others except Las Vegas, that is. Their local headlines read: 'ELVIS PRESLEY – His return to Las Vegas for a one-month engagement at the International Hotel draws record-breaking crowds.' The Showroom, with a capacity of 2,000, had to be upgraded to a capacity of 3,500 in order to accommodate the overflow.

Hurricane Camille, a billion-dollar catastrophe, was not just another storm; she was a killer. Biloxi and its neighboring cities along the coast took the full force of the storm's 200mph-plus winds for almost five hours.

A local apartment complex a stone's throw from the water's edge was completely destroyed, killing all but one of the twenty-three people who had refused to heed multiple warnings from the police and Civil Defense and had, instead, moved all their furnishings to a top floor in preparation for a 'hurricane party'.

Many of the finest homes on the coast, which had weath-
ered other hurricanes throughout the past hundred years,
were left with only their foundations remaining. A total of
141 lives were lost on the Mississippi Gulf Coast alone.

The peninsula of Biloxi, literally cut off from the rest of the
world by collapsed bridges, downed power-lines and trees,
was a living hell. Emergency crews from neighboring states
worked for weeks trying to restore power. The Red Cross, the
Salvation Army, and one charitable organization I remember
well, the Seventh-Day Adventists, worked around the clock
bringing in drinking water, ice, food and clothing for the
needy.

Fabian, worried about his many friends and family
stranded on the peninsula, took his fishing skiff and outboard
motor and drove it to the north side of Biloxi Bay. Now, with
a vehicle parked on both sides, he spent most of his time fer-
rying food and water to his loved ones. Feeling he could do
more if he didn't have me and the children to take care of, he
drove us to Mobile, Alabama, and put us on a plane to Las
Vegas, to stay with his brother Wally.

Wally had become friends with Elvis back in 1958, when
Elvis sat at Wally's twenty-one table to play Blackjack. Elvis
and Wally were a lot alike; tall and handsome, they both had
a way with the ladies. Wally introduced himself to Elvis by
announcing that his brother was married to June Juanico.
Elvis later introduced Wally to Joe Esposito, and the three
became fast friends, managing to get together whenever Elvis
was in Vegas.

Wally had worked his way up and was now a casino boss
at the International Hotel, where Elvis was headlining. And
headlining he was! Everywhere you looked you would see
enormous billboards flashing only one name: ELVIS! I had
been to Las Vegas many times, but had never seen a promo-
tion such as this. Not only the Strip, but the airport and all
roads leading to the city were dotted with billboards screaming ELVIS! ELVIS! ELVIS!

Knowing we had our favorite entertainers, Fabian's brother
always kept us informed as to who was headlining so we

could plan our trips accordingly. I knew Barbra Streisand had been at the International, and I was hoping she would still be there. I had no idea Elvis was going to be in Las Vegas until I stepped off the plane, and that same old nervous feeling in my stomach returned. By this time, Elvis had acquired the status of 'living legend'.

After the luxury of a shampoo and shower, Wally, without asking, picked up the phone and used his connections to get tickets to see Elvis the first night I was in town.

I could easily rest my elbows on the stage, we were so close. The house lights dimmed and the orchestra opened with a goose-bump rendition of the theme from *2001: A Space Odyssey*. Elvis made his entrance wearing a white jump-suit, looking positively flawless – still the best-looking man I ever laid eyes on. I had never liked his dyed black hair, but even that didn't take away from his resplendent appearance.

'C. C. Rider' was his opening song, and he sang it like he was at one with the beat. He was electrifying. His left leg was doing double-time to the rhythm, more of a quiver than a beat. My first thought was: 'Dear God, if his leg is going this fast, how fast is his heart beating?' I had overheard some people in the Showroom talking about how thin he was, and how fast he was moving; they thought he had to be on some kind of drug. No way, I thought, not my Elvis; he was too smart for that. However, hearing the remarks coming from more than just a few people did bother me. I could hear my mother's voice inside my head: 'Elvis is a grown man, June. He can take care of himself.' Sure, he was a grown man; he was thirty-four years old. So why did I still see him as a little boy?

Covering every inch of the stage, Elvis walked in the direction of our table and everyone stood up, including me. When he got close, at least a dozen or more fans ran up from behind me, stepped in my chair and pushed me face down on the table. They were using my back as a step to get up on the stage. Wearing a fashionable mini-dress, I was more concerned with my safety than the fact that my ass was visible to everyone behind me. Wally quickly put himself between me

and the stampeding fans; we both had bruises on our backs
from the high-heel shoes. Elvis quickly went back to deep
center stage, out of harm's way. The show stopped long
enough for security guards to escort unruly fans from the
stage. How foolish I was to think the fans would grow up and
not behave this way any more.

As soon as we arrived home after the show, Wally phoned
backstage at the International and paged Joe Esposito, telling
him I was in town and wanting to talk to Elvis. When Wally
handed me the telephone, Joe was still on the other end.

'Is that you, June?' Joe asked. 'Hold on, I'll get Elvis for
you.'

Holding a cocktail in my hand, and having had several at
the show, I wasn't the least bit nervous. It had been such a
long time, I wondered what I would say.

'June, is that you, honey?' Elvis asked.

'Yes, Elvis, it's me – and don't call me honey,' I answered.

'You haven't changed a bit, have you, baby?' he laughed.

'I've changed a little; hopefully for the better. You've
changed a little too; I saw your show tonight and you look
better than ever. Your voice is better than ever too, Elvis, I was
impressed!' I said, knowing Elvis loved praise – and this came
from my heart.

'Thanks, June, coming from you that makes me feel good.
You've been on my mind for the past few days. Did you and
your family survive the hurricane okay?'

'We had some damage, but nothing compared to most people. The sad part of it all is that there's nothing left on the
beach. The Sun 'N' Sand is gone, the Ko-Ko is gone, and the
only thing left of the White House pier is a few broken pilings.
You do remember the White House pier, don't you?' I asked,
hoping he would remember the place we had spent most of
our time on our first date.

'I remember it well, June. As a matter of fact, I remember it
like it was yesterday. How about Gus Stevens' Lounge? Did
Mr Gus make it okay?' he asked, remembering Gus had rolled
out the red carpet for him on every visit.

'A miraculous thing happened to Mr Gus. A tractor trailer

washed up, blocking the wind and surging tides from his huge
front windows, and he had only minor damage. He's keeping
his doors open to anyone needing food, water and ice; sharing
his good fortune, so to speak.'

'What about Gulf Hills, how did they do?'

'Not too bad. The villas are all gone and so is the boat
dock. The hotel and the Hack house are still standing.'

'How about you, June? Are you happy? Do you need anything? Is there anything at all I can do for you, baby?'

'I'm fine, Elvis. If things got any better, I couldn't stand it,'
I answered, using the same reply I always used when asked
that question, although it wasn't necessarily the truth.

'I've seen a few of your movies and your acting is improving,' I lied, trying to make him feel good about his acting
career.

'The movies are shit and you know it, June. I'm still just
spinning my wheels.' His voice was the same, but his diction
had definitely improved: ten years ago, Elvis would have said,
'Ah'm jess spinin' mah wheels.'

'I guess congratulations are in order – you have a beautiful
wife and a new baby girl. All you need now is a little boy, and
your life will be complete.'

'Whoa, June, don't rush me! I'm still trying to get used to
being a daddy. Yours must be getting pretty big now. How old
are they? You still have just two, right?'

'Right! Tony is eleven and Tori is seven. They're both beautiful,' I answered, like the proud mother I was.

'Seven and eleven, huh? They would be great at the crap
table. Forget I said that, June, my mouth is going ninety to
nothing I'm so hyped up. And I still have another show to do
before I can unwind.'

'I noticed how hyper you were on stage. Are you sure
you're okay? Is there anything I can do for you? How are you
unwinding these days?'

'Don't worry about me, baby. When I need to unwind, I go
to bed and read a good book.'

'What are you reading? Anything good?'

'June, you wouldn't believe me if I told you. On·second

thought, maybe you would. A long time ago, someone very special gave me a book to read. I've read it at least a million times, June, it's my favorite book. I try to keep a copy with me at all times. It's my unwinder,' he laughed. I was so surprised I couldn't think of a thing to say. I knew he was talking about *The Prophet*.

'Ain't it funny how time slips away? Shit, baby, I didn't mean to go and get sentimental. How's everybody in Biloxi? How's your mother and Mr Bellman?'

'They're all fine, Elvis, everybody's just fine,' I answered, only half hearing his question; my mind was still on the book.

'I see Pat every once in a while, and how's my old friend Buddy Conrad doing? I used to see him all the time, but not lately. He's the joker who told me you named your son Elvis.'

'Buddy died a few years ago, Elvis. He had cancer.'

'Damn! Damn! Why is it the good die young, June? Why? Damn! I sure hate hearing that about good old Buddy. I really liked old Buddy,' Elvis said, apparently at a loss for words.

'The last few days of his life, all he talked about was you and the good old days. Everything was E.P. this and E.P. that. He was grateful for the time we all had together.'

'I'm grateful too, June. They were the best years of my life. Listen, baby, I'll be here for another week, so if you need anything, just give me a call. Just ask for Joe. How long are you going to be in Vegas?'

'I'm not sure. At least until the power is restored back home. We live in the country, and without power we have no water, and no air-conditioning either.'

'You live in the country, June? Do you have any horses?'

'We have three horses and two cows, but no chickens. You know how I feel about chicken shit,' I laughed.

'You haven't changed a bit. I'm real happy for you, baby, you got your ranch after all.'

'It's not really a ranch, Elvis. We call it "Oleo Acres" – a low-cost spread.'

'That's good. Sounds just like you. Are you sure there's nothing I can do for you, baby?'

'I'm sure. Thanks for asking, though. I don't want to keep

you on the phone; I know how busy you are. I appreciate you taking the time to talk to me. Take care of yourself, Elvis. I love you.'

'I love you too, June. Take care, baby.'

The neon lights atop the International Hotel were clearly visible from Wally's front door, and I thought of calling many times during the next ten days. But I never did. On the way to the airport I noticed all the billboards with Elvis's name had been removed. Elvis had left the city.

EPILOGUE

Weekend of 4 July 1977

After an absence of over ten years, my friend Pat was in town for a surprise visit. A few mutual friends of ours had arranged a Fourth of July celebration in her honor.

Talking and laughing for hours, we had lots of catching up to do, and, as always, the conversation turned to the old days with Elvis.

'June, you know Elvis is now forty-two years old, and not in the best of health,' Pat said. 'Next month is the anniversary of his mother's death, and I'm worried about him. Really worried. If you remember correctly, Gladys was forty-two years old when she died on 14 August, and you, of all people, know how Elvis was with his premonitions of death, concerning either himself or his mother. Call it superstition or whatever, but there's something about their ages being the same. He might have a hard time dealing with it; maybe he won't deal with it at all. It really worries me, June. I think we should go to Memphis and see if there's any way we can help.' She was no longer laughing, but dead serious.

'Elvis is surrounded by people looking out for him, Pat. What good could we possibly do?'

'I know he's surrounded by people, June, but do they understand Elvis the way you do? Do they really care enough? You know how Elvis can be when someone tells him something he doesn't want to hear; but he'll listen to you, June. He always did.'

Surprised and shocked by Pat's intuition, it was hard to believe what I was hearing. We were both so in tune with Elvis and each other's thoughts, it was frightening.

'Well, do you think you can get away for a few days or what?' Pat questioned.

'I don't know, Pat; I'll have to talk to Fabian. He'll probably think I'm crazy, but I'll see what I can do.'

The hostess brought out a steaming platter of boiled shrimp and crawfish and placed it between me and Pat. I was so preoccupied with thoughts of how to swing a trip to Memphis I couldn't eat a thing. I knew no matter how much I talked, begged or pleaded, Fabian would never go for it.

My thoughts then turned to Red West; if only Red was still with Elvis. If Elvis was ever in any kind of trouble, Red had always been there for him. I always thought that if anyone truly loved Elvis Presley, it was Red West; but Elvis and Red had gone their separate ways in July 1976, just a year earlier. Red, close friend and bodyguard for over twenty years, had a better relationship with Elvis than any relative.

Suddenly I had a flash of inspiration. We wouldn't have to go to Memphis – Elvis was coming to Biloxi! In the midst of the excitement in seeing all my friends in one gathering, it had completely slipped my mind. Elvis was scheduled to be the very first performer to give a concert in our newly completed Gulf Coast Coliseum. The entire city was buzzing; how appropriate for Elvis to do the honors. He had made many friends along the Coast, and now he would be coming home; back to where it had all begun. Biloxi finally had a place large enough to accommodate the thousands who would turn out to see him.

Soon it was all settled; I was to phone Pat, give her the exact date, and she would fly in for the weekend.

My fifteen-year-old daughter Tori had been after me for

months, not only wanting to see Elvis in concert, but also to
go backstage and meet him in person. Tori had been hearing
about Elvis Presley – not from me, but from others – as far
back as first grade. By the time she reached fourth grade, she
managed to sneak one of my scrapbooks to school for 'show
and tell'.

With all the tight security surrounding Elvis, my daughter's
main concern was how we were going to let him know we
were in the crowd of thousands. Two years earlier, in mid-
1975, my first cousin, George, went to see Elvis in concert in
Shreveport, Louisiana, and his wife took along a sign she had
made on a poster board. The sign simply read: MY NAME IS
JUANICO. Within minutes of Elvis's entrance on stage, two security men working for Elvis approached the couple with the
poster and asked for me, wanting to escort me backstage. I
was sure, if all else failed, the same trick would work for us.

I couldn't wait to see the look on Elvis's face when he saw
Tori: she was the image of me the first time we'd met over
twenty years earlier. But, as fate would have it, it never came
to pass. The dedication and grand opening of the Coast
Coliseum, featuring Elvis Presley In Concert, was scheduled
for September 1977, just one month after he died.

'*If in the twilight of memory we should meet once more, we shall speak again together and you shall sing to me a deeper song.*'

The Prophet
Kahlil Gibran

LAST TRAIN TO MEMPHIS
The Rise of Elvis Presley

PETER GURALNICK

'Wonderful . . . Guralnick deserves to live in Graceland'
RODDY DOYLE

Last Train to Memphis is arguably the first serious biography that refuses to dwell on the myth of Elvis. Aiming instead to portray in vivid, dramatic terms the life and career of this outstanding artistic and cultural phenomenon, it draws together a plethora of documentary and interview material to create a superbly coherent and plausible narrative.

The first of two volumes, covering Presley's rise to prominence up to his departure for Germany in 1958, *Last Train to Memphis* will undoubtedly become the benchmark by which other biographies of him are judged.

'Unrivalled . . . [Elvis] steps from these pages, you can feel him breathe, this book cancels out all others'
BOB DYLAN

'It's hard to reclaim Elvis from the weight of history and slander, but Guralnick – as you might expect from his great book about the soul '60s, *Sweet Soul Music* – does it beautifully . . . [He] tells this twentieth-century myth with a fine regard for his subject's humanity'
JON SAVAGE in *Mojo*

'A wonderful book . . . Guralnick gives us an Elvis of real flesh and blood . . . The richest and most detailed portrait of Presley we have ever had'
TONY PARSONS in the *Sunday Telegraph*

An

paperback